T. H. HUXLEY'S DIARY
OF THE VOYAGE OF H.M.S. RATTLESNAKE

A native outrigger sailing canoe alongside "The Rattlesnake" in the Louisiade Archipelago (Chapter 8).
From a water colour (unsigned) in the possession of Mrs. L. Huxley.

Preface

THE notebook containing my grandfather's Diary of his voyage on H.M.S. *Rattlesnake* was found among the papers of my father, Dr. Leonard Huxley, after his death last year. He had received an enormous mass of papers, letters, drawings, and other material belonging to my grandfather and grandmother after the death of the latter in 1915. To sift the wheat from the very large amount of chaff would have been a tremendous task. When, during the last twelve months, they were finally sorted, letters from the most eminent Victorians were found cheek by jowl with laundry bills; the original MSS. of various of my grandfather's essays were piled among miscellaneous press-cuttings; the notebook containing this Diary was found among the group of old household account-books.

My father never had the heart to go through the mountain of material thoroughly. He had of course undertaken a similar task after my grandfather's death in 1895, when he had sifted a vast quantity of letters and papers in preparation for writing his father's *Life and Letters*. It was, I think, the knowledge that he had done this, and the belief that nothing of vital interest had escaped his efforts, which helped to deter him from renewing the task after 1915.

This brings me to an important question. Had this *Rattlesnake* Diary really eluded his previous search; and if so, how had this been possible? The relevant facts are as follows. In the *Westminster Review* for January 1854 my grandfather reviewed the official account of the voyage of H.M.S. *Rattle-snake*, written by its chief naturalist, MacGillivray. In this review, in order to supplement the book's rather bald and official account, he quoted long extracts from "the unpublished journal of one of the officers", which is none other than the present Diary. Some of this is quoted by my father in *L. & L.*,[1] vol. i, p. 46 *seq*. On p. 42 reference is made to incidents recorded elsewhere in the Diary; but a knowledge of these could equally well have been gained from the official history of the voyage.

There is thus no direct evidence of the present MS. of the Diary ever having been seen by my father. The evidence for his not having seen it is indirect, but very strong, for the Diary contains so much of extreme interest that it is inconceivable he should not have utilized it in the preparation of the *Life and Letters*. In that work, all the events of my grandfather's life up to the end of his voyage occupy a mere 54 pages, out of a total of over a thousand. The extensive quotations from the brief published portion of the Diary indicate how eagerly my father used such material. My uncle, Mr. Henry Huxley, agrees with me that it is most unlikely that the Diary was ever in my father's hands.

But if this was so, how was it so? For one thing, he knew of the existence of the Diary, and would undoubtedly have made every effort to find it. For another, we know that my grandfather had the notebook by him as late as seven years before his death, for at the close of it he had written out some autobiographical notes which take his career up to 1888.

My guess, for what it is worth, is that when my grandfather retired from active work and moved to Eastbourne, the Diary was mislaid owing to its resemblance to the account-books among which it was eventually found (a case of protective resemblance, in biological parlance!) and was humbly stacked away with them. My grandmother had a passion for keeping everything (or an aversion to throwing anything away—it comes to the same thing) and so there was ample opportunity for the Diary to lurk undiscovered for the next thirty-eight

---

[1] For brevity's sake I shall refer to the *Life and Letters of Thomas Henry Huxley* (2 vols., Macmillan, London, 1900) as the *Life and Letters*, or more briefly, *L. & L.*

years. However, whether this be so or not, and whether my father ever saw it or not, the essential fact remains that the great bulk of these sixty-odd thousand words have never been published, and that they are in my opinion—and that of several friends well qualified to judge—of the greatest interest, and in every way worthy of publication.

It is interesting that the publication of this Journal should follow so soon after that of Darwin's.[1] The two greatest British biologists of the nineteenth century each began his career as naturalist on a long voyage of scientific exploration. To both, the experience was of inestimable value, and indeed in Darwin's case, had it not been for his journey on the *Beagle,* it is on the cards that *The Origin of Species* would never have been written.

But there is a remarkable contrast between the two Diaries. That of Darwin, though revealing the most interesting glimpses of the writer's character and personality, has as its chief and absorbing interest the growth and development of his ideas on the mutability of species: in it we are assisting at the birth of the Evolution Theory.

Huxley, on the other hand, records singularly little about his scientific views in his Journal. He mentions that he has been busy examining this or that animal, that he has sent off an account of such-and-such a piece of work to England, that he thinks he has arrived at valuable conclusions. But as to what the conclusions were, or by what steps he arrived at them, there is scarcely a word.

Yet these were the researches which earned him a Fellowship of the Royal Society at the age of twenty-five, researches which laid the foundations of our rational understanding of the comparative anatomy of two major groups of animals, and paved the way for some of the broadest generalizations of Morphology, such as the germ-layer doctrine and Haeckel's use of it in regard to his theory of recapitulation.

But if Huxley's journal is meagre where Darwin's is generous, the converse also holds. There can be few other such abundant source-books for studying the growth of a great

---

[1]Charles Darwin, *Diary of the Voyage of H.M.S. Beagle,* edited by Nora Barlow (Cambridge, 1933).

scientist's personality. In these pages are revealed the many
sides of Huxley's complex temperament; his struggles with
himself, with his fellow-men, with nature; the steps in the
organization of his powerful character. Add to this that it
was during this voyage that he met and became engaged to
his future wife, and that the Diary contains a record of the
beginnings of that deep love which endured undimmed
throughout his life, and it will be seen that we have here a
document of the highest personal interest.

Huxley's character was indeed as remarkable as his scientific
achievements and his literary talent; and I venture to believe
that many to whom Huxley the scientist makes no special
appeal will find in this Diary a deeply interesting picture of
the growth of a great and rare personality.

In addition to Huxley's own Diary, we have the journal
kept by his *fiancée* during the latter part of his voyage. Most
of this is of no more than family interest, but I have incor-
porated a few extracts from it where these throw light upon
Huxley's personality or career, or upon the Australian scene
of a century ago which provided a background for so much
of his own Diary.

In addition, I have used some of my grandfather's sketches
and scientific drawings as illustrations. Reproductions of the
scientific drawings appeared in the *Philosophical Transactions
of the Royal Society* to illustrate the published accounts of his
researches, but the originals show his extraordinary delicacy
and skill in scientific draughtsmanship as the lithographed
reproductions cannot do. The sketches were for the most part
contained in a large album, which has been in my father's
possession since my grandfather's death. A few of these have
been published elsewhere,[1] but I have chosen either unpublished drawings or those which have suffered severely in reproduction. My grandfather had a natural artistic gift, as
these sketches will show. As one well-known artist to whom
I showed them exclaimed, "What courage amateurs have!
Huxley attempts what most of us would be afraid of tackling,
and only the greatest artists could tackle successfully: yet
sometimes he all but pulls it off." I especially commend the

---

[1]Notably in MacGillivray's official account of the *Rattlesnake's* voyage.

drawing of the native boy by the waterfall (p. 34), with its strange, almost Gauguinesque effect, and the brilliant treatment—highly selective yet extremely realistic—of tropical vegetation (p. 102). Huxley was a great scientist and a great man of letters; if he had had time and opportunity, he would have been a great artist as well.

One word more, and I have done with this long preface. My grandfather's handwriting, so neat and orderly at first sight, was in fact, owing chiefly to its speed, of a fearful illegibility. This defect increased with the years: but it was already present at the age of twenty-one, and the task of deciphering the Diary has not always been easy. In some cases, notably with a few proper names, I have had to leave a blank or hazard a guess, in spite of much poring over the MS. and much searching of maps and books.[1] I apologize for these defects, but do not think that they will in any way detract from the interest of the record as a whole.

My thanks are due to various relatives and friends who have read the MS. in whole or in part, and have made valuable suggestions; and in especial to Dr. C. G. Seligman, F.R.S., and to Professor C. M. Yonge, who have put at my disposal their special knowledge of the regions visited by the *Rattlesnake*.

[1]Such gaps and queries are inserted between square brackets. Square brackets have also been used for insertions in the text, *e.g.* for variant spellings of places used by MacGillivray in his official account, and to explain when passages have been added later by Huxley to the text of his Diary.

Contents

Illustrations

Those interested in Huxley's abilities as a draughtsman should look at MacGillivray's *Voyage of H.M.S. Rattlesnake,* in which eight plates and numerous figures in the text are from Huxley's pencil. As Huxley himself records (p. 286) these have suffered a good deal in reproduction, as is seen by comparing the Frontispiece to this Volume with its reproduction in MacGillivray's book—but they are still of considerable merit.

On vol. i. p. 83 is another picture of Kennedy's party cutting their way through the scrub, a counterpart of my Plate 7, p. 102. On Vol. i. p. 193 is a delightful picture of the incident with the pig, described on pp. 145–6 of this book. On p. 208 of vol. i. is depicted the watering-place on South-East Island. In spite of Huxley's remark on p. 150—"I tried to make a drawing of the place, but it disgusts me exceedingly compared with my remembrance of the reality"—it is a charming sketch. On p. 223 of vol. i. (with supplementary text-figures in later pages) is a drawing of one of the huts on Chaumont Id., but which MacGillivray refers to as Brierley Id., described on my pp. 156–7. On p. 264, vol. i. is a very beautiful drawing of the village on Brumer Id., described on my pp. 170–1. MacGillivray tells us that its name is Tassai, but in the legend to the plate erroneously puts it in New Guinea. The frontispiece to vol. ii. is a not very successful drawing of two natives from Redscar Bay, including one with the "Jewish" cast of countenance (see my pp. 122, 200). On p. 37 of vol. ii. is a very interesting plate of the *"waus"* or screen described on my p. 195.

Among the text figures may be mentioned ethnological drawings from the Louisiade—a lime calabash, a stone axe, a fishhook, a canoe of the type described on my p. 148, a bracelet made from a human jaw, as mentioned on my pp. 148–9, a Brumer Id. catamaran, a drum and a cooking-pot, shield and spears, panpipes, a wooden pillow; and a Darnley Island hut, doubtless one of those which Huxley describes himself as drawing on p. 204.

T. H. HUXLEY'S DIARY
OF THE VOYAGE OF H.M.S. RATTLESNAKE

CHAPTER 1

Introductory

THIS Journal, kept by Huxley between 1846 and 1850 during the voyage of H.M.S. *Rattlesnake*, throws new light on the early years of one of the great scientists of the nineteenth century. It cannot be read in its proper perspective without some familiarity with his life and career. The course of that career has already been set forth on numerous occasions—very fully in the *Life and Letters* (London, 1900) edited by Leonard Huxley, more broadly in such books as *Huxley, the Prophet of Science,* by Houston Peterson (London and New York, 1932), and *Thomas Henry Huxley,* by [Sir] P. Chalmers Mitchell (2nd ed., London, 1913), which devotes special attention to his scientific achievements. For all detail, I must refer my readers to those sources. But I feel that something is needed in this place as a background for readers of this Diary, and I shall here try to give a sketch, in broadest outline only, of what seems to me relevant.

Thomas Henry Huxley was born in 1825, a seventh child, the youngest survivor of eight. His father, George, was an assistant master in a large school at Ealing, and here Thomas spent his first ten years. His mother was a remarkable woman, dark and slender, of untiring energy and vivacity. Thomas took after her very closely in physical appearance and temperament, and was always devoted to her—passionately so as a child. From his father he inherited, according to his Autobiography, little except "an inborn faculty for drawing . . .

a hot temper, and that amount of tenacity of purpose which unfriendly observers sometimes call obstinacy".

When Tom was ten, the Ealing school broke up, and the family moved to Coventry. The boy got little regular education; but he had a passion for reading and self-instruction, combined with a queer turn for metaphysical problems which was well developed before the age of fifteen.

At the age of twelve he sat up at night to read Hutton's *Geology*. At fourteen he contracted a serious illness as a result of attending a post-mortem. At fifteen he started a journal called *Thoughts and Doings,* some interesting extracts from which are given in *L. & L.* By sixteen he had taught himself German; at seventeen he notes in his Journal that he has "for some time been pondering over a classification of knowledge", and produces a scheme of his own.

When he was not quite sixteen he went to London as a medical apprentice, first in Rotherhithe, and then with his brother-in-law, Dr. Scott, in north London. His experiences among the poor population of Rotherhithe made a great and lasting impression on his mind.

Meanwhile at Sydenham College he pursued his studies preparatory to a medical career. At this time he won his first prize—in Botany; and when seventeen and a half obtained a Free Scholarship at Charing Cross Hospital. There he studied under the well-known physiologist Wharton Jones, who encouraged him to publish a discovery concerning the microscopical structure of human hair which he made while at Charing Cross—no small achievement for a nineteen-year-old student.

In 1845, at the age of twenty, he took his first M.B., after an academic career full of honours and prizes. In the next year he obtained a post in the Navy Medical Service, and was soon in residence at the Naval Hospital at Haslar, under that notable explorer and naturalist Sir John Richardson. It was Richardson who, noting Huxley's talents, recommended him for the appointment, as assistant surgeon and naturalist aboard H.M.S. *Rattlesnake,* which was to have so profound an influence upon his life. Without that, he would in all probability have remained a medical man, his scientific talents perhaps afforded an outlet in human physiology of the more

Plate I

Two early portraits of T. H. Huxley.   The one in the top hat must have been taken prior to his appointment
to " The Rattlesnake."

From previously unpublished daguerreotype in the possession of The Hon. Mrs. John Collier.

medical sort. Just as later in his career it was the preoccupa-
tion with fossils enforced upon him by his post at the School
of Mines which led to his becoming a leader in palæontological
science, so the opportunities and duties provided by the
voyage, of becoming acquainted with lower forms of life not
easily accessible to stay-at-home naturalists, led directly and
immediately to his achieving distinction in comparative
morphology.

His voyage on the *Rattlesnake* ensured that he should
become a general biologist. It also opened his eyes to the
variety of the physical world, and made him acquainted with
primitive man. And last but far from least, it introduced him
to Henrietta Heathorn, his future wife.

In a later section I shall return to discuss the scientific fruits
which he gleaned from the four years of his wanderings, and
to give a more detailed account of the events which took place
immediately after his return to England. Here I will simply
complete the sketch of Huxley's life in the barest outline
needed to give it form.

Late in 1850 the *Rattlesnake* was back in England. Huxley's
immediate task was to secure proper publication of his scientific results. The Admiralty behaved in a most niggardly
manner, and in 1854 Huxley finally resigned his appointment
in the Service, and secured publication of his papers through
the Government grant to the Royal Society. He had already
been elected a Fellow of the Royal Society at the age—
astonishingly youthful for a follower of the descriptive sciences—of twenty-five, and at twenty-six he was awarded the
Royal Medal of the Society and elected to serve upon its
Council. But these honours did not provide him with bread-
and-butter, much less with a livelihood which would allow
him to embark on the marriage he so deeply desired. They did
not even help him to secure any of the various professorships
for which he applied—at Toronto and at Aberdeen, at Cork
and at King's College, London. His gloom was deepened by
his mother's death and his father's grave illness; and in spite
of regular journalistic work and a book, he was seriously
thinking of emigrating to Australia and setting up as a doctor
there. However, at the critical moment, he was appointed to

the School of Mines under the Geological Survey, and soon afterwards obtained additional lecturing work.

Miss Heathorn came over to be married in 1855, and then Huxley settled down into that career of incessant and many-sided activity which ended only with his death, forty years later. For the whole of that period, save the six years of his retirement, he lived and worked in London, though with many journeys on official business to different parts of the country.

The publication of Darwin's *Origin of Species* in 1859 was a turning-point in Huxley's career. The concept of organic evolution, and evolution proceeding by natural causes, gave point and focus to his varied biological researches. Biology became a unified science, the facts of adaptation, of palæontology, of embryology, of comparative anatomy, of geographical distribution, all fell into line. What is more, his passion for truth and his genius for intellectual controversy also found the widest scope in the storm which immediately burst and continued to rage and grumble for the remainder of Huxley's life. Had it not been for "Darwin's bulldog", as Huxley once dubbed himself, the permeation of every domain of thought by the evolutionary concept would have been neither so rapid nor so complete.

But this was only one of his activities. He continued to do valuable research of a technical nature. The list of his scientific memoirs occupies nearly 10 pages in *L. & L.;* and although the great majority of these were published between 1849 and 1879, he continued such work until 1888. He was also much involved in the applications of science, and served on three Royal Commissions concerned with fisheries and one on a medical subject.

In purely scientific education his insistence upon practical work led to the establishment of the first true laboratory of biology in 1871, and his methods, combined with an immense personal influence on his pupils, left a lasting impress on biological teaching. His interest in education, however, was far from being confined to his own special subject. His work on the London School Board, as a Governor of Eton, as a member of several Royal Commissions, and in many essays and addresses, helped to give natural science its due place in general education, while at the same time he fought against any narrowness or pedantry on the part of science as emphatically and vigorously as against the narrowness and pedantry of traditional studies. The whole range of our educational system, from the elementary school to the university, bears the mark of Huxley's work in this field.

Nor were his educational interests confined to the academic or the formal. His skill with the pen early led him to undertake scientific journalism and popular lecturing: and his disinterestedness led him to devote as much as possible of his energies in this sphere to truly educational work. His lectures to working men were outstanding examples of what such things should be—the lecture "On a Piece of Chalk" remains as a literary classic, a model of lucid, vigorous English—and set a high standard that undoubtedly influenced the subsequent course of events in adult education and extension work.

His interest in the general problems of philosophy, religion, and morals never deserted him. With the publication of his *Lay Sermons, Addresses and Reviews* in 1870, he came to occupy a unique position in the thought of his time—a position which he retained until the day of his death. In him the scientific spirit was combined with the speculative reason, scientific knowledge with an astonishing range of knowledge in other fields, and devotion to his work with a rare ethical passion. The result was a potent leaven.

The term "agnosticism", which he coined, became the focus for an important movement of intellectual liberalism. If this movement was at first in large measure a destructive one, this was inevitable in the face of the existing vested interests of thought; and the destruction was necessary to clear the ground before any new construction could be begun. Huxley's influence, however, was also constructive. His championship of rigid intellectual and moral standards, and his insistence upon a full and varied life, saw to it that his was no mere negative force.

Finally, he had a wide circle of general interests and personal relationships. His rich family life (he had eight children); his many friends in all walks of life; his relation with his colleagues and his pupils; his deep interest in literature, painting, and music—these provided the background against which his busy life was set.

There was unfortunately another side to that background. Never strong, he was early attacked by a dyspepsia which became chronic; and this, combined with the pressure of his work and public commitments and with the need for making both ends meet, brought on occasional crises of nervous prostration. Only a man of indomitable spirit could have persisted as he did in the tasks which he had set himself, or seen his efforts crowned with such success.

However, at the last even his energies flagged. He retired from active work and spent the last six years of his life in retirement at Eastbourne, where he died in 1895 at the age of seventy.

CHAPTER 2

Huxley's Diary: Outward Bound
DEC. 1846–JULY 1847

Huxley, like many diarists with a virgin diary before them, was full of good resolutions. He begins with a long entry written while still in port. But from then on his entries are sporadic, and he is often forced to write up from memory the events of a week, a fortnight, or even a month.

I have cut the text of the Diary into sections. The first section deals with the voyage from England to Australia. The *Rattlesnake* had a complement of 180. Among the names we shall meet in Huxley's Diary, besides that of Captain Stanley, are those of Lieutenant, later Commander Yule, who commanded the *Rattlesnake's* tender, the *Bramble*; Lieutenant Dayman, who seems to have been the second in command aboard the *Rattlesnake*; Lieutenant Simpson and Mr Obree, who were especially concerned with the surveying work; Brady, another officer; Heath, one of the midshipmen; Dr. Thomson, the surgeon, Huxley's immediate superior; MacGillivray, the naturalist;[1] Brierley, who accompanied the boat as an artist; and "M.", the ship's clerk, with whom Huxley had a violent quarrel (p. 260). Sailing from Spithead on Dec. 3rd, 1846, the *Rattlesnake* spent a few days at Plymouth, to take aboard £65,000 of specie for the Cape. Leaving Plymouth on the 10th, she called at Madeira, passed through the Cape Verde archipelago, spent over a week at Rio de

[1]Huxley spells the name M'Gillivray.

Janeiro, and then a month at the Cape. Their next port of call was Port Louis, in Mauritius, where they stayed for several days, and thence they sailed for Australia, breaking the voyage at Hobart in Tasmania to deliver specie. The voyage from Plymouth to Sydney lasted seven-and-a-half months. It was Huxley's first experience of the sea and of foreign lands and peoples.

·   ·   ·   ·   ·

Dec. 10th, 1846. In Plymouth Sound.

Thank God! fitting out is at last over. We have no more caprices to fear but those of the wind—a small matter after having been exposed to those of the Admiralty. I can at length sit down and form some clear idea of the things to be done and the plan I must pursue so as to turn to the utmost advantage the opportunities this expedition will afford me. Not that past experience gives me much reason for believing that I shall ever steadily adhere to a given plan—but still it is well to have such a guiding thread—be it but for the purpose of fixing the thoughts steadily on the main points and not allowing the mind to be frittered away on whatever falls across it.

I must keep two points in view, 1st. that I *am* simply a student; 2nd. from the peculiar circumstances in which I am placed, care and caution in observation may enable me to *become* a teacher with regard to particular points. And on my success in this latter matter my future prospects and my usefulness in this appointment clearly depend.

Not only my previous habits and tastes but the nature of the accommodation and opportunities afforded by the ship, clearly point to the study of the habits and structure of the more perishable or rare marine productions as that most likely to be profitable. Naturalising for systematic purposes is not à mon gré. My memory is not sufficiently selective of these facts to give me any hope of attaining profound systematic knowledge—and furthermore all the naming and determining of place is far better done by those who sit in museums at home.

But what I *can* do and they *cannot* and where therefore the chief value of my position is: I can observe 1. the "habits" of

living bodies, 2. their mode of development and generation,
3. their anatomy by dissection of fresh specimens, 4. their
histology by microscopic observation.

But here again if I take these points in all their generality
it is a field far too vast for me to hope to work out my plans
—I must restrict them still more narrowly. After much
thought I do not think I can do better than take the following
points for special investigation.

1. The procuring of as many as possible of the brains of
   fishes, as suggested by Prof. Owen.
2. The dissecting as many as possible of the Mollusca for
   the purpose of ascertaining whether their structure
   (especially of the Nervous System) is not reducible to
   some unity, such as that shown to exist by Mr [G ?]
   in the Acephala alone. The structure of the shells might
   be left to a future opportunity but their development
   should especially be looked after.

   Histology also must not be forgotten here although
   the thorough working out of this part of the subject
   might well be left till one's return.
3. The anatomy and especially the mode of generation of
   the large Cirripedes and Annellids [sic].
4. Diligent search after new Epizoa upon the gills, eyes,
   etc., of fishes.
5. Careful dissections of the large Radiata, especially of
   the Trepang.
6. Zoology—Anatomy—Histology of the Acalephae with
   especial care and for the purpose of being fully acquainted with this subject study carefully the works of
   Lesson and Will.
7. Careful study of all matters relating to coral and corallines, especially to the animals of the latter.

All these are things which I can attend to myself and in
which I neither interfere with nor need the assistance of any
one else. I shall strive after nothing else, but if opportunities
are set before me, e.g. with regard to dredging matters, I shall
by no means neglect them.

Dec. 26th.

A fair wind is carrying us fast away from Madeira.[1] What has a week's stay enabled me to say about the place? But little, if we leave out notes of admiration, for the feelings produced by the rival beauties of its scenery would require for their fit expression more eloquence than I possess. Nature is a true tragedian—her most painful throes, her wildest struggles have all within them some element of beauty—even in death she covers her face, like Caesar, with a graceful mantle.[2] So in this island, a huge monument of some awful volcanic phenomenon—made up of wild peaks with intervening deep gullies and ravines, often carrying within them clear evidence of the ravages of mountain torrents. Nature has so kindly and artistically arranged the various parts: has so softened the variegated brightness of the hills, with here a soft white cloud resting on its summit, here a deep unfathomable-looking valley, and there a patch of vegetation; putting in by way of frame a sky and sea of the bluest blue, and at times as it were in pure wanton sport half decking, half hiding the mountain scenery with rainbows, that the whole produces a soft and harmonious scene on which the eye dwells without tiring. Much of my own pleasure of course arises from mere novelty. Mountain scenery is new to me, and the semi-tropical vegetation, the bananas, the cactuses and the palm trees, call to mind all that I have ever read of foreign countries and give me a foretaste of the far south. But that cursed Master at Arms has come, with his "Three bells, sir".

Dec. 31. *Sat.:* at Mid-day 21° 12'. Within the tropics: but the weather by no means so warm on the whole as it was at Madeira.

To finish my record of the latter place: the town of Funchal is a regular whited sepulchre—fair to look upon but all stinks within. The style of architecture of the houses strikes one at once as something foreign and brought up in my mind the

[1]MacGillivray records that the voyage to Madeira was uncomfortable: the scuppers were in a bad state, and there were leaks in most of the ports and scuttles.

[2]Marginal note here:—Rather sublime than otherwise, I calculate. Jany. 1849.

pictures in an old French edition of *Gil Blas*. As to the public buildings it is quite impossible to say to what style they belong —Portuguese Gothic I imagine. The Cathedral is a most tawdry affair, by daylight at any rate. I visited it on Christmas Eve wh. I understand to be a great festival among the inhabitants, and heard some chanting of a most vile description. Add to this that it would be difficult to say who evinced more indifference to what was going on—the choristers or the people and Santa Maria! What a stink there was. I was glad to get away, even at the risk of being walked off by some of the Portuguese pimps who [? hail] you at every step.

So far as interiors go I can only speak as to the house of our kind and hospitable friend at the American Consulate. This was very comfortable and well fitted up, the beautiful tropical plants in the little courtyard in front giving it a most pleasant appearance. We tasted his wine in all stages of development from the raw new stuff up to the delicious "Poison" of ten years old.

I made two excursions into the country—one to the famous Corral [Curral, MacGillivray], the other to the Camera de Lobos [l'Obos, MacGillivray]. The ride to the Corral I shall not soon forget. The road is bad enough in itself and it needed not my indifferent horsemanship to throw the stimulus of danger into the general excitement. How we scuttled along those narrow pathways, Brady and Park and I, with a perpendicular rock on our right and an equally perpendicular precipice on our left, our hold on terra firma being entirely confined to some five feet of rough stones called a road, between these two.

What surprised me most was that though altogether unused to doings of this kind, the idea of danger never entered my head. On the contrary I cried "Vamos" and whacked my good steed with the lead. Extreme hunger produced by the keen mountain air was the only drawback on my enjoyment of the sublime and beautiful. Shall I confess it—that a crust of brown bread would have been worth much to me, even on the top of that glorious peak which looks into the Corral—and an orange much more.

(The new year has just come in, accompanied by one drum, one accordion, and a whistle.)

1847. *Jan.* 4*th.* To continue (if indeed I shall be able to rake together any thoughts in this hot noisy berth) :

On our descent we made many unsuccessful forays upon the buckets of the country people in search of proviant, until at length crossing the bridge we met a woman prettier than usual carrying a bucket of oranges and a quantity of bread. Along with her were several other country people, a horridly ugly old mendicant and the usual accompaniment of ragged boys. We dismounted and sat on the parapet while the people formed a circle round and doubtless stared to see that the Ingleses really had mouths and appetites like other people. One broad-shouldered fellow especially, was particularly attentive and polite. He seemed to have some authority among the others and I regret to believe, exercised it by plundering the woman of the greater part of the small remuneration we gave her. We cantered off in the midst of a high dispute among them and reached the house of our hospitable friend by five, dined, and in the evening went to a public ball.

This was to me a most stupid affair—quadrilles and waltzes badly played at intervals of half an hour, and in these intervals the males arrayed on one side, the females on the other. However, some English girls there were conversible enough, and so the time passed.

On the twenty-fourth Dec. I made a quiet excursion by myself. The people make a great day of Christmas Eve. Everybody is to be seen in the streets and the market places are filled with country people, buying pork and fish for the morrow's feast, so that it is a good opportunity for studying the costumes. The streets were very crowded but at no time did I see any drunken or disorderly people. After wandering about for some time I made a bargain for a horse wh. turned out a very bad one (memo: never bargain for a horse without seeing him again) to take me to the Camera de Lobos, to wh. place an English gentleman whom I met at the reading rooms recommended me to go, as being at once pleasant and accessible. The road to this village is by no means so dangerous looking as that to the Corral but in its intimate constitution is decidedly worse, being made up of rough stones set on edge. My beast, however, took precious good care to endanger neither my bones nor his own, by resisting all my efforts to work him up to a canter.

Vegetation on the whole appeared more luxuriant than in my previous journey, and some little spots of land embayed in trap dykes were beautifully clothed with cactuses, oranges and bananas. I met with one strong evidence of the destructive nature of the torrents here, in three half-ruined arches stretching into the bed of what must be at times a wide river, though, when I crossed, the brook was hardly two steps across for my horse, and had to wind its way humbly among the very boulders it had torn down in its prosperous days. These arches were evidently the remains of a strong narrow bridge.

Walking up one hill to relieve my horse, I picked up many shells of a species of Monodonta among the stones. I suppose the people eat them as we do periwinkles.

Camera de Lobos offers nothing remarkable in itself but the view from a promontory just beyond it is exceedingly beautiful. There is a still higher cliff just beyond but time would not permit of my ascending it.

At night I went to the Cathedral where I understood great things were to be done. I stood two hours of it and then bad music, heat and the insufferable stink of garlicky humanity drove me out. I consider that stink as one of the most remarkable circumstances in my travels.

We sailed on the morning of the 26th. And now we have passed the Cap de Verd Islands, passing between St Jago and Mayo, and have reached 6.85° Lat. and 22° 38′ long. West, right into the region of Trade Winds and flying fishes. In passing the Cap de Verd I looked particularly after the dust mentioned by Darwin, but although the atmosphere is never particularly hazy, no dust has been seen.

Every day except Sunday we heave to at 1 P.M. and take soundings, and at the same time a towing net is put overboard. Its contents have been Diphydes, Ascidians, Entomostraca in great numbers, nearly allied to Daphnia, and for three days past great numbers of transparent lanceolate bullheaded animals about 3/4 in. long wh. resemble Epizoa more than anything else. [Underneath, added later: Sagitta.] These animals possess a pair of strong comblike jaws moving similarly to those in the gizzard of Rotifera, a simple intestinal canal, with a pair of long tubular glands filled with cells (ovaries?) on either side. The tail is provided on each side with radiating filaments, so as to resemble that of a fish. There are no other appendages nor trace of eyes. They are exceedingly voracious and swim about frequently with their heads buried in some unfortunate ascidian.

The phosphorescence of the sea at night has been decidedly less since we left Madeira than before. The light is only visible when the water is violently disturbed round the ship, is in quite distinct globules, and ceases at a very short distance. I ascertained before we reached Madeira that it arose from a small medusa, and from its similar appearance I should imagine the case to be the same still.

I look forward to "schöne Tagen". I have a corner in the Chart Room to myself, and when I have once persuaded people that Microscopy is a thing requiring a great deal of attention and quite incompatible with being bothered to show something pretty, I shall get on capitally. I mean for the present to show them nothing but "interesting" [? elementary] structures in wh. they can see nothing and of wh. they will soon become thoroughly tired and so leave me to myself.

Jan. 10th. Lat. 2° 0′ 25″ N. Long. 22° (circa).

Light winds and calms have delayed us some days on this N. side the Equator but we have every hope of passing it tomorrow when I believe the usual buffooneries are to be practised. Squalls with thunder and lightning accompanied by heavy rains have occurred for some days past and more than one waterspout has been seen. Our friends the flying fish have quite left us, and sharks, dolphins and pilot fish have taken their place. The only other evident living creatures have been storm petrels. Several of them have been shot by the naturalist and declared to be the "Thalassidroma Leachii", a species as yet thought peculiar to England.

The deep-sea line was got ready to-day; but alack and alas as the weight (10 shot) began to show upon it the splicing came undone and away went the lead minus line, to investigate for himself. He has however not yet returned to report, and strong fears are expressed that he has absconded.

The humidity of the air has been astonishing, the difference between the wet and dry bulb thermometer being at times not more than 0°.75.

Our sick list has been of the largest for a week past: thirteen and fourteen, not exactly serious cases, but troublesome anomalous rheumatisms, and curious painful affections of the feet, among the boys sometimes the dorsum sometimes the ball of the foot, and in one case the skin on the ankle being red and puffy and very tender. Bathing with warm water, with rest and sometimes puncturing with a lancet appeared to be the best restoratives. These cases occurred principally among the boys but a marine and naval cadet have also been affected.

What a precious pack have I to deal with in these delightful messmates of mine, as might have been expected. I have five years of silence (that is to say of speaking from the mouth outwards only) to look forward to. Save the necessary courtesies of life, I shall make it my business to have very little to do with them. And yet I suppose that on the whole, they are good specimens of those whom My Lord Commissioners think fit associates for gentlemen, to say nothing of students and professional men!

[Added later, in pencil: Unjust—they turned out very good fellows.][1]

To-day, ruminating over the manifold ins and outs of life in general and my own in particular, it came into my head suddenly that I would write down my interview with Faraday —how many years ago?[2] Aye there's the rub, for I have completely forgotten. However it must have been in either my first or second winter session at Charing Cross, and it was before Christmas I feel sure.

I remember well how my long brooding perpetual motion

---

[1]Compare *L. & L.* i, 48. On board a ship of war, "how utterly disgusted you get with one another! Little peculiarities which would give a certain charm and variety to social intercourse under any other circumstances, become sources of absolute pain, and almost uncontrollable irritation, when you are shut up with them day and night. One good friend, a messmate of mine, has a peculiar laugh, whose iteration on our last cruise nearly drove me insane."

[2]This description of his interview with Faraday is one of the three passages from the Diary previously published (*L. & L.* i, 21-23, where, however, it is stated to be quoted from a letter).

scheme (which I had made more than one attempt to realize but failed owing to insufficient mechanical dexterity) had been working upon me, depriving me of rest even and heating my brain with châteaux d'Espagnia of endless variety. I remember too, it was Sunday morning when I determined to put the question, which neither my wits nor my hands would set at rest, into some other hands for decision. And I determined to go before some tribunal from which appeal should be absurd. But to whom to go? I knew no one among the high priests of science and going about with a scheme for perpetual motion was I knew for most people the same thing as courting ridicule among high and low. After all I fixed upon Faraday—possibly perhaps because I knew where he was to be found, but in part also because the cool logic of his works made me hope that my poor scheme would be treated on some other principle than that of mere previous opinions one way or other. Besides, the known courtesy and affability of the man encouraged me, so I wrote a letter and drew a plan, enclosed the two in an envelope and tremblingly betook myself on the following afternoon to the Royal Institution.

"Is Dr Faraday here?" said I to the Porter. "No sir, he is just gone out." I felt relieved. "Be good enough to give him this letter", and I was hurrying out when a little man in a brown coat came in at the glass doors. "Here is Dr Faraday", said the man, and gave my letter. He turned to me and courteously enquired what I wished. "To submit to you that letter, sir, if you are not occupied." "My time is always occupied, sir, but step this way", and he led me into the Museum or library, for I forget wh. it was, only I know there was a glass case against wh. we leant. He read my letter, didn't think my plan would answer. Was I acquainted with mechanics —what we call the laws of motion?

I saw all was up with my poor schemes, so after trying a little to explain, in the course of wh. I certainly failed in giving him a clear idea of what I would be at, I thanked him for his attention and went off as dissatisfied as ever. The sense of one part of the conversation I well remember. He said "that were the perpetual motion possible it would have occurred spontaneously in nature and would have overpowered all other forces", or words to that effect.

I did not see the force of this, but did not feel confident enough to discuss the question.

However, all this exorcised my devil and he has rarely come to trouble me since. Some future day perhaps I may be able to call Faraday's attention more decidedly. Perge modo! wie das Gestirn—(das Gestirn in a midshipman's berth!).

13th.

Crossed the Line—usual tomfooleries observed.[1] Sounded in 2400 fathoms yesterday and got no bottom.

17th. lat 12° 49' S.

Caught my first Physalia. It's the first Portugee that has been taken in the ship, whereby [? King] is decidedly thrown into the background. Made a most satisfactory examination of the said Physalia, wh. has completely disgusted me with the papers on the same subject in the *Suites de Buffon* and puts in a much clearer light the true analogies of these animals. These Frenchmen, except Milne-Edwards, are horridly superficial.

Our sick list has suffered a great increase in consequence of the Neptunizing, in the shape of Rheumatism, Pleurisies and Contusions. It has been up to 22. Memo: if ever I am surgeon of a ship I will make a written statement to the Captain of what these things end in.

Saturday, Jan. 23rd. Entered Rio Harbour.

I have used up all my notes of admiration for Madeira, otherwise I wd. describe Rio Harbour wh. beats it into fits. Schön! schön, wunderschön.[2]

Feb. 7th.

We staid at Rio a week, that is to say we did not sail until the first of this month. During all this period it was exceed-

[1] *L. & L.* i, 31. "I had the good luck to be ducked and shaved early, and of course took particular care to do my best in serving out the unhappy beggars who had to follow."

[2] In a letter to his mother, published in *L. & L.* i, 31, he expatiates further upon the beauties of Rio.

ingly hot. The thermometer in the sun on Rat Island (where observations were going on) rose as high as 140° and on board the ship it was not infrequently 86° in the shade and I do not think that at any time it was below 80°. The weather was fine most of the time, but always in the evening a bank of clouds collected about the Organ Mts and the lightning played about their peaks. One evening a complete storm of thunder, lightning and *tropical* rain descended upon us from the same quarter. It was lovely to see the solid zigzag rods of fire descending upon the high points of land, repeatedly striking the same place, and for the instant lighting up the whole scene.

Probably on account of the little time during wh. I have been exposed to the undermining influences of a hot climate, I have been in no way inconvenienced by the heat, at least not so much so as to interfere with my occupations. I have been about, on shore and in boats, without troubling myself about time of day, and so long as the ground was level walked at my usual pace with ease and comfort. Climbing, however, was a puzzler, and although the dense bush of the hill-sides kept the temperature comfortable, I found myself getting hors de combat before many yards were accomplished.

All my rambles at Rio were in the company of the Naturalist and therefore had or pretended to have a more or less naturalistic tendency. However, singular to relate, our investigations always took in the end a chemical turn, to wit, the examination of the nature and properties of a complex liquid called Sherry Cobbler. Oh Rio, thou Sodom-and-Gomorrha in one, town of stinks and beastliness, thou shalt be saved not because of one just man, but because of the excellence of the iced drink of the man [?]. We have a tradition, McG. and I, that one evening we consumed nine pigeons and eighteen Sherry Cobblers! Can these things be?

Cobblers or no cobblers, however, our liege lady Nature was not neglected. No end of curios have been collected, partly by our own activity in dredging and otherwise, partly by the golden hook on shore. I took part in two of the dredging expeditions,[1] and the most noteworthy fact about these is that we procured immense numbers of a species of Amphioxus.

[1] On the first occasion, he and MacGillivray were compelled, in the absence of a sieve, to use their hands as strainers (*L. & L.* i, 31).

They appeared literally to swarm in the sand in both Three-fathom and Botafogo bays, depth never more than 4 fathoms. They had just the habit and appearance of those I had seen at the Brit. Association procured by Prof. Forbes, but from Gamble's description of the British species it seems to me distinct. Of course I looked upon these as a great prize and employed the first specimens I procured in a reëxamination of the blood; to my great annoyance, however, I was unable to procure a specimen of blood sufficiently pure for the purpose. All I can say is, negatively, that I saw nothing to contradict my previous account.

These Amphioxus appeared to me to die sooner than those I had seen in England. Mine began to stink by the time that they had been 24 hours in my jar and even sooner than that, so that I prospered better in an investigation wh. did not require the animal to be alive. I mean that of the generative organs, of whose structure I have obtained a very clear idea. I rather reproach myself with not having made out the circulation in these live specimens. But I only had two sets of specimens. The first were fruitlessly employed in the attempt to procure blood, the second were entirely taken up in the examination of the generative organs wh. occupied the whole of the last day we were in Harbour. Besides I thought we should not sail until the Tuesday when I sh^d. have had another day for the examination of many points I had put off.

The market place here is worth attention from those whose stomachs are strong enough to stand the combined stinks of fish and nigger. They must eat queer things, as we saw numbers of cuttlefish (Loligo) and hammer-headed sharks, exposed in the stalls. The latter were small, none exceeding I should think three feet in length.

The only other notable thing in the town is the Rua do Ouvidor, wh. is the principal street for shops. The curiosity shops for feather-flowers, shells, insects etc. are the most remarkable among these. We patronized one Madame Finot, a talkative ricketty Frenchwoman. I procured a few peculiar curios from [?] from her. Notwithstanding the label in the interior of these she would persist in asserting them to be native but very rare, and consequently valuable. The trade in feather-flowers must I should think be somewhat considerable, as she had some forty females of various ages and colours busily at work in the large back part of her shop.

As for the Emperor's Palace and the Churches, they are heaps of brick and mortar in the usual Portuguese no-style of architecture—masses of ugly tawdriness.

It is a huge pity that the old Norse fashion of squatting is out of date. A few of the hungry Saxon millions now famishing in England, had they possession of such a country as this, and the Brazilians extirpated, might found a second Indian Empire.[1] There are two things that forcibly strike anyone going into the country here. 1st the enormous number, variety and beauty of the butterflies, 2nd the noise of the cicadas.[2] These fellows are as big as a man's thumb and fly about the trees like locusts. They emit a very acute loud continuous note, and when numbers of them are together it is really deafening. Singularly enough they seem to agree to short intervals of silence, then the note begins, at first weakly, then swelling into a grand chorus and gradually dying away again.

The harbour never looked more beautiful than the morning we sailed. The mountains stood out sharp and well defined, and the singularity of the Sugar-loaf was heightened by a band of clouds wh. trailed along about half-way down. We put the dredge down when we were well out, and in [left blank in MS.] fathoms got up a number of shells, mostly Terebratula; of these the larger were all dead but the small ones were alive.

Feb. 13*th.*

Some days ago the beautiful albatrosses first made their appearance. Nothing can be more easy and beautiful than the flight of these birds. We have also had [in] our train several species of Petrel, a huge Puffinus and a Thalassidroma. We don't at all keep in mind the fate of the Ancient Mariner, inasmuch as whole broadsides of small shot and rifle bullets

---

[1]He expresses similar sentiments in a letter to his mother (*L. & L.* i, 32). Here, after describing the negro slaves, he writes, "I have a much greater respect for them than for their beastly Portuguese masters, than whom there is not a more vile, ignorant, and besotted nation under the sun". Like other young men, Huxley at 21 was inclined to a sweeping impetuosity.

[2]The New South W. cicadas quite equal them. Jan. 1849.

are fired at them daily, but they don't keep to their part of the affair, never coming "for food or play" to the mariner's holla.

The towing net has contained very little of late. A few small crustaceans, among them Idotea; an occasional Velella (V. emarginata), a medusa (Geryonia) and a Diphye (Aglaisma) summing up the whole. Examined the manducatory and respiratory organs of Idotea.

Feb. 18th.

Lost my small drawing book with all the sketches therein contained out of the starboard quarter boat. Hiatus valde deflendus!

Feb. 24th.

To-day it was nearly calm, and the air was much warmer than it has been for some time. The sea swarmed with multitudes of marine animals. Physalia, Velella, three sp. of Ianthina, one or two large species of Idotea, a few Salpae, etc., attracted every one's attention by their large bladdery organs and the beauty and delicacy of their shells, so that from morning until dusk there were a continual succession of people in the quarter boats busy with the towing nets. The ordinary way of using the net did not suffice, but you had to wait till you saw an Ianthina coming and then throw it so as to catch him. The Physalia were all small (about 2 inches in length). The only difference I could observe between them and the larger P. pelagica was that they had a greenish patch round the posterior opening of the air bladder. I took advantage of the opportunity to renew my examination and verify the reproduced lost sketches. Not only did I succeed in doing this but many other new and singular points of structure came out of which I made detailed drawings.

Feb. 25th.

In the morning I made a drawing of the animal of the Ianthina. The figures in Mrs Grey's book are very bad. I also endeavoured to make a dissection of one, but what between the rolling of the ship and the small size and delicacy of the object, I did not succeed at all well. Another Physalia was caught and I carried out the examination further. There is a month's work yet in it; but notwithstanding its complexity I hope in time to get a very complete account of its structure and even of the forms through which its different organs pass. At the same time I think I can already perceive that it will form a great link in the chain of Acalephae, at once explaining and explicable by many as yet isolated structures in the Diphydes, the Physophoridae, and even the Medusae.[1] I feel half ashamed to put such a thought on paper but I have a feeling that by the more or less perfect manner in which this is worked out, my capacities for these undertakings must stand or fall, as at any rate it is a somewhat difficult investigation and not a bad test.

I should like to send a complete account from the Cape if possible but I am afraid I shall not get a sufficient supply of specimens—or rather, not a sufficiently well-regulated supply. If Dame Nature will send me one every day I shall do, but if she sends me a thousand one day and none for a week afterwards I shall be done. This is the misfortune and difficulty in working at these animals in hot climates. You get a day's work out of your specimen and on the morrow he is rotten and you have nothing to go on with although there were millions to be had the day before.

March 16th. Simons Bay.

We dropped anchor here on the 8th of this month at about three o'clock in the afternoon just in time to escape half a gale of wind. Indeed our passage has been reckoned singular as we have not fallen in with the regular hard-blowing south-easter common hereabouts; on the other hand we have met with nothing but light, unsteady sometimes contrary winds interspersed with fine calms. These calms would have just suited me, were it not that the incessant long swell . . .

---

[1]Jan. 7th, 1848. Capt. Stanley informed me this morning that the Paper had arrived, had been perused by Prof. Forbes who was "delighted" (?) with it, and was to be read before the Linnean Society. [But see p. 25 and p. 48, n.]

April 16th.

Precisely a month I see since my last entry—truly journal-
ising is not my forte. We remained at Simons Bay until the
9th of this month for the sole purpose so far as I can judge
of being present at a ball given by the Admiral on the 7th.
This was a very creditable affair. The fair "Afrikanders" did
honour in point of good looks to their native land and danced
bravely. Considering it was a dignity ball too there was a
remarkable absence of formality. Nevertheless I chiefly remember that I was very seedy all next day and wished I hadn't
been such an ass as to go.

I care not how long it may be before I see Simons Bay
again—so far as the town goes—for a more dull, dreary plati-
tude never met my eyes. Nothing but officials, stall-keepers
and Malays to be seen, and very few of these. The Malay
habitations too are as noisome as any Portuguese huts and the
place looks altogether unwholesome.

The surrounding scenery is grand and rugged, but very arid
and sad looking, the vegetation being mainly confined to low
dusty-leaved shrubs and heaths which show their beauty only
on a near approach. But perhaps to this very circumstance, the
absence of any foliage to interfere with the deeper and warmer
tints of the soil, may be owing the gorgeousness of the tints
assumed by the high mountain of the Cape Hanglip side of
the bay, when lighted up by the rising or the setting sun. I
have never seen anything more beautiful in paintings, where
indeed until now I always judged their more scenic effects to
be mere painter's licences.

Several of our officers made visits to Cape Town but the
accounts I received from them of Cape Town and the things
to be done there held out no prospect sufficiently inviting to
induce me to undertake the journey. So my rambles in South
Africa have been chiefly confined to zoological foraging among
the holes in the rocks on the seashore. These offer a great
quantity of marine animals but no very great variety. It was
curious to meet with Comatulae and Terebratulae above low
water mark. The former however were abundant and very
beautiful. A large [?   ] was very common in the same
localities. Several species of Haliotis too were found of good

size and tolerably abundant. During our stay I made several very careful and satisfactory drawings and dissections of Haliotis, Sipunculus, Bullœa, Patella, Fissurella. I examined a large Turbo also, but not very carefully in consequence of his being too much contracted. In every case I paid particular attention to the anatomy of the nervous system and was more and more confirmed in the ideas I had previously formed as to the unity of organization to be detected in it throughout the mollusca. It is not time yet to draw conclusions, but twenty or thirty careful dissections must decide the point and then, Corpo di Baccho, we will have a paper.

I have a grand project floating through my head, of working up a regular monograph of the Mollusca, anatomy, physiology and histology, based on examination of at least one species of every genus. But I fear me much that, as the old saying goes, my eyes are bigger than my belly. In any case, however, I think I will draw up a plan for such an undertaking, as it will at worst prove a useful guide in the study of such molluscs as I do work at. What other notions have I floating in my head just at present?

No. 1. A thorough account of all the Acalephae we meet with.

No. 2. The determination of the homologies of the parts of the head in Insects, for my own private satisfaction at any rate. Inasmuch as I am not at all satisfied with Newport's account as applied to the big Cape grasshopper (locust?). This, to do it properly, will require an examination of the principal types of head in Crustacea, Insecta, Myriapoda, Arachnida, Annelida, in the adult and embryonic states.

***   Modest notion this and about enough for the five years in itself.

No. 3. Mollusca monograph as aforesaid. Enough for five years and a half.

No. 4. An anatomy of the Actiniae and of the Polype animal if Mr McGillivray does not take the latter up. Dᵒ Velella and Porpita.

With all these on my mind I think it will be a hard case if I am obliged to be without occupation anywhere. God defend me from idleness! I should assuredly go clean daft, shortly, in my present environment had I nothing to do.

I finished up my paper on the Physalia at Simons Bay although not quite so completely as might have been wished,[1] and sent it home. I had at first thought of transmitting it to Forbes that he might do what he pleased with it. But the Captain suggesting that it should go to his father as President of the Linnæan, it has been thus disposed of, I stipulating only that it should go to Forbes in the second place. I think it is not improbable that the Bishop will get it printed in the *Linn. Trans.*, by no means on account of any inherent merit, but because it is the first-fruits of his son's cruise. They may do as they like with it. The working up the subject has done me all the real good that lies in the thing and I feel no more interest in it, particularly as I cannot possibly know anything about its fate for the next six months.

To-day I have been very busy upon the Diphyda, Aglaisma and Diphyes—the former was perfect, the latter only possessed the nuclear piece. These transparent creatures are vastly troublesome to depict, even in outline. You have to turn them about and study them for a long while before you can properly understand their strange and whimsical forms.

May 4th.

We made Mauritius last afternoon and having sailed round the northern extremity of the island were towed into Port Louis this morning by the handsomest of tugs. Towing was necessary on account of a fresh offshore breeze which would have precluded any mode of approach beside beating up, a process dangerous by reason of the narrow entrance of the harbour which is flanked on each side by a fringing coral reef. The aspect presented by the island as you approach its shores, is very beautiful, but will not give that idea of luxuriant fertility I had formed from the descriptions of Darwin and others. At a distance the character of the landscape reminded me partly of Rio and partly of Madeira, resembling the former in the shape of the mountains (one of wh. was singu-

---

[1] *Consequences of precipitation:* although I have not made any absolute errors I find by subsequent examination that I have overlooked some important points. N.B.—Don't be in a hurry again. Jany. 1849.

larly like the Corcovado), and the latter in the dry red volcanic-looking appearance of the high land. But as we gradually neared the land the rich plain of the Pamplemousses became a more prominent feature of the landscape, and its bright green richly wooded undulations, fully redeemed the character of the country. I have not yet been ashore but great things are spoken of the Town by those who have.

This is my twenty-second birthday—these birthdays are strange things to reflect on. Twenty-two years ago I entered this world a pulpy mass of capabilities, as yet unknown and save by motherly affection uncared for. And had it not been better altogether had I been crushed and trodden out at once? Nourishing me up, was as though one should pick up a stray egg, unconscious whether dove's or serpent's, and carefully incubate it. And here I am what a score of years in the world have made me—such a bundle of glorious and inglorious contradictions as men call a man.

"Ich kann nicht anders! Gott hilfe mir!" Morals and religion are one wild whirl to me—of them the less said the better. In the region of the intellect alone can I find free and innocent play for such faculties as I possess. And it is well for me that my way of life allows me to get rid of the "malady of thought" in a course of action so suitable to my tastes, as that laid open to me by this voyage.[1]

May 7th.

I went ashore yesterday and the day before to see what was to be seen. The aspect of the island improves even on closer acquaintance and many parts which from the ship looked dull and sombre brighten into a soft verdure.

The Town is remarkably clean but is not without a certain Rio flavour about it, as I suppose from the very numerous black population. It is very regularly laid out in streets parallel to and at right angles with the water. At least this holds good for the town proper; another portion continuous with this, but distinguished under the name of the Black Town on account of the prevailing tint of its inhabitants, cannot boast of any architectural elegance, consisting simply of a street of low two-

---

[1] Is it better with me now? A little. Jany. 1849.

story houses and shops and scattered irregularly behind this on the side of the hill a vast number of thatched huts. But as elsewhere, cleanliness prevailed, so much so that the very gutter in one place contained numerous small Physae.

The variety of costume of the people, from no costume at all up to the silks and satins of the French lady or the richly embroidered muslin drapery of the Hindus, is sufficient to render a walk amusing. You see in the space of a few yards, most Parisian-looking Frenchmen, graceful Hindoos, turbaned Mussulmen, Cingalese, Chinese with their tails carefully stowed away in their caps, and strangest of all the new Police, the very animal of Cockaigne himself, save that ten to one he wears a black face and speaks French. How the deuce they stand the buttoned-up coat and glazed hat in this climate I cannot divine—dispensation of Providence probably.

No place could have been more happily chosen for the site of a town than this; at the back is a mountainous mass of wh. the Peter Botte and La Pouce form two peaks and two spurs run out from this and include a sort of amphitheatre within which lies the town as far as half-way from the water's edge; and behind that a beautiful flat space laid out with a Champ de Mars where now some people who have come here with a sort of Batty's circus on spec. have erected their Booth. He must have been a bold man who first planned the getting up of an equestrian show here, but I understand that the first person who did so was exceedingly successful, making £2000. The blacks sold their very shirts to go.

On one side of the valley in wh. the town is placed a hill rises up, and on this the English have erected a very strong fort built of stone wh. completely commands the town and the entrance of the harbour.

The stone seems very hard and tough and would appear to be plentiful as I noticed that many of the tombs in the cemetery were constructed of it. The cemetery, by the bye, is one of the most beautiful places I have seen. It is placed towards the left point of the Harbour Fort William at the extremity of a noble avenue of Casuarinae. It is of considerable extent with a solid stone wall running round it. Within it is thickly planted with beautiful waving palm trees and flowering acacias, with here and there a bright parterre surrounding a grave.

The monuments are solid looking, and one (to English officers) of white marble and elegantly finished. In other catholic burying grounds I have seen the fashion of planting flowers about the graves, but here the custom was carried to, as it seemed to me, an absurd extent. Not a grave was without a household jug, more or less elegant in design, let into the substance of the stone and plastered there—into these jugs they had poured water and inserted a bouquet of flowers, some of which were sufficiently withered. I judged the date of the deceased's death by the seediness of his bouquet, seeing that Time and Lethe are one. In one case I suppose the disconsolate mourner had no spare crockery inasmuch as he had made use of some old pickle or preserve jar, with name of the manufacturer and contents in black letters on a white ground staring you in the face!

Above all things too I must not forget to note that I saw a fringing coral reef for the first time. It is beautiful to see its place marked in the softly heaving blue sea by a line of white breakers, and within a more yellow coloured water.

Saturday 8th.

Started off early in the morning in the big boat on a pedestrian excursion to the tombs of Paul and Virginia. It is many years since the *Chaumière Indienne* first fell into my hands and I have not forgotten the lively feelings it excited in me, though I fear that such feelings would not return by a reperusal; intercourse with the world the flesh and the devil having extinguished any latent spark of sentimentalism (of the French prudish kind especially) that may have existed in my bosom.[1] Nevertheless, sentimental or practical, nobody should leave Mauritius without seeing the ground consecrated by St. Pierre's classical tale, were it merely for the sake of the beautiful walk thither.

The distance from Port Louis to Pamplemousses is vari-

---

[1] "Though I never was greatly given to the tender and sentimental, and have not had any tendencies that way greatly increased by the elegancies and courtesies of a midshipman's berth,—not to say that, as far as I recollect, Mdlle. Virginia was a bit of a prude, and M. Paul a pump,—yet, were it but for old acquaintance sake, I determined on a pilgrimage." From a letter to his mother (*L. & L.* i, 34).

ously estimated, generally at seven miles, but inasmuch as it did not take me much more than an hour and a half to walk there I do not suppose it to be more than six. The road is excellent throughout, capitally macadamised, and often on either hand beautiful views in the intervals between the thickly set acacias and palm trees, on the one side, towards the gently undulated, English looking plain near the shore, on the other towards the fantastic mountain ridge which bears the Peter Botte.

All along the road at no great distance cottages inhabited by coloured people, and sometimes avenues leading to buildings of greater pretension, are scattered, and as I walked I met with great numbers of people of all colours and varieties of costume hastening to the market at Port Louis, some with loads of no small magnitude. The European people whom I met were all either riding or in carriages, and it seemed to me that some of them looked rather surprised at seeing a white man using his legs after my fashion.[1]

You recognize Pamplemousses at once by its white steepled church with its curiously shaped front. You pass by this and keeping well to your left walk for some distance down a lane well wooded on either side. I was directed to walk along here till I came to the house of a M. Garet Mechanicien, as I understood it, where were the tombs. At length I found this house seated at the extremity of a short avenue of Casuarina trees. Up here I marched and seeing a little intelligent looking boy come out towards me, I mustered up my best French to enquire if M. "Garet" was at home. My French must have been very bad for the boy immediately announced in good idiomatic English though with a slight foreign accent, "Mr Geary is not at home, sir, but I will show you the tombs". My disappointment at being thus openly convicted of bad French was swallowed up in the delight of being able to chatter at my ease, and I speedily became great friends with my youngster and his little sister, a young lady who, though only eleven, was more of a traveller than most folks, having been born in England and yet just arrived at Mauritius from Cochin China !

[1]Perhaps like the W. Indians they have a contempt for a "walking buccra". Jany. 1849.

My guide led the way to what had once been a beautiful garden at the back of the house, but now was a perfect wilderness. It was surrounded by beautiful trees and a grassy path led quite round it. In the middle of this path, towards the end of the garden, was placed on each side a vase with a square pedestal, surrounded by four tall Casuarinas; of these however two on Paul's side had been torn up by a hurricane.

Virginia's tomb[1] was on the right hand side, and near it, overshadowed by an overthrown cocoanut tree, was a low defaced stone marking the spot where the faithful slave rests.

My little guides made great complaints of the merciless ravages committed by visitors, memento collectors who knock off pieces of the tomb without mercy.[2] By way of hint I suppose they took care to let me know that some of these had been severely fined. I showed them that I had a full sense of the abomination of such practices and contented myself with plucking a couple of roses, which now scent my desk.

When I returned I made a sketch of the place from memory; by those who subsequently visited it this was pronounced to be accurate.

Some days after this Brady and I planned a pedestrian excursion to the Tamarin falls some 17 miles up the country and were joined in our project by King, notwithstanding the clamourous assurances of every body else that to think of walking sixteen or seventeen miles in a day in Mauritius was neither more nor less than stark madness. As usual all this only confirmed me the more in my determination and as the others were of the same mind, we started very early one morning. Not knowing what to expect in the way of proviant we provided ourselves with some brawn and sardines, to say nothing of sundry pocket pistols filled with strong waters— as . . .

Not in the humour to write any more to-night.

[1] I have half a suspicion that these tombs are mere "Quakers", in sea phrase— but I can't get at the rights of the story. Jany. 1849.

[2] In a letter to his mother (*L. & L.* i, 35) he adds that the souvenir-hunters were mostly English. He also tells us that Mr Geary was "an English mechanist, who puts up half the steam engines for the sugar mills in the island".

May 29th.   Lat. 36° 6 S.   Long. 74° 17.

Since leaving Mauritius we have had the loveliest weather, the sea calm and quiet as a river. It is getting cold however. Yesterday we saw a great flock of whales spouting in all directions. One of them rose up not more than 30 yards from the ship, and showed his real size to us. He was a finback certainly not less than 50 (?) feet long.

June 22nd.

Since my last entry we have had quite another sort of thing to the "quiet river". It has been cold miserable weather with occasional hard close-reefed topsail breezes, and to add to our discomfort the fuel was all of a sudden found to have fallen short some ten days ago. By way of meeting this alarming deficiency the galley fire was put out at twelve every day, and lately there has been no galley fire at all, all cooking being done in the coppers, and the fire in these even put out at 4 P.M.[1] It is astonishing what a difference this makes in one's small stock of ship's comforts. No hot grog, tea at half-past three, and other abominations. If the present state of things continues however we shall soon have an end of these things. We are within 200 miles of Van Diemens Land with a glorious 8½ knot breeze and expect to see land to-morrow evening at farthest.

I had one of my melancholy fits this evening and as usual had recourse to my remedy—a good "think" to get rid of it. It took me an hour and a half walking on the poop however to accomplish the cure. Among other thoughts that I thought I sketched out the plan of my next paper, "On the Diphydae and their relations with the Physophoridae". I have the material all ready and will send it from Sydney. It shall consist, 1. of a slight sketch of what is already known about the Diphydae. 2. The terminology I use compared with that of authors. 3rd. a general description of the Diphydae and of the typical genera of Physophoridae. 4th. an anatomical and genetical account of the organs of the two classes with comparison.

[1]Poor Denison! He thought himself a real martyr. I should like him to have tried three months on the reefs. Jan./49.

Suppose I finish my account of our trip in Mauritius. I left off where we started, provided with eatables and drinkables and altogether three "proper men". Away we trudged, full of life and spirits, and I confess that the whole scene, the bright sunlight, the brilliant foliage, the firm earth, so refreshing in its very resistance to the foot of one who has been for weeks reeling at sea, intoxicated me, and I would have readily undertaken to walk to Jericho if required. As it was we put a good ten miles between us and the town before calling a halt. By this time the sun was getting hot, and never was anything so sweet as the water of the little Belle Isle river on whose banks we rested.

But there are seven miles to go and we must not rest here. So on we go, asking our way from the innocent blacknesses who cross our path in the best French we can command, as it turned out to little purpose, for after crossing the Rivière du Tamarin and being quite elated at the prospect of leaving our carriage friends in the lurch, we took the turn to the Black River instead of that to the Cascades. We walk on some way and then inquire of a Frenchman who keeps a sort of wayside auberge for further directions. We get capital vin ordinaire at sixpence a bottle and our good friend, seeing us I suppose look somewhat vexed at having come out of the road, assured us that the Cascade du Tamarin is nothing so very grand—he himself has seen that, but that if we want to see the real beauty of the island we should go on to Chamarelle which is only twelve miles off. We must sleep somewhere, and there is nowhere else to sleep at but the Military Post at Black River from whence it is an easy stage to Chamarelle. Our friend assures us that we need be under no apprehension about a reception as M. le docteur at the Porte is a "tres joli petit docteur". Could we do else? No, so we agree to go on.

Meanwhile the appetite gets urgent and we get off the road to seek for a convenient resting and dining place. We descend towards the river, pass a very tempting looking banyan tree, cross a rude bridge, and get into a sort of waste garden in wh. stands a house. Here I found fast asleep in one of the rooms a Frenchman whom I laid under contribution for cold water. He provided us with this, and with first rate pillows on wh. we reclined at our ease "sub tegmine fagi". After

lightening our pockets very materially of the store of eatables
Brady and I went to sleep while King as usual conchologized
and sketched in the neighbourhood. We did not get under way
again till just three o'clock, when somewhat heavy and stiff we
bent our way towards Black River. Our progress was somewhat slower than in the morning so that the sun was setting
as we reached the port, and the rich colours of the evening
sky gave a peculiar beauty to the exquisite little bay at the
head of which the station is situated. In the absence of the
officers the soldiers brought out coffee and bread, the best they
had; after a while the little doctor, who fully merited the
epithet "jolly", returned and we were immediately invited
into his house and provided with a capital dinner. We slept
there that night and did not get fairly on our way again till
eight the next morning, thus exposing ourselves far more to
the heat of the day than was necessary. Our friend the doctor
provided us with a letter of introduction to M. Dinneuville
and accompanied us himself as far as the first river, where he
derived considerable amusement from seeing me wade over
with Brady on my back, the feet of the latter being rather too
sore to admit of his walking over the rough stones at the
bottom. We had to cross two or three streams in this way.

At length we came to a high table-land rising abruptly out
of the plain we had been traversing. Here we had to take to a
mountain path which led for about 1800 feet up the steep side
of a hill clothed with a thick wood. What between the heat
and our previous walk, this seemed a most tremendous exertion, and I got such repeated attacks of violent palpitation of
the heart with consequent faintness that I should never have
got up at all but for that invaluable pocket pistol. At last we
reached the crest and lay down awhile on the other side con-
templating the land of promise before us. The elevation made
a sensible difference in the heat, and the rest of our walk was
more agreeable. We found M. D.'s establishment to be a large
square of buildings in not the best condition. The centre was
provided with a large verandah and was inhabited by the
master, the sides were occupied by outhouses and buildings for
the servants. M. Dinneuville himself was stockingless and un-
shaven, but received us with all the courtesy of a French
gentleman. We found him to be a most agreeable well-

informed man, who had seen much of the world. He treated us most hospitably and would I believe have kept us for a month had we been so inclined.

After lunching with him we proceeded to the falls which are situated about a mile from his house. I shall never forget them —the scene struck me as the most extraordinary I had ever beheld. The Rivière du Cap rises among the high land towards the centre of the island, thence winds its way as a quiet rivulet, till it reaches Chamarelle, when it precipitates itself over the edge of a huge chasm, sheer down for 350 feet; at the bottom it breaks into rainbows of foam against the rocks and then becomes a dark still pool of many acres in extent, ultimately finding its way to the sea by a fissure in one side of the rocky basin. An old tree overhangs one edge of the precipice and hanging on by this you can look down and see the birds wheeling and soaring *below* you. A little Asmodeus of a boy, Sewan by name, accompanied us and I made him hang on to the tree for a foreground while I sketched. The sides of the pit are all covered with large trees and the whole aspect of the place conveys to the mind at once the strongest ideas of wildness and of richness. We bathed in the rivulet just above the falls and had a sort of small washing day so as to get rid of any rate the superficial layer of dust with wh. we were enveloped. In the afternoon King and I made another visit to the falls and saw them under a different point of view. At dinner we met the ladies of our host's family, and I fear that we did not represent the navy creditably in consequence of our imperfect knowledge of French. Chess-playing and conversation whiled away the evening, and we started early on the morrow on our way back to Port Louis, taking a somewhat different course to the way we came.

At noon we were going to bivouac at the bottom of a long avenue wh. led up to a gentleman's house, but he spying us out came down, and carried us up to lunch with him. M. Butte was not contented with entertaining us in first rate style, but seeing that Brady walked rather lame, he insisted upon his riding on a donkey for some miles, sending a black servant to bring the said donkey back. We reached Port Louis that night at ten, having walked thirty odd miles. Brady was disabled for some days, but the rest of us were ready for anything the next

Plate 2

THE CHAMARELLE FALLS, MAURITIUS,
with " the little Asmodeus of a boy, Sewan by name." Pencil drawing,
signed with monogram.

morning. And so ended one of the most pleasant trips I ever had.

Van Diemen's Land.

The sight of the bold land about S.W. Cape was I may venture to say the most pleasant thing that happened to us in our last cruise, always excepting, by the bye, the jolly face and English tongue of the old pilot who came off to us in Storm Bay. The pilot was a man well to do in the world. He lived on Bruny [?] island and we sent a boat to his farm to get such supplies of firewood, fresh meat, potatoes and other luxuries as he had at hand. Those who went brought back reports about a very nice well-furnished cottage, with piano and the like, and ladylike wife with three or four rosy children. And this in a place where fifty years ago you would have seen nothing but naked savages or kangaroos.

Light winds and calms detained us so that we did not get to anchor in Sullivan's Cove before the second day after leaving Storm Bay. I got ashore in the jolly-boat before the ship came up to her anchorage, and having done what business I had to do, got before a huge fire in the Ship Inn with McGillivray and there stuck, imbibing considerable quantities of toddy, until ten or eleven o'clock. We were all invited to a ball that evening but it had no charms for me compared with that splendid wood fire.

CHAPTER 3

Huxley's Scientific Work on the "Rattlesnake"

SCATTERED through the Diary are references to the scientific work carried on by Huxley on board the *Rattlesnake*. Here he mentions finding such and such an organism in the tow-net: there, that he has dissected or microscopically examined some other organism. Sometimes he congratulates himself on having understood to his own satisfaction the structural plan of a family or group; at other times he draws up a scheme for possible future research or tries to envisage how he will work up his results when he returns to England.

To the layman these references will inevitably be cryptic. The long Latin names are unfamiliar; the very types of animals investigated are unknown to the ordinary man; the problems that Huxley sets himself seem arid and formal. But even to the professional biologist, Huxley's comments on his work do not reveal much. If he did not know their authorship, he could deduce little from them beyond the fact that an ambitious young man was working on problems of comparative anatomy in various groups of floating marine organisms. What success the said young man was having in his investigations, and what value there was in the theoretical conclusions that he was drawing, would remain hidden.

In addition to the Journal, there exist in the collection of *Huxleiana* at the Imperial College of Science and Technology at South Kensington, two volumes of purely scientific notebooks, each of about the same size as the Journal, which I have been able to consult. I do not, however, propose to quote from them here. For the most part, they consist of detailed technical descriptions of what his scalpel or his microscope revealed, with references to the numerous drawings which he executed in separate drawing-books.[1] At the outset, the entries are in chronological order, all on one side of the page. But later, as specimens of the same type recur, he frequently inserts his later observations on the blank pages opposite his original account. Many observations concerning the final cruise, to the Louisiade, New Guinea, and Cape York, are inserted thus. In addition to these original observations, which are given not in the shape of rough notes but in remarkably full form, a large part of one notebook is given over to abstracts, again very full and detailed, of scientific papers he had been reading.

The material in these notebooks would provide a rich harvest for the historian of science, showing as they do the growth of Huxley's knowledge and ideas in detail; but they fall outside the scope of the present volume.

To understand what the young Huxley was after and what he achieved, we need to explain what animals he was investigating, the bent of his mind, and the results of his work as evidenced in his published memoirs.[2] Not only this, but we need to set ourselves back in time, and think of the problems in terms of contemporary zoological knowledge (and ignorance), and of contemporary zoological philosophy.

At the outset of the voyage, while still in Plymouth Sound, he begins his Diary by setting down, under seven heads, a programme of work (p. 9). In point of actual fact, he did very little work on five of the seven topics. The "suggestion of Prof. Owen" that he should procure as many as possible of the brains of fishes seems to have gone by the board, as

[1] These drawing-books seem later to have been cut up to provide the illustrations for his scientific papers. I have the remains of one in my possession, together with some isolated drawings, apparently cut from the same source. A page of them is reproduced as Plate 3 to show the remarkable quality of Huxley's scientific draughtsmanship (p. 50).

[2] Huxley's scientific papers were collected after his death and republished in four volumes under the title *The Scientific Memoirs of Thomas Henry Huxley*, edited by his pupils, Sir Michael Foster and Sir E. Ray Lankester (London 1900).

also the search for external fish parasites (Epizoa). There is no evidence of his having paid much attention to the "large Cirripedes and Annelids" (barnacles and segmented worms), nor to the "large Radiata" (Echinoderms)—although the critical review of Johannes Müller's work on Echinoderm development, published by Huxley in 1851, soon after his return to England, gives evidence that he must have carried out the intention expressed in the Diary of dissecting Trepangs, the large sea-cucumbers or *bêches-de-mer* extensively sold for Chinese consumption.

The most curious omission is his "careful study of all matters relating to coral and corallines". The *Rattlesnake* spent months cruising along the largest and most wonderful coral reef in the world, the Great Barrier of north-eastern Australia: in spite of this and in spite of Huxley's avowed intention of studying corals, there is scarcely a mention of them in the Diary, no publication by Huxley devoted to the subject, and no indirect evidence of his having acquired any special first-hand knowledge of them.

To this strange fact I shall return. For the moment, we have to consider the two items of his original programme which he did carry out. Of these, one is the structural organization of the Molluscs, the other the detailed study of the Acalephae, or, as we should now say, Coelenterates.

In both cases Huxley took advantage of the special opportunities provided by an oceanic cruise. The animal inhabitants of the sea's surface layers are in the majority of cases characterized by extreme transparency. This has a twofold biological significance. The animals of these regions must not sink far below the surface. To prevent this, a frequent method is to dilute the tissues of the body with water, so that the specific gravity approximates to that of the surrounding medium, and sinking becomes less rapid. The watery jellies which make up the bulk of the body in jelly-fish and comb-jellies are examples of this; and such watery jellies are usually translucent or transparent.

In the second place, natural selection has been at work to effect concealment. In a certain number of forms, such as the flying fish, or the sea-snail Ianthina, or the siphonophore Velella, the animal has been made to approximate to the colour of its surroundings and is blue. But in most cases protection is achieved by invisibility. Not only jelly, but living flesh itself is made crystal-clear. The very blood may be decolorized, as in the young of eels. Such organs as cannot for one reason or another readily become transparent—the liver and stomach and reproductive organs of some creatures, for instance—are massed together in tight knots and coloured to resemble a floating speck of weed. Both the eater and the eaten may take advantage of transparency, the one to approach unseen, the other to escape detection.

However the transparency may be brought about, and whatever function it may subserve, it provides the biologist with unique opportunities for observation. Without dissection, without the laborious process of cutting and mounting serial sections, he can explore all the main features of the creature's anatomy. Nerves, brains, blood-vessels, muscles, digestive system—they are all transparent, but all outlined in crystal for his observation. This was doubly important in Huxley's early days, before the invention of the microtome had enabled the zoologist to reconstruct the anatomy of a creature from the thin serial sections into which, with the aid of the microtome, he had cut it. Huxley was forced to make the best use of the method of direct observation, too often neglected by later zoologists.

Such animals are taken by means of tow-nets—special nets of bolting-silk with a tin or bottle at the end, towed behind a slowly moving vessel. The technique of tow-netting at various depths below the surface is now a fine art. In Huxley's young days it was in its infancy. Indeed, so new was it that MacGillivray, in his official account of the voyage, thinks fit to append a special note on the subject. Their tow-net, he tells us, was home-made. It consisted of a bag of ship's bunting, two feet long, attached to a 14-inch wooden hoop. This, by means of three 18-inch pieces of cord attached to the hoop at equal intervals, was fastened to a rope and towed behind the ship. Modern tow-nets are much longer and made of finer material: but this served its purpose.

The pelagic animals to be taken by tow-netting in the open sea are extremely various, and belong to all the main groups of marine animals. Even a few worms and sea-cucumbers may be taken, and transparent fish, especially in the larval state, are not uncommon. But the most frequent are Crustaceans, Molluscs, Arrow-worms, Tunicates, Coelenterates, and Protista. Let the layman not be discouraged by the unfamiliar terms: they conceal the most fascinating creatures. By Protista the biologist means unicellular organisms. Among these the plants are of extraordinary importance, for they are to the sea what grass is to the land—the main sustenance for all the other creatures of the region, the broad base of the food-pyramid of the open sea. However, the majority of them are not only microscopic, but small even within that range of size. The details of their structure were not readily observable with Huxley's microscopic equipment, and in any case they were not of great morphological interest at that time. The problems that attracted Huxley were problems of form and structural plan, of morphology, not of "scientific natural history", or, as we should now say, ecology.

Crustaceans are familiar to all in the shape of lobsters and crabs, shrimps and sandhoppers; but the population of small transparent crustacea, especially Copepods, in the sea's surface layers is of great importance as an essential link in the food-chain between the microscopic plants and the larger animals like fish. However, Huxley, though he doubtless examined a great many of these creatures, seems not to have been especially interested in them at the time of the *Rattlesnake* voyage. It was not until many years later that he turned to the Crustacea and wrote that book on the Crayfish which for decades served as a model of what a well-balanced zoological monograph should be.

All the other groups, however, came in for his more intensive interest.

On January 4th, 1847, he becomes much intrigued with "great numbers of transparent lanceolate bull-headed animals about three-quarters of an inch long . . . which are exceedingly voracious and swim about frequently with their heads buried in some unfortunate Ascidian" (pp. 13–14).

It is interesting to find that his meagre zoological training had left him quite ignorant of what these animals were; he adds a note of a later date, presumably after he had had access to scientific books in Sydney, that they were Sagitta.

Sagitta or the arrow-worm is a widespread predatory marine creature which in our seas lives largely on herring larvae. It is an aberrant type of animal—the only type apart from vertebrates to possess a true tail, or part of the body reaching a distance behind the end of the digestive tube. This feature struck Huxley, who notes very pertinently that the tail resembles that of a fish.

He did not, however, publish any scientific paper on Sagitta. Most of his attention was thus given to the three groups of Molluscs, Coelenterates, and Tunicates.

To all three of these Huxley devoted a great deal of time and thought. I will deal with the results in what seem to me to be the ascending order of their importance. The Tunicates are a very fascinating group of animals, the most familiar— or perhaps I should say the least unfamiliar—members of which are the fleshy sea-squirts to be found on any rocky seashore. They are interesting above all in being degenerate relations of our own Vertebrate group. When young they pass through a microscopic tadpole stage which reveals the basic essentials of vertebrate structure—a dorsal and tubular central nervous system, a notochord or primordial backbone, which even in ourselves appears transitorily in early embryonic life as a precursor of the definitive vertebral column, and gill-slits piercing the wall of the pharynx. Later they lose all these badges of their tribe, and, in the case of the sea-squirts, settle down to a sedentary and vegetative existence.

This extraordinary metamorphosis, however, was not revealed until the 70's, when the Russian zoologist Kovalevsky startled the zoological world with his discovery of it. At the time of the voyage of the *Rattlesnake,* the vertebrate affinities of the group were unguessed at. More than that, the limits of the group were not clearly defined, and its general position in the animal kingdom was wholly obscure.

Besides the sea-squirts, which live sedentary lives attached to rocks or weeds, the Tunicates comprise some extraordinary actively-swimming creatures which inhabit the open sea. One group of these are the Appendicularians—tiny animals which manufacture amazing temporary "houses" of gelatinous material that serve to entrap microscopic plants and other food debris. These animals had proved a complete puzzle to earlier

investigators. Chamisso, their discoverer, had thought to de-
tect a resemblance to Venus' Girdle, a member of the tribe of
Ctenophores or comb-jellies; another zoologist was satisfied
that they were Molluscs; while the great Johannes Müller,
with characteristic frankness, had confessed himself wholly
unable to place them satisfactorily in the system. Huxley,
however, gave excellent reasons for believing that it belonged
to the group of Tunicates.

Huxley, in a paper published in 1851, once more showed
himself an adept at detecting the fundamentals of structural
plan through the deceitful veil of superficial appearance. He
showed that their basic organization was in essentials similar
to that of Ascidians, Salps, and other Tunicates. He further
suggested that their peculiar tail might be regarded as a primitive larval feature retained throughout adult life, in this
anticipating not only much of Haeckel's theory of recapitulation, but some of the modifications which, under the stress of
modern criticism, it has recently undergone.

Here again we are made to realize the chaotic state in which
invertebrate zoology then found itself, and the masterly insight displayed by Huxley in reducing this chaos to order,
carving up the unnatural groups which satisfied earlier workers
and reuniting their elements into the units of a rational and
natural system.

Besides these, other and more conspicuous forms abound in
pelagic waters. The most striking is the animal known as
Pyrosoma, or "fire-body", from its amazing luminescence. It
consists of a colony of Tunicates arranged round a central
space, in the shape of a thimble with a hole in the tip. Sometimes these giant thimbles attain a length of ten feet or over.
What is more, they glow with an intensity and variety of light
approached by no other phosphorescent organism. Anatomi-
cally, however, they do not provide any great puzzle. Their
organization in its broad features clearly resembles that of the
humdrum sea-squirt. The *Rattlesnake* on her homeward
voyage passed through swarms of these creatures on several
nights in June 1850, and Huxley was struck by the beauty of
the sight,[1] but only on one occasion was he able to procure

[1]See p. 260. In his Royal Society paper of 1851, he writes "a more beautiful
sight can hardly be imagined than that presented from the decks of the ship

one for examination. He confirmed the observations of previous workers, showed that they were closely related in their anatomy to the common Ascidians or sea-squirts, and made a few interesting notes on their emission of light.

The remaining group of Tunicates includes the Salps and their allies—those "strange gelatinous animals, through masses of which the voyager in the great oceans sometimes sails day after day" (I quote from Huxley's introduction to his paper on the subject, published in 1851). The anatomy of these creatures is very peculiar: but Huxley succeeded in showing that it was but a variant upon the fundamental plan of Tunicate organization.

However, his chief interest centred in their modes of reproduction. Some time previously, in 1821, the biologist and man of letters Chamisso, zoologist for the nonce, but better known as a botanist, traveller, and man of letters,—Chamisso had published an account of the life-history of Salps which in Huxley's words "was received with almost as much distrust as if he had announced the existence of a veritable Peter Schlemihl".[1] Chamisso had asserted that Salps occur in two quite distinct forms, a solitary form and a chain form. Inside its body the solitary form produces a chain of young forms of a somewhat different anatomical construction. The chain is later liberated, and grows up, its members still united into the chain form which may reach a length of several feet or even yards. Each member of the chain produces a single embryo which later is freed to develop into a solitary form, thus completing the cycle.

Huxley examined Salps on numerous occasions, and finally, in November 1849, when the *Rattlesnake* was anchored at Cape York, was able to put Chamisso's statements to detailed test. The sea for miles around was crowded with Salps in all stages of growth and reproduction. He found that Chamisso's remarkable assertions were in all essentials true. The Salp in its life-history does exhibit this invariable and necessary alter-

as she drifted hour after hour, through the shoal of miniature pillars of fire gleaming out of the dark sea, with an ever-waning, ever-brightening, soft bluish light, as far as the eye could reach on every side." The scientific convention allowed more scope for romantic writing then than now.

[1]The story of Peter Schlemihl, the man who sold his shadow, had made Chamisso famous as an imaginative writer.

nation of distinct forms. Huxley, however, went further. He showed that whereas the chain Salps possess sexual organs and give rise to the young solitary forms by sexual reproduction, the solitary forms are asexual. They produce the chain of young chain-form Salps by a process of budding, through the growth and repetitive constriction of a special proliferative tube or stolon. Thus in the life-cycle of Salps, there is not only an alternation of forms, but an alternation of generations, sexual alternating with asexual.

These observations were important and valuable in themselves. They also served as part of the basis for Huxley's first incursion into philosophical zoology. In what was probably his first public lecture, delivered in 1852 at the Royal Institution, he chose as his subject "Animal Individuality". But to this I shall return after discussing his work on the Coelenterates.

Meanwhile there remain the Molluscs. These are to all appearances a very heterogeneous group comprising not only the snails and slugs of land and sea, the chitons with their armadillo-like armour, the tusk-shells, and the pteropods, that important item in the food of whales, which flap their way through the open water with wing-like appendages, but also such astonishingly diverse creatures as the active big-eyed cuttlefish, octopuses, nautiluses, and ammonites on the one hand and the headless sedentary clams, mussels, cockles, and oysters on the other.

The Molluscs had been somewhat of a zoological dumping-ground. Molluscs merely means soft-bodied creatures, and the group had been taken to include almost any such soft animal, with or without an external shell, which was not segmented or elongated like a worm, or of a radiate structure like a sea-cucumber or a sea-anemone. Whole groups which are now classified quite apart from the Molluscs, like the sea-squirts we have just mentioned, the little sea-mats and other Polyzoa, and the Lampshells or Brachiopods, were for long grouped with the Molluscs.

In the introduction to his remarkable memoir on the subject, which was published in 1853, Huxley points out that it is still uncertain whether the "back" of a cuttlefish corresponds to the upper or lower surface of a snail, and that opinion is still quite uncertain "with regard to the archetypal molluscous form, and the mode in which (if such an archetype exist) it becomes modified in the different secondary types". In modern terms it was doubtful if the Molluscs as then envisaged represented a natural group: and if they, or some of them, did represent a natural group, it was uncertain how the different sub-groups were related and how the ancestral plan of structure had been modified during the evolution of the separate groups. Huxley deliberately restricted himself to the "Cephalous Molluscs", as zoologists of that period usually called them—the forms which, unlike the bivalves, possess a well-marked head, such as the snails and slugs and their marine relatives, and the cuttlefish, octopuses and squids. Scientific opinion, as he pointed out, was not yet agreed as to the relationships between these types, and this was the crux of the matter. If it were possible to establish the notion of an "archetype" or ideal structural plan which would be basic to all these forms and from which the structure of the separate sub-types could be readily derived, this would serve as a touchstone for the whole Molluscan problem. The question of the position of the outlying groups, like the bivalves or the Ascidians, could wait: it would solve itself with the aid of the tested concepts derived from the central cephalous group of forms.

A word must be said on the subject of archetypes. The modern zoologist, imbued from the outset of his training with the evolutionary outlook, is apt to read an evolutionary meaning into discussions such as those of this paper of Huxley's on the Molluscs, where the whole emphasis is laid on finding a general plan of construction which by slight modification can be made to fit the actual structural plan found in the animals as they exist here and now. For the modern zoologist, community of organization automatically implies community of blood relationship; the common "archetypal" plan is taken as the ancestral type; and the modifications of this seen in the separate existing groups are assumed to be the results of actual historical processes brought about in the course of evolution.

As a matter of fact, the concept of archetype had no such implications. Even Huxley, in later life the protagonist of

Darwin's views, was in 1853, only six years before the publication of *The Origin of Species*, definitely *not* thinking in evolutionary terms.

This idea of archetypes or general plans of construction each common to large assemblages of animals or plants had fixed itself inevitably upon biologists. Two contrary tendencies had been at work leading to the state of thought to be found in the 1840's and 1850's—in briefest phrase, the study of resemblances and the study of differences.

The study of resemblances had shown unexpected correspondence in constructional plan between different creatures. The wing of a bat, the flipper of a sea-cow, and the foot of a dog could readily be reduced to a common plan. The whales, in spite of their fish-like look, resemble mammals in their structural plan as well as in their warm blood and mode of reproduction. Creatures so remote in appearance as starfish, sea-urchins, and sea-cucumbers turned out to have the same general system of organs arranged in the same general way. The empirical fact of this constructional resemblance led to the formulation of the idea of an archetypal plan in which all the common features were embodied.

Goethe had done a great deal to establish the principle that many organisms may ring the changes on a common plan. For him, however, the variants were different expressions of a common *idea*. The very notion of an ideal type is taken from platonic philosophy, and in the hands of Oken, the German zoologist, the notion of archetype blossomed into strange metaphysical forms. More sober biologists, however, like the botanist de Candolle, refused to follow Goethe in his use of the term *idea* and preferred to employ the non-committal word *type*. It is in this empirical sense that Huxley uses the concept of archetype, as a common basis of structural plan which will serve as a ground for classifying certain animals together.

Meanwhile the study of differences had led to the belief that a fixed and definite number of archetypes existed, and that there were no transitions to be found or expected between them. Baron Cuvier, the great French zoologist, had been especially concerned in establishing this point of view. His contemporary, Lamarck, had employed the old conception of the *scala naturae* in his classification. For him, the main groups of the animal kingdom, of which he distinguished fourteen, beginning with infusoria and polyps and passing through insects to molluscs and up to fish and finally to mammals, constituted a single ascending scale, *l'échelle des êtres.* Cuvier would have nothing to do with this. He classified animals into four branches or *embranchements,* each constructed on a particular plan or type—the *vertebrate* type with backbone; the soft-bodied or *molluscan* type; the *articulate* type with numerous segments and jointed limbs, like Crustacea, insects, and segmented worms; and the *radiate* type, built on a radial plan, like sponges, sea-anemones, jellyfish, starfish, sea-urchins, and various other lowly creatures.

This was a considerable advance on the ideas of Linnaeus, who had grouped all invertebrates into "Insects" (in an extended sense) and "Worms", and had left the Vertebrates as four groups—mammals, birds, reptiles, and fish—each of equal classificatory value with *Insecta* or *Vermes.* But it left a great deal to achieve: how much, will be realized from the fact that from his Mollusca and Radiata modern zoology has carved out one sub-kingdom—the single-celled Protozoa—and at least ten major groups or phyla, each of equal classificatory rank with Vertebrates, say, or Molluscs in the modern sense.

Huxley shares with Johannes Müller, von Baer, and a few others the distinction of having been a notable pioneer in reducing this chaos, this classificatory mess, to order. And he did so by holding tight to the one guiding thread then available, the notion of archetypes. If you classified with regard to fundamental structural plan, you were more likely to be right than if you used as your criterion some superficial resemblance in form or some similarity in mode of life. This belief had at the time no real justification, either philosophical or scientific; but it was later justified by Darwin, for with the acceptance of the evolutionary idea, it at once became clear that common plan was the badge of common descent.

In the particular case of the Molluscs, the archetype which he framed to clarify his ideas was a creature of the following construction. It was bilaterally symmetrical, externally and internally, in this unlike a snail or a limpet; like them, but unlike the cuttlefish and their allies, it was a crawling animal, possessed of a flat muscular sole or "foot" on its ventral surface; dorsally it was equipped with a simple humped shell; between the shell and the foot was a space, the mantle cavity; internally its chief distinctive characteristic was the concentration of nerve-cells into three main centres or ganglia, one in the head, one in the foot, and one in the region of the body containing the main viscera.

From this archetype the types of the sub-groups of Molluscs could readily be derived—certain Gastropods by twisting of the body and sometimes the shell too into an asymmetry, the cuttlefish and octopuses by the sub-division of the foot into a series of movable arms and by the overgrowth and reduction of the shell, and so on.

It is remarkable how closely Huxley's archetypal Mollusc of 1853 resembles the ancestral type of Mollusc as deduced by zoologists eighty years later: only in minor details has there been improvement. Never was his engineer's instinct of grasping the essence of a construction better exemplified than in this work. Let us, in passing, recollect that the ease with which he could trace the position of nerves and ganglia, heart and other viscera, in the transparent floating forms he caught in his tow-net undoubtedly offered him advantages denied to zoologists ashore: the open sea offered him certain opportunities, and he took full advantage of them.

I have left to the last his work on the Medusae and other members of the group then styled Acalephae because it was the most fundamental, and also because it was of most importance to him in his career. He had early realized the significance of the new facts and ideas he had arrived at, and hastened to finish off his paper. Captain Stanley transmitted it to his father, the Bishop of Norwich, who communicated it to the Royal Society.[1] Huxley, after much heart-burning at not hearing anything of its fate, found on his return to England that it had already been printed and published in the *Philosophical Transactions* for 1849, under the title "On the

[1] In the *Life and Letters* (vol. i, p. 43) it is stated that the papers written by Huxley in Australia were sent back to Edward Forbes. However, in the *Phil. Trans.* for 1849 Huxley's paper on the Medusae is stated to have been "Communicated by the Bishop of Norwich, F.R.S." Later papers, such as that on the Salps, were communicated by Forbes.

Anatomy and the Affinities of the Family of the Medusae", and that his zoological name was already made.

Huxley fully realized the importance of his own ideas. In a letter to his sister (*L. and L.* i, 33) he anticipates that "this paper will achieve one of the great ends of Zoology and Anatomy, viz. the reduction of two or three apparently widely separated and incongruous groups into modifications of the single type".

Acalephae means *nettles*. The "sea-nettles" to which the name was applied in Huxley's day comprised the jelly-fish, large and small, the Siphonophores like the Portuguese men-of-war and numerous exquisite but unfamiliar colonial creatures, and the comb-jellies. To-day the name has been dropped —largely because of Huxley's work, and his demonstration that these creatures had a fundamental plan of structure which they shared with the polyps, and as later research showed, with the corals and sea-anemones. They were an artificial assemblage of sub-groups from within a larger group—what we now call the Coelenterates. In Huxley's time, however, they were pitchforked with sponges and sea-urchins and various other uneasy bedfellows into the *omnium-gatherum* of the Radiata—a group even more ill-assorted than Cuvier's Mollusca.

Medusae were among the most frequent captures of his tow-net, and he seems early to have been fascinated by their beauty and their unfamiliarity. After examining a number of them, he came to the conclusion that they were all built up, large and small alike, on a common plan—two "foundation membranes" (which we should now call cell-layers), one covering the outer surface, the other lining the stomach and its ramifications, and the two separated by a structureless gelatinous mass. Round the edge of the animal's umbrella-like disc there exist a row of tentacles and various special sense-organs. Of blood and blood-vessels there was no trace: the tubular canals to be seen here and there in the interior are all prolongations of the stomach.

Though these facts constituted a definite advance in zoological knowledge, they did not go very far. It was obvious that all jelly-fish showed a fundamental resemblance, and what I have described of Huxley's work merely gave precision to this, at the same time showing that the Medusae had nothing essential in common with other Radiates such as star-fish or sea-urchins.

However, Huxley was not content with this. Siphonophores of the two families Diphyidae and Physophoridae (the names recur in the Journal) were also abundant in his tow-nettings— long trailing glassy objects, with swimming-bells and tubular feeding-organs and protective bracts and long stinging tentacles, all attached, often in groups or bunches, to a central hollow stalk. Huxley found that these too lacked blood and were composed of the two foundation membranes with jelly-layer between.

Finally, when ashore, he took the opportunity of examining various polyps from the tidal zone. Even in these he discovered the two lining membranes, and saw that their mouth and the tentacles surrounding it conformed to the same essential plan as those of the jelly-fish, although the jelly-fish were free and solitary, the polyps stalked and grouped in colonies. The Siphonophores he also considered as colonial organisms, built on the same general plan. Thus he picked out of the Radiate hotch-potch three groups, very dissimilar in superficial appearance, and grouped them together as possessors of the same type of structural plan.

Later research added the corals and sea-anemones and one or two other forms to the assemblage: but Huxley had already characterized what is now a cornerstone of animal classification—the group *Coelenterata,* differing from all higher forms in being composed of two primary layers—Huxley's foundation membranes—instead of three. The modern zoologist is so used to the fundamentals of the classification which he imbibes from his earliest acquaintance with his science that he is apt to take it for granted. Reading Huxley's paper to-day, he would be tempted to dismiss it as *vieux jeu*—it seems so elementary. It is elementary: but Huxley was the first to seize on these elements. It is *vieux jeu* to-day: but in 1850 it was intensely novel.

Not content with this, Huxley drops in at the end of the paper, half casually, what is in a way the most pregnant and original of the ideas contained in it. He compares the fundamental plan of his medusa-polyp-siphonophore archetype to

Plate 3

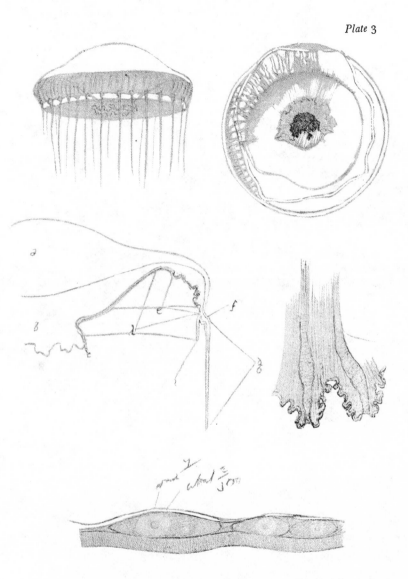

HUXLEY'S SCIENTIFIC DRAWINGS. FIVE SKETCHES OF A PELAGIC JELLY-FISH

Top left, the whole animal in side view; top right, from below. Centre left, vertical section of half the animal; centre right, portion of the "lip" surrounding the mouth. Below, a portion of the body-wall, under the microscope, showing egg-cells. These represent a selection from the eight pencil sketches on a single page of Huxley's scientific drawing-book. The page is labelled "LXIII. Oceania [the name of the animal], Feby 6th, 1848."

the fundamental plan of the very early chick embryo. Von Baer in Germany, as Huxley had read, had recently shown that in a certain stage of development the vertebrate embryo is built of two layers or membranes, outer and inner. Huxley now took the step of comparing these with the two foundation membranes he had discovered in the adult coelenterate. "It is curious", he writes, "to remark that throughout, the outer and inner membranes [of a jelly-fish or a polyp] appear to bear the same physiological relation to one another as do the serous and mucous layers of the germ . . ." and so on for a few more sentences.

In this brief passage Huxley anticipated the Haeckelian doctrine of recapitulation in its most ambitious flights. Von Baer had noted that the embryos of different vertebrates grew to resemble each other more as they were traced back to earlier stages. But the notion that there could be any real or significant resemblance between an adult jelly-fish or polyp and an embryo man or bird was in the year 1850 outside the range of zoological discourse, though now we accept it as basic and as signifying that all higher animals have during evolution passed through a two-layered stage of the essential Coelenterate type. The young Huxley was held back by the atmosphere of his time from doing more than note the fact of resemblance, without attempting to draw any conclusions from it. But during his middle age he was destined to see how such ideas made sense with evolution, and to find them becoming of great importance in zoological research and theory.

Finally I come to the question of zoological individuality. These colonial creatures like the Portuguese man-o'-war, where it was often difficult (and remains difficult in certain cases to-day) to be sure whether a given part represented a whole polyp or medusa modified to serve as an organ of the colony, or was only some enlarged organ of a polyp or medusa: those fantastic creatures the Salps, with their alterna-tion between two forms, of different structural type, one solitary and the other colonial, one asexual and the other sexual, prompted Huxley to philosophical speculation. What, in such cases, represented the individual within the species? Was it the single material aggregate, whether colony or solitary form? Was it the organization of given structural plan, whether this chanced to be solitary and independent, or to exist as a mere organ of a colony? Was it the whole succession of forms from fertilized egg to fertilized egg? Huxley liked clear-cut answers, and, in his Royal Institution address of 1852, he plumped for the last of the three solutions to the enigma. Biologically, he averred, an individual is a cycle: individuality inheres in a recurrent succession of forms, not in any single form: and the beginning of the cycle he fixed in the act of fertilization of the egg, setting aside the budding and other asexual processes of reproduction as in some way less fundamental.

In this last point we now know that he was wrong: there is no biological reason for dating the birth of an individual by the act of fertilization rather than by an asexual act: if it were so, we should have to say that a pair of identical twins were not two individuals but one individual—which, in Euclid's words, is absurd. But he was right in perceiving that a biological individual is a process, a cycle, and that individuality must be defined in dynamic, not merely in static terms. He was right also in assigning special significance to the sexual process of fertilization—merely wrong in linking this significance with the quite distinct significance of individuality.

With the idea of evolution at the back of our minds, we can think of grades of individuality, and of a structure like that of a polyp, say, passing from being an independent individual in its own right to becoming a mere organ of a colonial individual of higher grade—individuality can wax or wane in the course of evolution. In Huxley's day anything of this sort was hardly possible, even in abstract thought. However, his ideas forced men to ask themselves what they really did mean by an individual, and were a real stimulus to later advance: and his method of cutting the Gordian knot by introducing one definite fact—the cycle from one fertilization to the next—as the differential of individuality, is characteristic. Although there is no reference to it in the Journal, we can assume with a good deal of probability that his first philosophizings on the subject floated through his mind as he paced the *Rattlesnake's* deck on fine tropic nights before turning in to sleep.

One could add more about this or that detail of Huxley's scientific work on the cruise, but what has been said will suffice

to lend meaning to the scattered references in the Journal, and
to give some comprehension of the zoological importance of
the work itself. Before concluding this chapter, however, I
should like to say a few words on two further points—the
conditions under which the work was done, and the limitations
imposed by Huxley on the work itself.

Let me take this latter point first. In the young Huxley
there is little trace of the variety of scientific interests displayed by Darwin on the *Beagle*. Darwin paid much attention
to the general geology of the places he visited, and to their
general natural history. It was through a combination of these
two interests, in eastern South America, that he gained his first
flash of evolutionary insight—by noting that the fossil fauna,
though different in detail from the very distinctive existing
fauna of the region, yet in a general way resembled it and
differed from the fauna of any other region. Again, it was
detailed faunistic study that, on the Galapagos Islands, took
his evolutionary speculations a stage nearer certitude.

Almost everything is grist which comes to Darwin's mill.
He is interested in the natural products of the countries he
visits, and excogitates a brilliant theory on the origin of coral
reefs; he collects botanical specimens, and gives an account of
the physiological effects of high altitude on miners in Peru.

Huxley shows little of this scientific catholicity. His Journal
reveals him as very sensitive to natural beauty, as interested
both in literature and in people, as much preoccupied with
moral problems. But scientifically he confined himself, for all
practical purposes, to the stern discipline of anatomy and comparative morphology. Partly this was due to his temperament.
To the end of his life he could never summon up any great
interest in what is broadly called Natural History, or in systematics. The discovery and description of a species new to
science, which was the chief zoological interest of MacGillivray, the ship's official naturalist, had no attractions for him,
nor had he naturally the collector's passion.[1] As he himself

---

[1]In spite of their differences in scientific temperament, Huxley and MacGillivray seem to have got on well with each other. MacGillivray, in the preface to
his official account of the voyage, writes: "It also affords me great pleasure to
record my obligations to T. Huxley, Esq., R.N., F.R.S., late Assistant-Surgeon
of the *Rattlesnake,* for the handsome manner in which he allowed me to select
from his collection of drawings those which now appear as illustrations" [the

has put on record, his natural interest was what we may call biological engineering—to understand the construction and working of animals, and to deduce general laws from specific instances. He had strong visualizing power, and, though he might well have become a great physiologist had circumstances allowed him to follow his early bent for this science, the study of comparative anatomy came naturally to him.

Undoubtedly, however, the restriction of his work was in part due to the restriction of his previous training. Darwin, besides being a born collector, had paid considerable attention both to geology and botany while at Cambridge, and had profited by his intimate association with the distinguished and catholic-minded botanist Henslow. Huxley had received a medical training. Besides some elementary chemistry and physics, all of science that he had studied was human physiology and anatomy, with a little botany and comparative anatomy thrown in by the way. Such branches as geology, faunistic zoology, and anthropology had not come his way. Yet in later life he became eminent both as a geologist and as an anthropologist. We can only speculate as to what he might have achieved on the *Rattlesnake* if he had received a more systematic training in science. But quite possibly the restriction was all to the good. To the end of his life he worked best when concentrating on getting the utmost out of a particular problem: the way of collecting rather miscellaneous facts and gradually piecing them together into a coherent mass of evidence with a drift and a theoretical bearing, so ably practised by Darwin, or by the great systematists like Hooker, was not for him. It may be that his lack of interest in natural history and systematics on the one side, and on the other his lack of any preparation to study geological or anthropological prob-

originals of most of which, I may add, seem to have been lost], "and I may express the hope, which in common with many others I entertain, that the whole of his researches in marine zoology may speedily be laid before the scientific world" [referring to the dispute with the Admiralty as regards publication: p. 3]. And Huxley writes to his mother, after his first joint collecting expeditions with MacGillivray at Rio (*L. & L.* i, 32): "By the way, tell Cooke, with my kindest regards, that —— is a lying old thief, many of the things he told me about Macgillivray, e.g., being an ignoramus in natural history, etc., etc., having proved to be lies. He is at any rate a very good ornithologist, and, I can testify, is exceedingly zealous in his vocation as a collector . . ."

Plate 4

H.M.S. Rattlesnake.   *From a print in the possession of Mrs. L. Huxley.*

lems, conduced in the long run to a greater concentration upon comparative anatomy, and to a degree of penetration below the multiple surface of appearance to the unity of plan, which otherwise he might not have achieved.

That is mere speculation. What, however, is not speculation but matter of record is the difficulty of the conditions under which his work was carried on. The *Rattlesnake,* an old 28-gun ship, with her complement of 180 officers and men, was small and crowded. In the Journal we hear echoes of her creakings and rattlings, catch a whiff of the rich variety of shipboard smells, sympathize with Huxley in his discomforts in a gale, over the poor food and occasional short rations of water, overcramped quarters in sweltering muggy heat, at springing a leak.[1]

Even the collection of specimens was difficult. I have mentioned the home-made tow-net. MacGillivray records an even odder contraption which, under stress of necessity, they devised. It was on their first scientific collecting parties, carried out with the aid of a dredge near Rio de Janeiro. Not even a boat was provided. All the ship's boats and their crews were needed on the more official tasks of surveying and hydrography; and they had to charter a local one, together with a crew of negro slaves. On the first occasion, "no sieve having been supplied, we were obliged to sift the contents of the dredge with our hands—a tedious and superficial mode of examination". So next time they sallied forth "provided with a wire-gauze meat-cover and a curious machine for cleaning rice; these answered capitally". What would your modern zoologist aboard one of H.M.'s Research Ships say to a home-made bunting tow-net or to a meat-cover and a curious machine for cleaning rice as his main aids to the capture of his specimens?

Even this was not the end of their difficulties. The navigation officers were given to complaining that the tow-net stopped the way of the ship, and the traditions of the senior service were affronted by the messiness of marine animals

[1] See *L. & L.* i, 49, for Huxley's account of the "tone of feeling very unfavourable to scientific exertions" which characterized the regular naval officers in the 1840's.

aboard one of Her Majesty's ships.[1] So it came about that Huxley was not always able to net when he wanted to, and that even when this had been permitted, his cherished specimens were sometimes pitched overboard when his back was turned.

And when the specimens were at last safe, they had to be examined. This provided the greatest difficulties of all. Huxley's "laboratory" was a small part of the chartroom. The light there was poor. In all weathers but a dead calm, he had to lash his microscope to the table. Only those who have attempted microscopic work or fine dissection on shipboard know the continual nervous strain induced by the ship's motion. However, by one means or another Huxley managed both to secure and to study the queer marine creatures that the midshipmen nicknamed his Buffons—in allusion to what appears to have been the backbone of his scientific library, the *Suites à Buffon*. This in itself marks the scientific remoteness of that time from our own. We still read Buffon with pleasure for his majestic style and with interest as showing what natural history meant a hundred and fifty years ago. But a modern zoologist would no more dream of having him in his working library than he would Gesner or Aristotle.[2]

Undoubtedly microscopic work or dissection under such conditions was difficult. However, Huxley himself declared that the difficulties had been exaggerated. In any case, he surmounted them: and we may hazard that the need for surmounting them brought his pertinacity and concentration to a higher pitch and endowed him with experience and confidence that stood him in good stead later. Throughout his life he

[1]For Huxley's comments upon the *Rattlesnake* see *L. & L.* i, 47. ". . . Exploring vessels will be invariably found to be the slowest, clumsiest, and in every respect the most inconvenient ships which wear the pennant. In accordance with the rule, such was the *Rattlesnake;* and to carry out the spirit of the authorities more completely, she was turned out of Plymouth dockyard in such a disgraceful state of unfitness, that her lower deck was continually under water during the voyage."

[2]Before sailing, Huxley was optimistic as to the facilities for scientific work which he was to enjoy (*L. & L.* i, 26–27). But later he changed his tune. For instance, whereas in 1846 he wrote that he had *carte blanche* from the Captain as to books, in his account of the voyage written in 1854 (*L. & L.* i, 47), he states that, as regards scientific books of reference, the ship "sailed without a volume, an application made by her Captain not having been attended to". See also *L. & L.* i, 49.

made it a practice to verify any anatomical or zoological fact for himself before utilizing it in book or lecture. This may have been time-consuming, but it gave him and his scientific utterances an unprecedented weight. I should be pretty certain that the foundation for this practice of his was laid aboard the *Rattlesnake,* in the necessity for depending on his own resources, and in the discovery that his own observations often showed that accepted zoological authority was wrong.

There were other difficulties besides the material. He worked in scientific solitude, in complete isolation (apart from some talks with Macleay in Australia) from any kindred mind, for MacGillivray had no interest in the hard framework of comparative morphology and its remote inductions, and poor communications cut him off all but completely from his few scientific acquaintances at home. Yet even this may not have been without its advantages. A man of different temperament and less mental energy would not have kept the intellectual pitch. As it was, Huxley was often discouraged; at intervals the Journal reveals him wondering whether his work and the conclusions he had drawn from it may not be worthless after all. Yet he always recovers and goes on. Here again he early learnt the secret of true self-reliance, without undue diffidence on the one hand or too-easy confidence on the other. More than that, he was driven in on himself and his own reasoning powers. Uninfluenced by elder men to whose opinions he might well have given too much weight, in him the younger generation of Early Victorian zoology found itself and worked out its own destiny.[1]

One thing at least is certain. If it had not been for Huxley's appointment to the *Rattlesnake,* not only the matter but the manner of his scientific work and achievements would have been different, and almost without doubt less original and on a narrower foundation of experience.

Let me conclude with Huxley's own estimate of the value of his voyage aboard the *Rattlesnake* (*L. & L.* i, 29).

"Life on board Her Majesty's ships in those days was a very different affair from what it is now, and ours was excep-

[1]Professor Virchow, in the Huxley Lecture for 1898, took a very similar view of the effect upon the young biologist's scientific character of the intellectual freedom and isolation thrust upon him during the voyage.

tionally rough, as we were often many months without receiving letters or seeing any civilized people but ourselves. In exchange, we had the interest of being about the last voyagers, I suppose, to whom it could be possible to meet with people who knew nothing of firearms—as we did on the south coast of New Guinea—and of making acquaintance with a variety of interesting savage and semi-civilized people. But, apart from experience of this kind and the opportunities offered for scientific work, to me, personally, the cruise was extremely valuable. It was good for me to live under sharp discipline; to be down on the realities of existence by living on bare necessaries: to find how extremely well worth living life seemed to be when one woke up from a night's rest on a soft plank, with the sky for canopy, and cocoa and weevilly biscuit the sole prospect for breakfast; and, more especially, to learn to work for the sake of what I got for myself out of it, even if all went to the bottom and I along with it."

CHAPTER 4

The Diary: Australia
JULY 1847–MARCH 1848

THE voyage out had been important for Huxley's scientific development; his stay in Sydney was destined to change the general current of his life, for it was here that he met Miss Heathorn. She was keeping house for her married half-sister, Mrs Fanning, at New Town, just outside Sydney.

In the three months spent at Sydney, Huxley not only did a great deal of work putting his scientific material into shape for publication, made the acquaintance of the naturalist Macleay, whose store of knowledge and stimulating ideas he found very valuable, attended numerous balls and parties, and made a trip to Stroud, some hundred miles to the northwards —but he also found time to fall in love and to become engaged.

In this round of activities, the Journal suffered. But luckily he repaired some of the more important omissions in a long retrospective entry in November.

By this time he was at sea again. The *Rattlesnake* sailed on Oct. 10th for Moreton Bay, the harbour of the infant city of Brisbane. After a short stay here, they made their way six hundred miles up the coast to Cape Upstart, then turned and were back at Sydney on Jan. 14th, 1848. This short cruise seems to have been in the nature of a reconnaissance for the later voyage (the Third Cruise), when the survey of the Inner Passage between the Barrier Reef and the mainland was undertaken.

A brief fortnight in Sydney and they were off once more— this time to Bass Straits and Tasmania, to inspect the light-

houses in that region. During this cruise Huxley visited
Melbourne, and was surprised to find that it contained more
than 10,000 people, only ten years after its foundation. They
were away for a bare five weeks, and then had another seven
weeks, until April 29th, 1848, in Sydney.

This brief statement of date and fact will serve to intro-
duce a section of the Diary which contains some passages of
the deepest personal interest, and others brimming over with
characteristic charm and humour.

.   .   .   .   .

October 16th.

Poor Journal! no entry for five months. Five months of the
most pleasant I have ever spent, and fraught with events. We
left Sydney on the 1st and are now anchored off Moreton
Island, the wind not permitting of our entrance into the bay.
So much to keep up one's dates. For a statement of "Was ist
geschehen", some dull day.

Nov. 25th.

Yet another month. I'll make an effort. Van Diemen's Land
was without question one of the best places we have sojourned
in. The people were very hospitable—really hospitable, and
not inviting you to their home merely for the sake of your
coat as they do at Sydney. Our introduction (by Capt. Stanley) to Dr Bedford gave me some very agreeable acquaintances there and except that I was rather confined to the ship
by the Surgeon's absence, I enjoyed myself very much. I entered into all that was going on, much more than I should
have done by the bye. And what between Balls, dinners and
other things my residence there was little less than a round of
lesser and greater debaucheries. At Hobart Town I saw an
ether operation for the first time; it was quite successful, so
far as the patient's declaration went, although he kept up a
kind of reflex (?) moaning the whole time. He answered
questions quite rationally.

So much for Hobarton. I trust we shall return there some
day or other. (God forbid! Jany. 1849.)

We left on the 8th of July and arrived in Sydney on the

16th. I procured some very fine specimens of Diphyes by the way and completed the materials for my paper upon them.

We beat up that splendid harbour Port Jackson and as we neared Sydney and its homes and shipping became gradually more and more defined my heart throbbed with joy at the near prospect of obtaining news from home after seven long months of absence. The boat went off to the Post Office, and returned with a cartload of letters and newspapers, but no line for me. I damned everything and everybody but sat down to dinner in a temper that Satan need not have envied, vowing I would never write home again. After all, this explosion was little necessary as when my letters arrived a month afterwards I found my disappointment was purely accidental.

In the meanwhile began a round of humbug—ship scrubbing, painting, calling, and being called upon—Govt. Balls and the like. If I remember right I managed three balls and two dinners in the course of a week. I can't say I liked all this. For the nonce it was an agreeable change enough, and I justified it to myself on the principle of the expediency of acquiring a few pleasant acquaintances—perhaps even one or two friends—but on the whole it was a dog's life, altogether making a toil of pleasure. At first, too, I must needs join a considerable amount of private dissipation to all this. But this, thank God, was checked by a serious and painful illness which lasted some three weeks. To recruit my strength when I had recovered, I went to Tahlee [?] and from thence with Philip King to Stroud. Here misfortune followed me—I had not been three days on my visit when I was attacked with severe rheumatism in the foot, not to say gout, which kept me partly in bed and partly on the sofa for the ensuing ten days. And had it not been for Philip King's unremitting and most kindhearted attention, I believe I might have suffered far more severely. I was greatly annoyed to find myself helpless and thrown entirely upon the kindness of utter strangers, but I really believe the annoyance was confined to myself. An indifferent person might have thought I was the brother of my host and hostess.

Consequent on this calamity was another, which to say truth I did not feel—viz., I was absent from the *Rattlesnake* picnic, which as everybody said went off with so much éclat. I thought that the Fannings would be there, and a shade of disappointment passed over my mind, why I could not tell—what were they to me except very pleasant people?

In returning through the bush to Raymond Terrace I met McClatchie and urged by him changed my intention of leaving for Sydney, putting it off until Saturday and in the meanwhile visiting old Caswell, which was done, and on Saturday evening I got on board, and the old life began again. I was particularly glad to find that I had been inquired after by the New Town folks. Cary B. had been particular in her inquiries, but, as she took the trouble to explain to her informant, not on her own behalf; I was still more pleased—by instinct I suppose, for I could not have told myself why at the time.

Then again, I remember, I was particularly anxious to make some very proper calls—very proper and polite doubtless, but they were at New Town, and so in reflection I doubt if politeness could have been the whole and sole motive. I made one or two appointments with S. which were each time prevented so that it was a week before I managed the matter and then I went alone after all.

I called at Fannings first (instinct again?) and a pleasant merry hour we had of it, Mrs Fanning, the three girls and I. And of all subjects the one under discussion was my reception into the family. Fraternization—Cary Bose would have none of it, professed to oppose me tooth and nail, in her liveliest way. Sister Alice was in my favour. And sister Henrietta, what said she? Cast down her eyes, smiled, and would take the matter into consideration. So it was agreed at last that the decision of the matter should lie in her hand. My heart leaped. But I thought to myself, Tom, you are a fool, what on earth is there in you, and you have only seen one another four times, besides, it is wrong. So time passed on. The sisters were going to walk to Tempe, whereupon I found it highly expedient that I too should have a walk, and proposed myself as chevalier on the occasion. We set out and Sister Henrietta was my companion, not by my contriving I vow.[1] The other two mis-

---

[1][Footnote added in his wife's handwriting]: Why, you said you could not offer an arm to three and so offered one to *me!* And you twined the flowers yourself round my bonnet and observed they looked very like orange blossoms! —*Nettie.*

Plate 5

Holmwood, The Fanning's House, at New Town, outside Sydney, where Huxley met his future wife. Water colour, signed T.H.H. The words " Holmwood, Sydney, 1850 " are in his wife's handwriting.

chievous girls could find nothing better to do than plait a
wreath of white flowers for her—and there was some hint
about orange flowers.

We called at Mrs Steele's on our way, and renewed our
discussion. I proposed myself as a son, but Mamma gave me
no hope of adoption—inquired even with a very sly look
whether there were no other relation I would prefer. (Tom,
Tom, where art thou going to, like a lamb to the slaughter?)
And then came the rest of the walk. H.H. was my companion
as before and I began to find that there was something inexplicably pleasing to me in the expression of her mild "seelenvoll" countenance, in the tone of her voice, and still more in
her sensible and yet thoroughly womanly conversation. I
strongly suspect I was in love without knowing it, for after I
left Tempe (when to my everlasting credit for discretion be
it said I did not stop two minutes, the lady of the house being
absent) I do remember looking back more than once. And, ass
that I was, feeling half disappointed when I no longer saw her
at the window.[1]

I got back to Fannings' about four o'clock and immediately
requested to have my horse brought round, but F. requested
me with so much frank courtesy to dine with them that I could
not refuse. And I never spent a happier evening.[2] We sat
round the fire and I told no end of auld wives tales—there
was something that put me in mind of the happy old days at
S's. I saw Mr. H[eathorn] there too, a curious man of strong
natural talent evidently, but rather ingenious than sound. On
the whole I rather liked him. On my ride home that night I
felt happier than I had for months. Time wore away. We
were in the last days of September and were to sail early in
October. Some days after my visit, M. told me that he had
seen H.H. in a carriage and had received a very polite bow.
We were then very good friends (i.e. laughed and talked
together) but I felt disgusted and half angry at hearing her
name from the mouth of a heartless profligate,[3] such as he.

[1]"Mrs. Fanning has a sister, and the dear little sister and I managed to fall
in love with one another in the most absurd manner after seeing one another—
I will not tell you how few times, lest you should laugh." From a letter to his
sister Lizzie (*L. & L.* i, 37).

[2][Added later as footnote]: *Before*, perhaps—but *since* (?). '49.

[3]Too strong—too strong—though there is little love lost between us now. '49.

Whether this, or the increased value that purity and worth were attaining in my eyes as I insensibly felt a more personal interest in them, made me less disposed to put up with his humours than before I cannot say, but certain it is we quarrelled in a day or two, and spoke no more. Nor shall we, unless I strangely alter, again meet on friendly terms. My eyes are open to the influence he had on my disposition, bad enough naturally.[1]

A French frigate came into harbour and a grand final ball was to be given at Government House. A full dress affair. A number of us went, I among the rest, for I knew H.H. was to be there, and that night settled my fate. We danced together and when we did not dance we walked up and down the hall under pretence of getting cool. Without intention, without thought, our conversation became more and more interesting. We found corresponding events in our past life, we found that taste and habit of thought in each harmonised, and more than all each found that the other was loved.

Her hand trembled on my arm, but when, half mad with excitement as I was, I would have taken it, it was drawn back with such shrinking maidenly modesty that I feared after all I had mistaken. No word of love was spoken but we understood one another.[2] As I handed her to the carriage we appointed to meet again on Monday. Those miserable three days. I was half mad, unable to apply myself to any occupation or to rest anywhere. I felt that my happiness depended upon the issue of our next interview. I felt that I had already in honour pledged myself, and yet I would have given worlds to be able at any personal sacrifice to retract. What had I, a young man, poor, prospectless, I had almost said hopeless, to do with her? What right had I to disturb the even quiet tenor of her life, to give her new anxieties and undeserved cares, to take her from her pleasant friendly circle, to what, even after years, must be the hearth of a poor and struggling man? At times I cursed myself, and then as I thought over each look and word I felt so happy in the belief she loved me that all obstacles were forgotten. Anxiety brought on my old nervous

[1]M. was the ship's clerk, between whom and Huxley there was a smouldering feud: see p. 83, note, and p. 260.

[2]Very presumptuous statement that—scratch it out if you think so, darling. '49.

palpitation and I became less and less fit for quiet thought. Her image was ever before my eyes waking and sleeping, and her voice, sounding softly in my ears: "We shall see you on Monday?" In utter perplexity I determined to consult Mc-Clatchie who introduced me to the New Town folks, and had I not had other reasons I should have acquainted him with my state of the case as I strongly suspected him of leanings in the same direction. His advice was that of a friend of us both, advising strongly to let the matter drop, as a matter of duty, so after I had had some hours' conversation with him the end was as might have been expected. "Go on Monday I must and will, come what will of it." Poor fellow, I fear he had sadly wasted his breath. But I rather look upon him as a *particeps criminis* as he promised to ride over with me—and not stop.

But I, on my part, promised to behave very prudently. And so I did. For blessed be the Gods (and Mrs Fanning), Netta came down alone to receive me. She tried very hard to look indifferently at some prints on the table, but it was no good. My secret (and hers too) was soon out and we were both very, very happy when—when what? why that abominable soft-stepping butler came in to announce lunch. But I admire that man—he never changed countenance a muscle.

And this is what you call prudence, Signor Tom, is it? Certainly. Waste of time is the highest improvidence, and I lost none.

Happy day, short happy week that followed. I thank the Almighty humbly and heartily for this one bright spot[1] if it should so happen even that another never occurs in my life. I felt awakened to a new life, pledged by all the confiding tender love of that dear girl, to a new course of action—nobler and purer. My personal character, my personal devotion is all I have to offer her in return. And shall not that be made worthy of her? The thought that it is my duty to discipline myself for her sake, that she may have less reason hereafter to repent her choice, nerves my better feelings—and often her image is my good genius, banishing evil from my thoughts and actions. Bless you, bless you, dearest, a thousand times. You have purified and sweetened the very springs of my being which were before but waters of Marah, dark and bitter were they.

[1] Succeeded by how many, many more happy ones. '49.

And strangely enough, too, not merely is your influence powerful over my heart, but my intellect is stronger, my thoughts
more rapid, my energy less exhaustible, I never could acquire
more rapidly or reason more clearly. Wicked little witch, you
would have been burnt for sorcery in our great-grandfather's
days.

(*Courteous Reader*.[1] My good sir, this is doubtless all very
interesting to you—very—but to me rather dull. You have
given us some six pages of your love-making, forsooth, and
not one word about the ship or the expedition in general. Be
pleased to go on with the narrative, the really important
events. Were the *Rattlesnake* and *Bramble* wrecked or did
they go on their journey while you were in the clouds (?)
Courteous reader—you are an ass. Not events merely but
those which influence a man, are of importance. These formed
a new era in my life, a matter to me of much more importance
than all H.M. navy put together. And for your impertinence
not another word from me to-night.)

Dec. 5th.

We left Sydney on the 10th Oct. I for one felt downhearted
enough, but as usual chewed my own cud, and said nothing
to anybody. I had been with Netta the two preceding days and
the pain of parting from her was the feeling uppermost in my
mind. But I am not one of those who "put finger i' the eye"
and whine over the unavoidable so I determined that her dear
image should not be a mournful monument of past joys but
rather be ever present with me in my wanderings as a Penates,
an ark of promise in the wilderness of life. And so far did I
conceive it my duty to set her aside, as it were, lest too frequent regretful thought should deprive me of the energy and
temper required for the proper prosecution of my studies, that
I made up my mind to think of her only at one particular time,
to wit, for an hour before I slept.

(*Cts. R.* "And this resolution you doubtless kept as well as
the other before-mentioned?"

The writer begs to decline answering this question. If pages
of books will turn into people's faces, he cannot help it.)

[1]Dec. 4th. All this discussion means simply that I was tired of writing. This
journal was never meant to be read by any one but myself. '49.

Our first destination was Moreton Bay. We arrived and anchored under Moreton Island on the 17th Oct. I went ashore several times cockatoo shooting and several times met with the natives. They were miserable poor devils enough but very sociable and to all appearance happy as sandboys.

I had in Sydney had an invitation to visit Leslie [?] on the Darling Downs and as I found McBrady intended paying him a visit I determined on accompanying him.

Capt. Stanley was going to Brisbane with the *Asp* and 1st galley, so we took advantage of the opportunity and sailed up with him. Brisbane River is a considerable stream but much obstructed by shallows. Its lower part is bounded by mangrove flats, but towards Brisbane its banks become higher and it takes several picturesque turns.

We had to wait two days at Brisbane before we could procure horses but at length we were fortunate enough not only to get tolerably well mounted, but to procure a guide in the shape of a Mr Hay, a squatter who was going up to his station on the downs, and a most agreeable addition to our party he formed. By way of preparation for the journey I set up a pair of corduroys and a cabbage tree hat and when mounted, with thong [?] on saddle (especially taking the moustache into consideration) I flatter myself no one could have distinguished me from a genuine squatter. We set off in high spirits on our 100 miles ride, notwithstanding sundry predictions of a knock up on the part of our good friends at Brisbane, and I shall not soon forget the exhilaration of my spirits as we rode through the bush—free from all constraint and careless where there were not such things as ships in existence. Our first stoppage was at the house of Dr Simpson (Crown Lands Commissioner) at Woogeroo. Here we dined. Our host was a man of great intelligence—white-haired and white-bearded, but active and merry as a young man. I remembered his name in connexion with Homoeopathy, of wh. branch of physic he had been an eminent defender and professor in England. He commenced life as a cavalry officer, then studied law, finally took to physic, which he studied in Germany and Italy, last of all, the world as I suppose not agreeing with him, he came out to Australia and according to his own account was more content in his present position than any other. His place at Woogeroo was one of the prettiest I had seen in New South Wales.

In the afternoon we continued our journey as far as Lernis-town [?], 25 miles from Brisbane. This settlement is on the uppermost navigable point of the Brisbane and hence it is important as a depot from whence the wool of the squatters of the district is shipped.

2nd day. We talked of getting away early but with true colonial dilatoriness we did not start till 9 o'clock, thereby having much more of the heat of the day than was at all necessary. We rode thirty miles to a little inn just on this side the Dividing Range, kept by one Petteyman, stopping in the middle of the day for an hour at a water-hole to refresh. The third day was the stiffest ride of all—forty-five miles, and the range to cross. We crossed by a new and as they call it improved road. What the old one must have been I cannot conceive. We dismounted and even then it was one of the toughest climbs up the last pass, that I ever had. I thought my heart would have burst, and my horse was not much better. I must say, however, that I was well rewarded by the beauty of the scene. The road shelf lay through a thick brush, with its beautiful, dense dark green foliage and whimsical fes-tooned creepers clinging to the huge trees and thrown from branch to branch like a fantastic drapery. Here and there too high up on the trunk of some bare gum-tree the graceful stagshorn fern stood out like a corinthian capital; a deep still-ness reigned over all, broken only now and then by the sweet musical chime of the bell-bird. Once arrived at the top of the range a few steps led one to quite another scene—a wide spreading view over the distant mountains, the dense forest clothing varied in hue only by distance and the shadows of the passing clouds. But we might not spend too long a time here— yet a long journey was before us and noon was passed.[1]

[Here a space of nearly two pages is left.]

Left Moreton Bay Nov. 4th, and at Port Curtis Nov. 8th.

[Here a space of a page.]

[1]Lazy again, but I think I gave you all the particulars in my letters, dearest. Jany. 1849.

Cape Upstart. *Dec.* 12th. *Sunday.*

This day should have a red mark. Our head is turned towards Sydney again. We arrived here on the evening of the tenth, and early the next morning parties were sent in search of water. I accompanied the only successful one. After travelling with considerable labour up the bed of what must be in the rainy season a very considerable torrent, we arrived at two reservoirs of water among the rocks but not of the best quality and three quarters of a mile from the shore. The nature of the ground and the distance together rendered it impossible to water the ship and as the "element" is beginning to run short (each man is on an allowance of 6 pints per diem for all purposes) there is nothing for it but to cut and run down to Moreton Bay. Cape Upstart is one of the most barren places I have seen, but the rock scenery is grand and rugged.

Dec. 14th.

We have beaten back as far as Whitsunday Passage, where we are now anchored, intending at peep of day to go into Port Molle, where we lay a week ago. Sydney in five weeks! Bravo.

Dec. 24th.

Not so fast. We have had strong contrary breezes for some days past and are now only off Curtis Island. The ship has been knocking about and everything at the minimum rate of comfort. I feel especially disgusted this evening. Christmas Eve! a time that one   [continued on foot of p. 70].

[On opposite page.]

(Christmas Eve 1847 was signalized by an event and may be conveniently noticed on this accidentally blank page. At ten o'clock I went on deck for my usual walk. The night was beautifully clear and the moonlight brilliant. The officer of the watch had just gone into the chart room with the captain to lay off the ship's position. By a mistake in a bearing as it turned out they laid her ten miles further from the land than

she was. Only two officers were on the poop. Suddenly one of
these turned his attention to a white form not very far ahead
of us under some lowland. There was a rush to the chart room
and as sudden a rush out. "Breakers on the lee bow" shouted
the look-out rather behind-hand. "Hands about ship. Down
with the helm", and round went the old ship like a whisk (for
the first time that day without missing stays, curiously
enough). Then we saw clearly enough what our danger had
been. About 150 yards off were some nice low rocks with the
prettiest breakers dashing and foaming with no small roar
over them. Had we continued on our course a few minutes
longer we should have spent our Christmas day on Curtis
island off whose north end these rocks lie. The look-out men
must have been asleep. They got a tremendous objurgation
from the skipper and were blacklisted for a month—a long
price for a short nap.)

---

has been used to consider as sacred to social pleasures and an
occasion of pleasant meeting among friends. And here I am in
this atrocious berth without a soul to whom I can speak an
open friendly word. But it is all good discipline doubtless and
I am indeed already reaping the benefit, for I find myself
getting more and more satisfied and content with my own
sweet society and that of my books, not by any means forgetting dear Netta's letters. Only the process is somewhat painful
at times—the very eels don't get used to being skinned without a writhe or two.[1]

When I feel very rebellious and discontented I take up
Carlyle and read the Life of Heyne or Jean Paul, and when
I think of the old father writing church music and composing
sermons with the children cutting about on the table, I feel
ashamed of myself and try once more to abstract myself from
the neighbour's noise and balderdash.

Dec. 25th.

I will not think it Christmas day. There shall be no more
Christmas days or festive days of any kind for me in a ship.

[1]Grumble, grumble—but it's ower true. '49.

It is cruel mockery to call a drinking bout among a parcel of people thrown together by the Admiralty "spending a merry Christmas". It is a more than Egyptian feast, for *all* the guests are skeletons. Where is the social ease, the comfort, the heartfelt kind words, the friendly influences of a home circle? It is now two years since I formed part of such an one and that one alas! was but the last ray of a happy sun, followed by a dark night of misfortunes.[1] Oh Lizzie! dear Lizzie, dearer to me than any but one in this world, what endless misery hast thou seen since then—would that I could have been ever by you—I would have tended you and cheered you with a care passing that of a brother—for of all of us, you and I were the only two I believe who really loved and therefore understood one another.

Where shall I ever find another sister like you at once endowed with more than man's firmness and courage in adversity and yet gifted with tenderest heart, and mind and taste capable of the highest cultivation? And yet we may never meet again, nay in all human probability never shall.

But you once said "my highest hopes are centred in that boy" and may the Almighty forget me when I forget you or shrink from serving you or yours.

Next summer it will be six years since I made my first trial in the world—my first public competition.[2] Small as it was, it was an epoch in my life. I had been attending (it was my first summer session) the botanical lectures at Chelsea. One morning I observed a notice stuck up, a notice of a public competition for medals etc. to take place on the 1st of August (if I recollect aright). It was then the end of May or thereabouts. I remember looking longingly at the notice and some one said to me "Why don't you go in and try for it?" I laughed at the idea for I was very young and my knowledge of Botany somewhat of the vaguest. Nevertheless I mentioned

[1]His brother-in-law Dr. Scott (referred to as S.) and his sister had been forced by private difficulties to emigrate to America.

[2]This is another of the three passages to have been previously published. See *L. & L.* i, 17–19, where it is stated that it formed part of a journal he kept for his fiancée. However, from internal evidence it seems clear that in 1847 he was still keeping the journal as a purely private record; probably the idea of using it as a partial substitute for letter-writing did not take shape until he sailed in May 1849, when Miss Heathorn also began a journal.

the matter to S. when I returned home. He likewise decidedly advised me to try and so I determined I would. I set to work in earnest, and perseveringly applied myself to such works as I could lay hands upon—Lindley's and Decandolle's systems and the *Annales des Sciences Naturelles* in the British Museum. I tried to read Schleiden, but my German was not perfect enough. For a young hand I worked really hard, from eight or nine in the morning until twelve at night[1] besides a long hot summer's walk over to Chelsea two or three times a week to hear Lindley. The day of examination came and as I went along the passage to go out I well remember dear Lizzie half in jest half in earnest throwing her shoe after me, as she said for luck. She was alone (beside S.) in the secret and almost as anxious as I was. How I reached the examination room I hardly know, but I recollect finding myself at last with pen ink and paper before me and five other beings, all older than myself, at a long table. We stared at one another like strange cats in a garret, but at length the examiner (Ward) entered and before each was placed his paper of questions and sundry plants. I looked at my questions but for some moments could hardly hold my pen, so extreme was my nervousness, but when I once fairly began my ideas crowded upon me almost faster than I could write them. And so we all sat, nothing heard but the scratching of the pens and the occasional crackle of the examiner's *Times* as he quietly looked over the news of the day. The examination began at eleven. At two they brought in lunch. It was a good meal enough, but the circumstances were not particularly favourable for enjoyment, so after a short delay we renewed our work. It began to be evident between whom the contest lay, and the others determined that I was one main competitor and Stocks (he is now in the E. India service) the other. Scratch, scratch, scratch. Four o'clock came, the usual hour of closing the examination, but Stocks and I had not half done, so with the consent of the others we petitioned for an extension. The examiner was willing to let us go on as long as we liked. Never

---

[1][Inserted in pencil on opposite page]: A great deal of the time I worked till sun-rise. The result was a sort of ophthalmia which kept me from reading at night for months afterwards.

did I see man write like Stocks—one might have taken him for an attorney's clerk writing for his dinner. We went on. I had finished a little after eight, he went on till near nine and then we had tea and dispersed.

Great were the greetings I received when I got home where my long absence had caused some anxiety; the decision would not take place for some weeks and many were the speculations made as to the probabilities of success. I for my part managed to forget all about it and went on my ordinary avocations without troubling myself more than I could possibly help about it. I knew too well my own deficiencies to have been either surprised or disappointed at failure, and I made a point of shattering all involuntary "castles in the air" as soon as possible. My worst anticipations were realized. One day S. came to me with a sorrowful expression of countenance. He had inquired of the Beadle as to the decision and ascertained on the latter's authority that all the successful candidates were University College men—whereby of course I was excluded. I said "Very well, the thing was not to be helped", put my best face upon the matter, and gave up all thought of it. Lizzie too came to comfort me and I believe felt it more than I did. What then was my surprise on returning home one afternoon to find myself suddenly seized and the whole female household vehemently insisting on kissing me. It appeared an official-looking letter had arrived for me, and Lizzie, as I did not appear, could not restrain herself from opening it. I was second, was to receive a medal accordingly and dine with the Guild on the 9th November to have it bestowed. I dined with the company and bore my share in both pudding and praise,[1] but the charm of success lay in Lizzie's warm congratulation and sympathy. Since then she always took on herself to prophesy touching the future fortunes of "the boy".

Dec. 26th.

Still beating about here off Hervey's Bay. Wind dead on end and showing no symptoms of alteration.

[1] All this will interest you if ever I succeed in the path I wish to follow, Dear Nettie, and if I fail, perhaps still it may interest *you*, though to any one else it might seem puerile. Jany. '49.

Jan. 7th, 1848.

We got into Moreton Bay again on the 30th Dec. and took up our old station at Cowan Cowan. For a day or two before we arrived there was great excitement as to the probability of our meeting with the *Bramble* and various false reports had caused great expenditure of rockets, blue lights [and] guns. Great was the rivalry as to who should catch the first sight of her masts as we went into the Bay and great was the disappointment when no trace of her was visible. A boat was sent ashore and came upon very recent tracks of her— a saw unrusted, and recently felled trees—she must have been there but a day or two before us.

So the conclusion was arrived at, that she could only have moved up to the entrance of the Brisbane and some very imaginative folks even could see a topsail quite distinctly over Mud Island. The next morning the galley was dispatched to fetch the urgent mail in case it should be at Brisbane and to warn the *Bramble* of our arrival should she be there. There was great watching and looking out all that day. But the *Bramble* did not appear till next morning. As she hove in sight, what chuckles everybody indulged in, some hoping to revel in letters and newspapers. As soon as she was near enough a signal was made to inquire if there were any letters. They seemed an hour making the signal and when it was gradually made out: "No letters, no August mail", the poor old "Scratcher" was universally consigned to a region that shall be nameless. Recently however Yule came on board with dispatches for the Captain and satisfactorily explained all matters. He had great news, mostly of the horrific cast, the death of Lady Fitzroy and the Aid du Camp [*sic*] being the staple.

In the afternoon Capt. Stanley took into his head to go in the *Bramble* to the mouth of the river again so as to get his letters a little sooner. That evening it came on to blow, and on Monday, Tuesday and Wednesday it blew a gale of wind with a tremendous swell. Of course we saw no *Bramble,* no galley and *par consequence* no letters. But on Thursday the weather grew fine again and in the afternoon came the welcome sight of the galley laden with two huge mailbags. I got half a dozen letters, one from Sydney which was almost more

than I had ventured to hope—and that I read first—so true
is it that a man shall leave his father and his mother and
cleave unto his—ah! would I could call thee—wife, dearest.

Good night, darling, within a week if the gods be not very
unpropitious, I will answer that letter orally.

Jan. 13th.

Would that the good ship *Rattlesnake* were the veriest old
smokejack of a steamer. Here we have been laying with our
sails flapping against the mast—in sight of the Heads for the
last five hours, and the people in that confounded Hunter
River steamer which passed close under our stern hours ago
are by this time forgetting their journey among cheery home
faces. Never mind! to-morrow at worst I too will see my home
face.[1]

Feb. 25th.

Nothing for a month! It is a sign that I must be happy and
therefore think little of the present.

We anchored in Sydney harbour on the afternoon of the
14th Jany. and as soon as etiquette would permit, I was on the
back of a horse and off to New Town—where a happy meeting
made up for long separation. Would it were the last or the
longest.

The fortnight we remained passed, to me at least, like a
dream, out of which I awoke only when on the second of
February I found myself out at sea again. Two events of
importance occurred; in the first place we gave a grand turn-
out on the Regatta day, and secondly Brother Archie found
out he was in love, a circumstance which produced some
singular results.

We had delightful weather on our way to Bass Straits, but
the weather as we neared Port Philip [*sic*] became very
peculiar. There was a dense thick mist, and at the same time
the temperature was very hot so that the thermometer on one
occasion (after we arrived at Port Philip) stood at 90° in
the shade and 137° in the sun. It struck me as being similar

[1] Amen! to every word on this page—circumstances are similar. Jany. 14th,
1849.

to what I had heard described of the weather on the Coast of Africa. I procured some exceedingly interesting animals, among others a new Diphyes and two species of the genus Phacellophora. Besides these I examined a Diphyes very common in the Straits and the *Rhizostoma mosaica* plentiful in Port Philip Harbour, so that I had plenty to do.

The calmness and the misty state of the air caused us more delay in entering Port Philip, which we did however on the 10th February. The tide produced a furious ripple at the mouth of the harbour so that it appeared almost as if there were a bar across it—indeed the little whirlpools were so strong that the ship was completely swung about by them. A Pilot came off to us from the fine lighthouse at the entrance and led us safely to our anchorage at Williams Town—some 15–16 miles up.

Port Philip is a most magnificent harbour, wide and deep and capable of accommodating half a dozen navies but as appears to be the usual case with these Australian harbours its entrance is narrow and dangerous.

The country about Williams Town was dried up (they had had no rain for four months) and appeared certainly by no means prepossessing. As for Williams Town itself it consists of merely a few weatherboard houses and stores and offers no attraction of any kind.

Owing to the very unpromising look of the country and to having plenty to do on board, I did not go ashore until we had been some days in the harbour. And then McClatchie and Thorpe and I made an excursion up to Melbourne together. Melbourne is seated on the small river Yarra Yarra which debouches into Port Phillip, and lies some seven or eight miles away from Williams Town, but a communication is kept up with this place and with the town of Geelong which lies at the other extremity of the harbour by means of steamers which run five times a day. We had intended to go up the river in the steamer but were disappointed and accordingly landed on the shore opp. to Williams Tn. whence it is only about a two miles walk to Melbourne. We landed at a ricketty pier belonging to a small inn at the place, getting nearly swamped by the rollers in so doing, which gave rise to an urgent necessity for brandy and water, so we went into the inn and got warmed externally and internally (the weather had become clear and very cold, thermometer down to 58° or 60° in the shade) and then proceeded on our way in the mail cart which had just returned from Melbourne. "Mine host" was a most singular individual had been in the Guards, on the strength of which, I suppose, his sons and servants called him "Captain" and he himself cultivated an enormous twirling moustache. Malicious people however did say that he had occupied the less distinguished situation of a private. He was a most amusing person—a very dashing haw! haw! sort of person, one of those scheming ingenious ne'er-do-weels who are always rolling about and gathering no moss. His son (the flower of the flock) who drove the mail-cart was much such another, and another branch of the family who pulled the stroke oar of the whale boat in which we returned talked loudly of his intention of going to the ball. Altogether it struck me that these gentry were great vagabonds.

Two miles of a very dusty road brought us to Melbourne and I must say I was much surprised, knowing that the place had been not more than ten years in existence, to observe its size and the many tall chimnies which rose near the river —evidently indicating manufactories of considerable size. The town itself has fine wide streets, but the houses are of course irregular. It contains about 12,000 inhabitants. Altogether it much resembles Hobarton. There are several very good hotels. We went to the Royal, procured horses, rode about the Town, and then took our way to Brighton, an attempt at a town situated upon the shore of the harbour and about eight miles from Melbourne. The road to Brighton was pretty enough and had there been a little rain would have been quite beautiful. As it was we were half choked with dust. After seeing what was to be seen, and performing various nautical feats on our horses, we returned to our inn, had a capital dinner and returned by the way we came. And that was all I saw of the shore about Port Phillip.

There was a grand ball before we left, and tickets were sent to us. Some went but I did not—faith, I'm getting staid I believe.

On the 19th I believe we were all very glad to leave Port Phillip. The wind was in our teeth and blowing so strongly that we found it expedient not to leave the harbour until the 21st and we might just as well have remained where we were as we have been only kicking about ever since. Now however the weather has become calmer and we have great hopes of putting into Port Dalrymple by to-morrow. We are in sight of the Northern shore of V.D.L. opposite Mt. Valentine. The land is bold and grand in its outline—finer than most of the country I have seen.

I have nearly finished my paper on the Anatomy of the Medusae. I mean to send it to Sir W. Burnett requesting him to present it to the Royal Society, at the same time taking care to let him understand that I do not take such a step by any means through sycophancy. I feel that I owe the old man much, and I would do this as a simple matter of respect. I mean to make this same paper a turning point. If I hear well of it when we return from our long cruise, I shall consider that I am fit for such occupations and shall go on accordingly. If on the other hand, it does badly (and I am often troubled with great misgivings) I will give these things up and try some other channel towards happiness for dear Menen and myself.[1]

Febr. 3rd.

Happiness for myself—truly I may as well be more modest and be content if I can only establish hers—as for me I no longer look forward to halcyon days—even under her auspices. My temperament, I know too well, is incapable of allowing me this so-called happiness were it ever attainable by mortal in this world. I am content with nothing, restless and ambitious, and yet scorning the prize within my reach—the fruit of my endeavours seems to me like the fabled fruit of the Dead Sea. Once reached it is but dust and bitterness, and I despise myself for the vanity which formed half the stimulus to my exertions and perhaps leads me to overestimate their values.

Oh would that I were one of those plodding wise fools[2] who having once set their hand to the plough go on nothing doubting, who so long as they only go along care not for the

---

[1] [Note in pencil]: It was this paper which was published in *Phil. Trans.* [Actually it was sent to the Bishop of Norwich (p. 48)].

[2] Not a wise wish—very possibly I *am* a fool of another sort without knowing it. Jany. '49.

motives by which they are actuated, nor whom they sacrifice to their selfishness.

February 6th.

Dearly beloved self—from the tone of that last paragraph I should say you were rather grumpy when you wrote, but it was the first day at sea after leaving Port Dalrymple.

We reached Port Dalrymple on the 25th. The country even at a distance has a more cheerful aspect than the opposite shores. It is well wooded and bold, indeed sometimes almost mountainous. The entrance to the harbour is narrow but once in there is a fine expanse of water. We anchored three miles below George Town, and therefore between forty and fifty miles from Launceston, as the passage up the river Tamar, though quite practicable for vessels of greater draught of water than the *Rattlesnake* (15 ft. 6 in.), is somewhat difficult and dangerous.

George Town is a very pretty little village quite in the English style, indeed crossing Bass's Straits appeared to have brought us much nearer home than we really were. Everything from the rosy-faced girls and children to the fruit trees bent down under their weight of apples or pears put us in mind of England, and the resemblance increased on going further into the country.

A steamer runs between George Town and Launceston and on board of her a number of us embarked on the afternoon of the 28th (Monday after our arrival). The river Tamar is one of the most picturesque I have ever seen consisting of a series of pretty reaches with high well-wooded banks, and here and there you came upon a cleared spot, with its house and fields yellow with stubble (the harvest was just over) and in the far distance lay the blue summits of the distant hills of the interior. As we neared Launceston the cleared spots became more frequent till at length the woods were altogether driven back and the town itself appeared, encircled by a great extent of land in a high state of cultivation.

At Launceston the river Tamar ends or rather begins, being formed by the North and South Esk, two pretty streams which take their origin at no very distant point in the interior.

Heavy ships lie at some distance from Launceston below what is called the Bar. But small brigs and the like ascend to the town.

March 7th.

We met with a hospitable gentleman, Mr Penny, on board the steamer, who invited us to go out to his house the next day, so in the morning we procured horses and rode over to his farm which is about six miles from Launceston. We passed through an exceedingly pretty country, in a high state of cultivation and very like some of the midland counties of England. On all sides of us were fields yellow with the stubble of the lately reaped corn, divided from one another by hedgerows and shady lanes, and here and there might be seen an orchard, the trees absolutely bending down under their weight of fruit. I think that the resemblance to dear old England struck all of us, and all partook of the exhilarating feeling produced by galloping through such thoroughly *home* scenes. We lounged through Mr Penny's orchard, devoured his fruit, made a very substantial lunch with him and returned to Launceston just in time to dress, and dine with the Mess of the 11th.

We spent a very pleasant evening with them and the next morning started in the steamer back to George Town having compressed into our visit about as much as could well be done in the time. I suppose that bluecoats are rare even hereabouts, for we met with the utmost attention and kindness from everyone.

The next day (March 2nd) we left Port Dalrymple and made a very good run to Goose Island, doing 10½ knots for some hours together—a rate of speed which quite caused a sensation in the old ship. We dropped anchor under the lee of Goose Island in the afternoon and the Captain and a party of us went ashore to view the lighthouse. The island is a strip of granite about two miles long covered with a crust of light soil on which a scanty long coarse grass grows. At one end of the Island is the lighthouse, a fine old tower some eighty feet high. I was exceedingly pleased with the mechanism of the lantern which is of a superior construction. There is a lamp with three wicks in the centre—supplied with the finest oil by

a tube leading from a cistern rather above it. By this means
the wick is kept constantly fed, the surplus oil flowing over
into a reservoir. The mechanism for concentrating the light
consists of (1) eight compound lenses (nine pieces?) on
the —— [blank in original] principle. Then to catch all the
stray light they have (2) a number (365) of plane plate-glass
mirrors fixed at the proper angles for sending the rays out
parallel.

[Here, in the original, a sketch of the apparatus.]

The Island is tenanted by Gulls and Mutton Birds, the latter
of which as it became dusk flitted about over our heads in immense numbers and rendered walking rather troublesome on
account of the immense number of holes they had dug and out
of which they rose sometimes like spectres in the gloaming.
Besides them there was the superintendent and his wife and
children, three convicts and a flock of goats.

The superintendent was away but I had some conversation
with this wife—a pretty little woman of some eight and twenty
years. She seemed very contented with her lot, said she was
never dull as her children of whom there were five kept her
hands full. She and her husband had been five years on the
island and he was now absent for the first time.[1] Their only
hardship was that they were sometimes left without food, for
which they were dependent upon a neighbouring island, only
to be reached in certain states of the wind.

It was dark before we left the island and I had a view of a
nebula for the first time through Capt. Stanley's long refrac-
tor. It was that in Orion's sword and as the night was remarkably clear I saw it very well, the trapezium of stars being
well defined. I could have looked at it for an hour. We had a
look at some good double stars as well.

On returning to the ship we found an addition to our ship's
company in the shape of a dog, which had swum off from the
island. We were lying six-tenths of a mile (the distance was
accurately known) from the shore and what could have induced him to leave his old friends and come to us I cannot

[1]What do you think of a little establishment of this kind, Nettie darling?
Shall I try for a lighthouse. Fancy, you could howl without restraint. Jany. '49.

divine. He swam straight off and then once or twice made the circuit of the ship howling in order to attract attention. When he was seen the jolly-boat was lowered to take him in and now, under the name of "Lighthouse", he is a regular denizen and on account of his good manners a favourite on board. His breed would be difficult to define—he has the head of a Scotch terrier, the body of a turnspit, the legs of a spaniel and a tail altogether anomalous and sui generis.

The next morning we got under weigh and stood on for Swan Island where was another lighthouse to be examined. I did not go ashore here but according to the accounts of those who did, it is much superior to Goose Island. There was evidently considerable vegetation upon it, whereas at Goose Island they had some difficulty in raising potatoes and a cabbage was a chef d'œuvre.

Our westerly wind kept us company till we go away from among the islands, then chopped round and has ever since been easterly and consequently foul, so that we have had the pleasure of being in sight of Cape Howe for the last two days without being able to weather it. I wonder if Job was ever at sea? Every day we are knocking about in these cussed straits is one day lost from Sydney and all that I hold dear therein. If I were a Catholic I would invest a little capital in wax candles to my pet saints, but as it is I have alas no remedy but patience.

I was finishing the drawings for my paper yesterday in the chart room when Capt. Stanley came in, and after looking at my work for some time asked me what I was going to do with them. I told him my plans, when he suggested that I should send the paper to his father who would, said he, "if it were on account of the ship merely, push it to the utmost in the proper quarters". He offered furthermore to write to any one whom I would name and whose influence would be of use in getting it read and printed. All this was purely his own suggestion and indeed I thought he seemed pleased at the idea of sending it to the R.S.

I must say this for the skipper—oddity as he is, he has never failed to offer me and give me the utmost assistance in his power, in all my undertakings, and that in the readiest manner. Indeed, I often fancy that if I took the trouble to court him a little we should be great friends—as it is I always get out of his way and shall do so to the end of the story. That same stiffneckedness (for which I heartily thank God) stands in my way with others, my "superior" officers in this ship, who if I consulted their tastes a little more and my own a little less would I am sure think me what is ordinarily called a "capital fellow" i.e. a great fool. They will understand me I hope before we part company, though in truth it is a matter of little consequence whether they do or not.

Just now I am on good terms with everybody. No. 1 is absolutely overpoweringly polite, and on M.'s apologising we resumed speaking terms again at Launceston. I kept my word for five months, however, so that he for one, will know that I am "tenax propositi" and not worth offending. How will it be this day six months?[1] All adrift again I fear, but my equanimity will remain.

[1]Haven't quarrelled with a single soul, but I have found it expedient to drop my dearly beloved M. to the outside limits of politeness—he and I are incompatible, but I rather think it is my fault. Jany. '49. [As regards M., see pp. 63–4, 260.]

CHAPTER 5

The Third Cruise: "Wanderings of a Human Soul"

O N APRIL 29th, 1848, the *Rattlesnake* left Sydney on her
third cruise. The main objective was to make a survey of the
Inner Passage, running between the Great Barrier Reef and
the mainland and emerging to the northwards at Cape York.
The *Bramble,* under Lieut. Yule, of whom we shall hear a
good deal later in the Diary, was attached to the *Rattlesnake*
as tender for light draft work, under Stanley's orders. They
were accompanied by the *Tam o' Shanter,* a barque which was
transporting Kennedy's ill-starred expedition. At Rockingham
Bay, 1200 miles to the northward, Kennedy disembarked his
stores and men, in preparation for his overland march. The
purpose of the expedition was to explore the mainland between
Rockingham Bay and Cape York, in what is now northern
Queensland. Huxley accompanied Kennedy on a preparatory
trip to "feel the way a little" and to see the character of the
country through which he would have to pass. In the Diary
(p. 99) he gives a vivid account of this five-day expedition.

It was at one time suggested by Kennedy that Huxley
should accompany the definitive expedition on its long northward trek, but this was disallowed, rather to the young naturalist's disappointment, for he was thoroughly bored and
depressed with his life aboard ship. However, when the *Rattlesnake* arrived at Cape York before Kennedy, and finally
had to leave without any news of him and his party, Huxley
felt relieved that he had stayed by his ship: as he writes in a
footnote dated January 1849 (p. 104): "Fancy my disgust at

finding the ship gone (had I been with him) on our arrival at Cape York".

He was indeed luckier than he thought. Had he accompanied Kennedy, it is more than possible that he would not have returned alive; at best he would have lived through an experience shattering alike to body and mind.

The expedition finally left its base on June 3rd. Quite soon they began to suffer seriously from malaria. Within a month they had run into hostile blackfellows in place of the friendly natives near Rockingham Bay. Their rate of progress was far slower than had been anticipated as possible. Already in early August they found their stores running low, and this in a country where game was unexpectedly poor. On November 10th a number of the men were so weak from undernourishment that they were left in camp at Weymouth Bay, while a small party of the stronger members, under Kennedy's leadership, pushed on to fetch help from the settlement at Cape York. One after another of this little party succumbed to exhaustion or to the attacks of the natives, until only Kennedy and his faithful blackfellow Jacky (mentioned by Huxley in his account of the reconnaissance) were left.

Finally Kennedy was killed by the natives, and Jacky, with wonderful pertinacity and devotion, made his way through hostile tribes to Cape York, reaching the settlement on December 23rd.

A rescue expedition was at once dispatched, but on reaching Weymouth Bay found all but two of the party dead of starvation, and the two survivors in immediate peril of being murdered by hostile natives. The tragic news did not reach Sydney until after the *Rattlesnake* had left on her last cruise—hence the absence of any reference to it in the Diary.[1]

But if Huxley was spared this physical ordeal, he seems on this same cruise to have passed through some ordeal of the spirit, scarcely less trying for being intangible, wholly inescapable because it was played out within his own mind and soul.

However, before we enquire into the nature of this mental crisis and the reasons for it, we must set forth our reasons for

[1] A full account of the expedition, including a report by one of the survivors, is given as an appendix to MacGillivray's *Voyage of H.M.S. Rattlesnake*.

believing in its existence. The evidence is to be found by setting MacGillivray's official account against the record of Huxley's Diary, supplemented by that of his scientific notebooks preserved at the Imperial College of Science and Technology in South Kensington. In evaluating this, I have had the advantage of consulting Professor C. M. Yonge, of Bristol, who spent a long period in these regions as leader of the Great Barrier Reef Expedition, and has been able to give me valuable notes on the topography and marine fauna of the various islands mentioned.

The detailed survey of the passage between the Barrier and the mainland was begun on their arrival in Rockingham Bay, and continued by an unbroken series of triangulations over the 600 miles of coast-line and channel to Cape York. For four and a half months the *Rattlesnake* was engaged upon this task, moving slowly up the coast, anchoring a day here or a week there, sending shore parties on to this or that coral islet. For four and a half months they were within the Great Barrier Reef, sailing through a coral sea, its waters rich in tropical animals, with every opportunity for study.[1] Huxley, in the programme he had drawn up for himself on leaving England, had expressly mentioned corals as one of his chief zoological objectives. Yet now that he was actually in the world's most remarkable coral region, he scarcely gave it or them a thought.

Let us confront the records—his own, in his Diary and his scientific notebooks, and MacGillivray's, in the published account of the voyage. On the voyage up to Rockingham Bay, Huxley continued his observations on the pelagic life taken in the tow-net. There are seven entries in the scientific notebook, and the beauty of one siphonophore merited a mention in the Diary. His interest is concentrated on the two groups on which he had already expended so much labour—the Siphonophores and the pelagic Molluscs.

[1] In a letter to his sister, written shortly after the completion of this cruise (*L. & L.* i, 44) he writes: ". . . a parlous dull business it was for those who, like myself, had no necessary and constant occupation. Fancy for five mortal months shifting from patch to patch of white sand in latitude from 17 to 70 south, living on salt pork and beef, and seeing no mortal face but our own sweet countenances . . ." To which it may be said that MacGillivray did not seem to find it dull, nor would it have been dull for Huxley if he had been able to find the mental energy to become interested in the corals and other fauna of the reefs.

The survey was begun at Dunk Island. MacGillivray speaks of a successful seining party, which obtained many interesting starfish and some new crustaceans. Huxley on the other hand does not mention this at all, but writes (Diary, May 28): ". . . Rain, Rain! The ship is intensely miserable. . . . One can do nothing but sleep. . . . I try to pass the time away in thinking, sleeping and novel-reading, which last is a kind of dreaming."[1] And then follows a passage to which I shall later return, where all the doubts about his capacity press upon him.

Next day, however, he went off on the reconnaissance with Kennedy, and the novelty and activity of this little expedition with new companions and in new surroundings served to rouse his interest. The stimulus which it provided is evinced by the long and vivid account in the Diary.

But then comes the month of June. During this period there is no entry in the scientific notebooks. In the Diary he mentions Barnard Islands, but only with reference to an exploring trip ashore and some account of the natives. Then come the Frankland Islands, with a bare mention. MacGillivray on the other hand records a reef collection, with rich and varied results, as well as the remarkable abundance of sea- and land-shells, which was enough to stimulate the collecting instincts of the crew. One sailor seen climbing a tree was asked if he were bird's-nesting, but he replied, "No sir, it's these Geotrochuses I'm after"—Geotrochus being a tree-living mollusc. They next move to Fitzroy Islands. Huxley again records the fact, and gives a good deal of space to an incident there concerning a strange vessel and her encounter with hostile blacks, but neglects the large flying-fox roost and the botanical points mentioned by MacGillivray. All these three groups of islands, Professor Yonge tells me, are rocky, and have fringing reefs.

From June 21st to August 2nd there is but one entry in the Diary: "*July 7th.* Anchored under Low Ids.", with a footnote added later: "All this part of the cruise is a perfect blank in my memory".[2]

---

[1]His description of the wet heat on the fourth cruise (p. 136) shows that the physical conditions were as bad or worse then; and yet, as we shall see, he was on that cruise mentally much more his normal self.

[2]In his review of MacGillivray's official account he wrote (*L. & L.* i, 49): "Any adventures ashore were mere oases, separated by whole deserts of the

However, the scientific notebooks show that he had not lost all interest in his work, though even so, there are entries for three days only, on eight specimens. One of these was on July 5th, at one of the several stations recorded by MacGillivray before the ship reached Low Isles, another at Eagle Island on August 1st, both referring to sea-snails (gastropods). A third refers to a siphonophore on July 31st. The rest were collected at the Low Isles on July 8th—two molluscs, one polyp, one jelly-fish, and a short note on a crustacean.

Yet the Low Isles were chosen as the headquarters of the Great Barrier Reef Expedition. They consist of a coral and a mangrove island, and provided Professor Yonge and his colleagues with unrivalled facilities for the study of corals and of animals inhabiting the coral reefs and mangrove swamps (see Yonge, *A Year on the Great Barrier Reef*). MacGillivray notes the abundance and variety of the reef fauna found during the *Rattlesnake's* four-day stay, mentioning especially the rock-pool fish, the crustaceans, molluscs, echinoderms, and coelenterates (corals and related forms).

Huxley makes no mention of Hope Islands (July 19th), which Professor Yonge tells me are coral isles of the same type as Low Isles and with an equally rich fauna, though Mac-Gillivray records the interest of the mangrove swamps, the variety of the shells, and the striking birds. Nor does he mention Eagle Island, close to Cape Flattery, where MacGillivray speaks of the fishing eagles.

At Lizard Island they anchored on August 2nd, for a fortnight. Here Huxley makes no mention of the fauna, but records his impressions of the scenery. This, as Professor Yonge notes, is very fine, the summit of the 1160-foot peak affording the best view of the Barrier Reef. It has fine fringing coral reefs. MacGillivray notes finding the remains of native turtle-feasts, and records the best collection of showy mollusc shells he had ever seen. He also notes in passing that during this cruise he had landed on thirty-seven islands, and

most wearisome ennui. For weeks, perhaps, those who were not fortunate enough to be living hard and getting fatigued every day in the boats were yawning away their existence in an atmosphere only comparable to that of an orchid-house, a life in view of which that of Mariana in the moated grange has its attractions." This clearly shows how he craved for the stimulus provided by purely external events.

on every occasion had secured something new in the way of specimens.

During the next seven weeks there are but two entries in the Diary—one a bare statement that they had moved to the Howick Islands, the other a long account of the impression made upon him by Dante's *Inferno*. This latter entry ends, "I have been getting very apathetic of late, and I think I never was so mortally sick of anything as of this wearisome monotonous cruise. . . . I care for little else but sleep, and I have a great mind to coil myself up—hibernate until we get letters at Cape York; another week, thank Heaven! must bring us there."

Yet the Howick Islands, according to Yonge, have a very rich fauna, characteristic of the three habitats, rock island, mangrove swamp, and coral reef. MacGillivray here notes the vast numbers of flying-foxes, in flocks "like rooks", and the only song-bird seen on the N.E. coast, in the shape of a honey-sucker. MacGillivray also has notes on the following stations: Cape Melville, a remarkable promontory of granite; Pelican Island, inhabited by many pelicans and other interesting birds, and scene of several shooting-parties; Claremont Islands, where turtle nests were found; Night Islands, swarming with pigeons; Sherrard Islands; Cape Direction; Cape Weymouth, where they anchored for a week; Piper Islands, lovely with pink-flowered Erythrina trees, and exhibiting the remains of a trepang-curing establishment; Young Island, an "infant island" in process of growth; and Sunday Island.

None of these are even mentioned by Huxley, save the last, apropos of which he writes, "We are laying at present under Sunday Island, a kind of repetition in miniature of Lizard Island. I have not been ashore and don't care to go, what's more." His scientific notebook contains entries on four days out of the fifty, referring to six specimens—a marine worm, four mollusc dissections, and a jellyfish.

At Bird Island, however, he becomes interested, but in some natives, not in zoology; and at Cavin Cross Island next day he for the first time shows an interest in the abundance of bird life, though he does not seem to have found much enjoyment in a couple of pigeon shoots.

That is October 3rd; and then as he himself records,

"Three months passed and no journal". During that period, after reaching Cape York on October 7th and picking up letters from Sydney, they spent nearly four weeks at Cape York itself. There they made many interesting contacts with the natives, duly recorded by MacGillivray: but even these seem not to have broken Huxley's apathy. Nor does he record the two cases of scurvy which appeared among the crew, although these must have come to his professional notice, nor the wonderful pinnacled termite nests on the mainland, nor the kangaroos and opossums, the cockatoos and parrots, the snakes and monitor lizards that occupied MacGillivray's attention.

In his retrospective entry of December 31st, Huxley records their visit to Port Essington, on the other side of the Gulf of Carpentaria. Here what chiefly interested him was the dreariness of the settlement, and the strange life and death of the Roman Catholic missionary Don Angelo. There is, however, an entry concerning the extraordinary abundance of jellyfish— the only record in the Diary during this cruise on any subject connected with his own scientific interests. This entry is confirmed by the scientific notebooks, which during the fortnight beginning November 11th contain entries, most of them of considerable length, concerning four species of medusae and two siphonophores. The examination of these latter prompts him on December 1st to a disquisition on the proper classification of the group to which they belong. Finally, during the sixty-eight days' cruise home, there are five more entries, all referring to siphonophores. In the Diary this part of the voyage is not mentioned at all, save for the impression of the peaks of Timor from the sea.

From these facts it seems clear that Huxley during this cruise never investigated any corals, betrayed hardly any interest in the remarkable natural history of the places visited, and carried out very little zoological work in general. The animals to which he did give more attention were almost entirely those in which he had become interested on the voyage out—Medusae, Siphonophores, and Molluscs.

On the other hand, many of his own statements in the Diary reveal his troubled state of mind. On his birthday, May 4th, a few days after leaving Sydney, he looks back on the past twelve months:—"What an immense change has this twenty-third year made in me! Perhaps taken all together it will turn out to be the most important of my life. My first year of sea-life—my first year of scientific investigation—the success or failure of which must determine my prospects—my first year, last but not least, of love, which has and will model my future life."

It is this uncertainty of his future prospects which is constantly in the background of his thought, coupled with his uncertainty of the merits of his scientific work. He believes his work to be good—and is then assailed by doubt. If he has over-estimated his abilities, and his prospects are no prospects at all, but an illusory hope—why then to have allowed himself to declare his love, to have allowed Henrietta Heathorn to plight her troth to him, will have been the act not only of a fool, but of an unworthy fool. The same intensity of feeling which glowed in his love conferred a horrid vitality upon his doubts and scruples.

His doubts and worries were fostered by the total lack of news as to the fate of the scientific papers which he had prepared and sent back to England during the three months spent at Sydney in 1848 after the voyage out. These included the paper "On the Anatomy and Affinities of the Family of the Medusae", in which, as I have explained in an earlier section, the youthful Huxley set our understanding of the great group of Coelenterates upon a new and clearer footing, and made a notable contribution to the proper morphological classification of the animal kingdom.

As a matter of fact, this paper had been at once communicated by Captain Stanley's father, the Bishop of Norwich, to the Royal Society, and was published in the *Philosophical Transactions* in 1849. It was on the strength of the results set forth in it that Huxley was made an F.R.S. at the age of twenty-six, and received the Royal Medal of the Society at the almost unprecedented age of twenty-seven.

But of all this the young naturalist in his cramped quarters on the *Rattlesnake* knew nothing. Forbes, it appears, was merely waiting until he could report the acceptance of the papers for publication. But, as it happened, his silence was interpreted by Huxley as evidence that the work had not been well thought of.

The emotional upheaval caused by his falling in love had been profound. The sense of a new way of life, different in quality from all that had gone before, thus opened before him, caused him to repudiate many of his old attitudes and to indulge in acute self-blame for what appear to have been the minor peccadilloes of a normal young man (pp. 60–1). All true lovers have experienced the sense of committing the entire self, even the deep unconscious springs of it hitherto hidden or unrealized, into the hands of another human being and into the impersonal or superpersonal charge of love: and have known how this can not only increase joy and energize the faculties, but also on occasion magnify unhappiness and multiply doubt. Huxley seems to have had this experience in full measure. The separation from his beloved, the climate, the uncongenial company aboard the *Rattlesnake,* the uncertainty whether his scientific investigations, pursued with such ardour, were really of the importance he had fancied—all these seem to have conspired to throw him into a painful and unbalanced mental state in which lethargy, broken by rare spurts of activity, alternated with self-questioning and depression.

I have quoted from his entry of May 28th, where he complains that the hot, wet weather takes away all his energies. But the rest of the passage proves that the wet weather was perhaps an unconscious excuse, at best but a partial cause:

"Have I the capabilities for a scientific life or only the desire and wish for it springing from a flattered vanity and self-deceiving blindness? Have my dreams been follies or prophecies? If in old times these questions have pressed themselves painfully upon my mind when my own fate was all that hung in the balance, how shall I cease to think over them now that the fate of one whom I love better than myself, depends upon their right or wrong solution? There is something noble, something holy, about a poor and humble life if it be the consequence of following what one feels and knows to be one's duty. And if a man do possess a faculty for a given pursuit, if he have a talent intrusted to him, to my mind it is distinctly his duty to use that to the best advantage, sacrificing all things to it. But if this capacity be only fancied, if his silver talent be nothing but lead after all—no Bedlam fool can be more worthy of contempt. The man who has mistaken his vocation is lost and useless. He who has found it is, or ought to be, the happiest of the happy."

In place of investigating the anatomy of marine organisms he spends much time reading. On August 2nd he notes that he has begun on the *Divina Commedia,* and adds:

"Since I began Italian I have read (1) the first part of Sforzi's *Storia Romana,* then (2) *Il Cortegiano Questo,* then (3) *L'Avare* and *Tartuffe* in Italian, then *Le Cerimonie,* then *L'Arte Poetica* of Metastasio (or rather of Horace) besides some of his Canzones and letters. Somehow or other Italian does not seem to come home to me as German does. The elegant smoothness seems cold compared to the glorious rugged 'seelenvoll' old Saxon Deutsch."

Eight weeks later, on September 30th, he records his impressions of the *Inferno,* which he has just finished, and concludes with the passage already quoted about his intense boredom and his not caring to go ashore.

At Port Essington he read *Candide* and *L'Huron.* In the Diary, his chief interest is reserved for the character and religious beliefs of Don Angelo.

Finally, there is an entry made during the long return voyage, undated, but apparently at the turn of the year:

"What has the year 1848 done for me? is a question I may well ask, and yet perhaps not find the true answer these ten years. What have I done for it? All too little. I have spent time that should have been occupied with work in idleness, that should have been occupied in fruitful recollections in foolish discontent at the present and still more foolish anticipation of the future, and yet, as poor Gretchen sings:

> *Alles was dazu mich trieb*
> *Ach! war so schön,*
> *Ach! war so lieb . . .*

So true is it that the growth of our virtues involves that of our faults also, and the very circumstance that prompts my better actions is a source of discontent and vain regrets."

The doubts and the uncertainty were to continue. So too was the gloom. On the succeeding cruise, under date June 4th, he writes:

"I am becoming a very morose animal, worse than I was last cruise, I think. It annoys me at times to hear others talk, and I could sometimes bite anybody who speaks to me. . . . I feel like a tiger fresh caught and put into a cage."

However, on this final voyage the appearance and habits of the natives provided him with a new and very real interest, as the pages of the journal testify, and it is only when there were none of them about that he relapsed into his lethargy. For instance:

"*July* 31*st*. . . . No canoes have been near us for some days, and were it not for a few friendly 'Buffons' I should be in a state of utter stagnation."

There we may leave the matter. Huxley was of highly-strung temperament, with a self-questioning mind. Although he himself writes (April 6th, 1850) that he is not of a "subjective" disposition, this seems hardly to have been true. He was all his life much concerned with morality and the ordering of his intellectual ideas on the conduct of life. An entry made on his twenty-second birthday, during the outward voyage from England, before ever he met his future wife, reveals a Faustian temper (p. 26):

"Morals and religion are one wild whirl to me—of them the less said the better. In the region of the intellect alone can I find free and innocent play for such faculties as I possess— and it is well for me that my way of life allows me to get rid of the 'malady of thought' in a course of action so suitable to my tastes as that laid open to me by this voyage."

As he truly says in writing the conclusion to the main part of the Diary (p. 208):

"Here is the end of a *History of Four Years,* dearest. It tells of the wanderings of a man among all varieties of human life and character, from the ball-room among the elegancies and soft nothings of society to the hut of the savage and the grand untrodden forest. It should tell more. It should tell of the wider and stranger wanderings of a human soul, now proud and confident, now sunk in bitter despondency—now so raised above its own coarser nature by the influence of a pure and devoted love as to dare to feel almost worthy of being so loved.

"Could the history of the soul be written for that time it would be fuller of change and struggle than that of the outward man, but who shall write it? I, the only possible historian, am too much implicated, too interested, to tell such a story fairly."

The voyage aboard the *Rattlesnake* provided for Huxley not only an unrivalled apprenticeship in his chosen science; it was also an apprenticeship in the affairs of the spirit. Huxley was great not only as a scientist, but as a man: his character was as interesting and exceptional as his achievements. During this third cruise he was passing through the fire. Knowing the self-mastery to which he later attained, we can find in the record of this black time of struggle and depression a document of deep human interest.

CHAPTER 6

The Diary: Third Cruise
APRIL 1848–JAN. 1849

T<small>HE</small> preceding chapter is sufficient introduction to the next section of the Diary, and the map at the end of the volume will allow the reader to follow the *Rattlesnake's* course in detail. There is, as usual, no entry during Huxley's busy and happy stay in Sydney during March and April. We are plunged direct into the sadness of departure.[1]

· · · · ·

April 29th.

We are leaving Sydney again on our long cruise with the *Tam o' Shanter* in company. I have no heart to write.

May 4th.

My birthday again. What an immense change has this twenty-third year made in me! Perhaps taken altogether it will turn out to be the most important of my life. My first year of sea-life—my first year of scientific investigation, the success or failure of whose results must determine my prospects—my first year, last but not least, of love, which has and will model my future life.

I have had a good day of it. First as it happened to be past twelve before I went to bed last night I consider I had a right

---

[1]In the *Life and Letters* this cruise is called the "Second Northern Cruise", and that to the Louisiade and New Guinea, which I have called the fourth, is called the third.

to read dear Nettie's letters—which I did accordingly and derived great comfort and happiness therefrom.[1] Secondly— the calm which has existed for some days has allowed many "Buffons" to come to the surface and this morning I was fortunate enough to catch a beautiful "Stephanomia" which was floating quietly along the surface of the blue mirror. I have been very busy examining it all day.

May 21st. Rockingham Bay.

After a tedious voyage interspersed with many calms and contrary winds we anchored at Cape Upstart on the afternoon of the 19th and we remained until three o'clock on the following afternoon for the purpose of taking observations. Twenty- four hours' sail brought us to Gould Island under whose lee we are anchored to-day. Out towards the other shore lies the *Tam o' Shanter.* She arrived yesterday morning, having parted company with us before we entered the reefs. We have this time taken a peculiar route, entering the Barrier between the Capricorn and Swain's Reefs where there is an opening of some sixty miles width; and from there we have made a straight course up to the Percy Islands.

This passage is altogether outside the other and is con- sidered to be more convenient by the "conoscenti".

Mount Hinchinbrook is a very fine rugged mass more than two thousand feet high; its summit was enveloped in dense white clouds. Altogether it looked very like Madeira. Three of the natives, an old man and a boy in one canoe and a young man in another, came off to the ship as soon as we had anchored. The old man came on board and was received with due attention of a host of gaping youngsters and Jacks. He seemed very much disposed to make himself at home. He could speak no English but showed great signs of admiration of my white shirt and black neck-ribbon. The canoes of these people are very different from any I have yet seen, though like the others made of bark. These are more neatly made, have a dis- tinct broad and narrow end, either serving however to go foremost indifferently, and are strengthened by ribs of some

[1]Rather curious association of your dear letters with a "marine nastiness" you may think, my dearest, but they are more closely connected than you may think. '49.

flexible wood. They paddle themselves along by pieces of bark held in each hand—squatting on their heels rather towards the stern of the canoe so that its afterpart forms a sort of well into which the copious leakage runs. Every now and then they cease paddling with one hand, put it behind them, and bale out, scratching the water out as it were with the paddle. The action is excessively ludicrous. Many of these fellows had a bar of red paint across the bridge of the nose and under the eyes— one had his hair confined in a sort of net like a cabbage net and his beard was done into a flat elongated band fastened together and squared at the end by some white stuff.

[Here, in the original, a small sketch of the man's head to show the beard.]

These men did not understand the use of a pipe or tobacco. They brought off fish-hooks and lines which they readily parted with for biscuit.

23rd.

Moved over from Gould Island to one of the Family Ids. near Dunk Island.

24th.

All the ship's boats (except the dinghy) and half of his men away debarking Kennedy's horses and sheep. I spent the day on the Island in an unsuccessful search after cockatoos, numbers of which had been seen perched on the tops of the trees, but were put out of our reach by the dense jungley character of the brush covering the interior of the island. We found a singular parasite (Balanophora) upon the roots of the Gum Trees in the brush. I made a coloured drawing of it which I gave to McG. to send to Hooker.

26th.

Finding no convenient watering place on the small island we weighed anchor and took up a position about 1½ miles from Dunk Island.

It rains incessantly.

Plate 6

Hal. being painted

HUXLEY BEING PAINTED BY A NATIVE ACQUAINTANCE

Pencil, with red paint on the forehead, the bridge of the nose, and behind
the eye, in both figures.   Unsigned, undated : the legend is in his wife's
handwriting.   The scene is probably Rockingham Bay.

28th. Sunday.

Rain, Rain! The ship is intensely miserable. Hot, wet, and stinking. One can do nothing but sleep. This wet weather takes away all my energies. I do not mind dry heat to any extent but to be steamed in this manner is too much for me. I try to pass the time away in thinking, sleeping and novel-reading, which last is a kind of dreaming. The novel I have been reading is not exactly a first-rate one and yet interested me much as corresponding to and awakening many old thoughts—I could have fancied that I myself had written *Ranthorpe.*

The author well and clearly points out the difference between *aspiration* and *inspiration,* and the fatal wreck that has been made of the lives of those who have mistaken the one for the other. God knows how often the very same thoughts have arisen, how often they do arise, in my own mind. Have I the capabilities for a scientific life or only the desire and wish for it springing from a flattered vanity and self-deceiving blindness? Have my dreams been follies or prophecies? If in old times these questions have pressed themselves painfully upon my mind when my own fate was all that hung in the balance, how shall I cease to think over them now that the fate of one whom I love better than myself, depends upon their right or wrong solution? There is something noble, something holy, about a poor and humble life if it be the consequence of following what one feels and knows to be one's duty and if a man do possess a faculty for a given pursuit. If he have a talent intrusted to him, to my mind it is distinctly his duty to use that to the best advantage, sacrificing all things to it. But if this capacity be only fancied, if his silver talent be nothing but lead after all—no Bedlam fool can be more worthy of contempt. The man who has mistaken his vocation is lost and useless. He who has found it is, or ought to be, the happiest of the happy.

Monday, June 5th.

This day week I went away with Kennedy to see his camp at Tam Point. I remained in his tent that night and returned the next day with Capt. Stanley in the galley, but not before I had made an agreement with Kennedy to form one of his light party which was to start for the purpose of feeling the way a little on the morrow. He intended to be away not less than four days or more than six and it was his intention to penetrate thirty or forty miles if possible into the country. I was delighted at the idea of the trip and the little modicum of adventure involved in it—so much so indeed that I found myself up before sunrise the next morning and ready to start with the first cutter which was to convey us down to the camp. Giving our letters into the safe custody of Capt. Marienberg who was to sail that morning, and taking K. on board as we passed, we soon reached the camp. Here we had a capital breakfast à la bush—damper, tea and chops to wit—and by 9 o'c were mounted and off, exploring and no mistake. Our party consisted of Kennedy, myself, and three men—Douglass, Luff, and "Jacky" the blackfellow. Each man had pistols in his holsters and a double-barrelled carbine slung by his side, cartridge belt and etceteras, so that, though I fear no sergeant would have marched through Coventry with us as "regulars", we should not have been badly equipped for a guerilla raid.

Each man had besides one or two of those inestimable quaint tin pots hanging to his belt—Jacky had his bush axe strapped above his cloak at his saddle bow, and one of the men led a pack horse laden with the eatables, viz., flour, damper, tea, sugar and a little salt pork that I had provided.

"Are you all ready?" "All right, sir!" "Come on then." And we are fairly off into the bush. Kennedy rides ahead, ever and anon taking a bearing with his pocket compass. I follow, somewhat inconvenienced at first by my carbine, and we two beat down the long grass into a road for those who come after us. We go along swimmingly at first but presently we come to a high ridge. We skirt first along one side, then the other, but there seems no end to it. We try to climb it but it is composed of vile loose blocks of stone most unsatisfactory to the shins of the climbers whether man or horse. We find it requisite to halt and Kennedy goes up to the top of the ridge with Jacky and Luff leaving two of us in charge of the horses. He is gone a long time (which I occupy by making studies of the horses in my sketchbook) and when at length he returns it is with rather a long face and the information that the ridge is not to be passed and that if it were the country round about is too thick to allow of passage in that direction.

"Never mind! faint heart ne'er won fair lady" and with that observation venerable at once for its antiquity and its truth, we turned our horses' heads back to the camp, as the day was well spent and no advantage to be gained by bivouacking.

On these as on all other occasions K's only anxiety was on the journey out. When he made up his mind to return, he signified his intention to Jacky who immediately put himself upon our track and led us back like a dog following scent.

Thursday morning.

We started again and after one or two ineffectual attempts to circumvent the ridge we gave up the attempt and made our way along the sea beach to the first river. Having reached it we first attempted to follow up its left bank, but fruitlessly, as it was densely wooded with scrub. On this bank we fell in with a party of natives who immediately rushed off in great affright. They had an unfortunate child diseased in some manner so that it could only crawl on all fours. It appeared at first not to be aware of the cause of the sudden departure of its friends but suddenly perceiving us it set up a series of the most unearthly yells and scuttled off as fast as it could get along. As we rode along we heard shouts and coo-eys on all sides of us without being able to see any one. I am free to confess I was not sufficiently used to this to feel quite easy, and began to see that my pistols were handy and occasionally to speculate upon the kind of sensation that would be produced by a spear between the shoulders. But without doubt the poor wretches were far more afraid of than inclined to disturb us. Still they did not seem to be at all badly inclined for when we returned to the mouth of the river a number on the opposite side held up their arms in sign of peace and pointed out to us the way we should follow in order to ford safely. It was fortunately low water and by keeping close to the line of breakers made by the sea dashing on the bar we crossed without wetting our horses' bellies. As we advanced our black friends retreated and beckoned to us to keep away from them.

We kept along the sea beach for a little way then entered the bush and rode for some distance through a beautiful open forest land with very high grass. Our hopes rose. This was the way undoubtedly, nothing could be better—when suddenly we came to a soft boggy creek, evidently leading on the right hand down to the river we had left. Now the question was where did it end on the left hand. We rode for a long way but when the creek ended we came to a tea-tree marsh altogether boggy and impracticable and the marsh seemed to get worse and worse the further we went so that K. had little doubt but that it would terminate immediately in the second river. We were in fact on a kind of island. This much was consolatory: Jacky sent up into a high tree reported clear forest land in the distance and a road might be made through the marsh.

Nothing more was to be done in this direction and as the tide would not be low enough to permit us crossing until after midnight, the next matter of importance was to find out a place for our bivouac. We picked out a clear spot close to the sea shore near a water-hole and about half a mile from the river. Close to us but further away from the river was a black camp and presently a party of our friends of the morning came very cautiously sauntering with their hands behind them towards us. When the horses were tethered and everything made snug I went towards them and entered into conversation by jabbering and gesticulation. I fancy we were sources of great amusement to one another. I bound my handkerchief round the head of one, and obtained in return some sliced edible root wrapped up in a leaf. They invited me to their camp but I declined as Kennedy did not wish to have any close intercourse with them. After the regular tea and damper I kept first watch (8–10 P.M.) yarning, and then spreading an opossum rug over us thought we would get two or three hours sleep. But alas! for the vanity of human wishes. It speedily began to rain, at first gently and then as it rains in tropical countries only, with all the appearances of a very dirty night. We were soon wet to the skin, and then as matters could not be worse we tried to make ourselves jolly "under creditable circumstances" over our smouldering fire. Half-past twelve soon came and then finding our horses and feeling out their equipment with some difficulty we determined to attempt the

Plate 7

KENNEDY'S RECONNOITRING PARTY CUTTING ITS WAY THROUGH
THE BUSH, JUNE 1848

Pencil, unsigned. A note on the margin in his wife's handwriting
indicates that the nearest figure represents Kennedy ; the next,
Huxley.

ford, full of anticipation of a dry tent and blanket at the camp. But when we reached the river's bank it grew darker and rained harder than ever. Even our guide, the line of breakers, was not to be seen. We floundered a third of the way over, leaving trains of light behind us in the phosphorescent water, and contrived to reach the first bare sand of the bar—and then the whole aspect of affairs was so very unsatisfactory that we made up our minds to return—soaking was better than drowning; so we returned to our old ground determined to make ourselves happy, blew up the embers of the dying fire, got a little warmth into our watery garments, and fortified the inward man with quarts of hot tea and damper. Then we unstrapped our cloaks and I coiled myself up in mine so as to be impenetrable to rain and went fast asleep. When I awoke it was broad daylight and still raining. Kennedy was standing before the fire, as I left him, endeavouring to believe he was getting dry. The men were standing round half asleep. Altogether it was rather a dull look-out and I wished myself asleep again.

Happily it left off raining about eight, and then we got some breakfast. The clouds still hung heavily over and I finding myself now drier went and cut down a few Pandanus trees by way of exercise, much to K's amusement.

Time wore away and about two o'clock we tried the ford once more, succeeded in crossing it and were soon snug and comfortable in the tents again.

There was yet left one possible direction for the road into the interior and this was northward by the E. coast, so in the morning (Friday) we set out once more. Our first progress was more favourable, through fine open country covered with long grass. Every now and then a red kangaroo would start up within a short distance of us and bound away. The day was bright and cheerful and everything boded well—but after a few miles we came to a dense jungle scrub stretching out on either side so as to bar our further progress. This brush was as bad as any I had seen on the islands. The same rope-like climbers, the same prickly rattans, the same dense high forest. We determined to cut our way through this in the hope of reaching clear land on the other side; and great was the trouble we employed to this end.

We got through a mile of this stuff and at length emerged upon some fine open forest, but we had not proceeded far when we were brought up again by a turn of our old friend the river. This was to be escaped only by cutting through more scrub and so Kennedy gave up all attempts in this direction. Before leaving, however, we ascended a high hill close to us and thence we perceived the course of the river, and the impossibility of making any progress along its left bank. K. determined finally on crossing the river and attempting the passage by its right bank and we returned for the last time to our camp.

The next morning Capt. Stanley and Simpson came over with first galley and pinnace to assist if necessary in helping Kennedy on for a first stage. The remainder of Saturday was occupied in packing. We got into motion early on Sunday morning, as soon as the state of the tide would permit of the pinnace crossing the bar. First went Kennedy finding out a good road along the beach. Then followed the three carts, then came the sheep and finally the horses in the rear brought up by the indefatigable Niblett. Altogether the procession was somewhat patriarchal-looking and imposing. All day was taken carrying over the carts, stores and sheep in the pinnace. A little before sunset we got the horses across fording at the bar, and just as it was getting dark found ourselves all assembled (minus one unfortunate dog which had not the courage to swim across but remained miserably howling on the other side) on a little sandy spit running out from the opposite bank of the river. It was too late to move so the horses and sheep had to be fastened up without food or water. The men made themselves happy round the fire and we, i.e. Kennedy, Simpson and myself, spent the evening in sweet discourse variously interrupted by eating and drinking under the tent.

Early in the morning we marched to our old bivouac where the horses were to have a day's rest and food, breakfasted and then with all wishes for our friends' success took our leave.[1] I should well have liked to have gone on to C. York

---

[1] As I suspected, ma'amselle, you rejoiced over my disappointment. However as Kennedy was absent—when we left—to tell you the truth I am not sorry myself. Fancy my disgust at finding the ship gone (had I been with him) on our arrival at Cape York. Jany. '49.

with him as he proposed to me, but it was impossible to leave the ship for so long a period.

I liked much what I saw of Kennedy. Wholly without pretension, he seemed to me to be well up to his work, and admirably fitted to manage his party well, which in these expeditions is half the secret of success. I believe he will succeed if his undertaking be possible.[1]

4th June.

Ship moved to Barnard's Islands.

5th June.

Went away in the first cutter with Simpson and McGillivray to explore a small river which had been noticed by Brown and Dayman a little to the southward of our present position.

The opening of the river is not easily perceived as its embouchure runs almost parallel to the coast. As we approached many natives came down. They had, some of them, necklaces, and cylinders through their noses. One or two large fishing nets lay on the beach and some of them had fish spears but they brought down no other arms. They appeared to be very desirous of making our acquaintance and beckoned to us to land.

The river was nearly fresh down to its very mouth and a strong current was running down it, so that we hoped to find a considerable body of water further up. At first the banks were flat and mangrovey, and a channel of five or six feet was to be found near one or other bank; higher up the banks became hilly and were clothed with thick brush in which the Livingstonia and   [left blank in original][2]   abounded. As we advanced shoal banks abounded and at three miles from the mouth we could nowhere get more than two feet

---

[1]In a letter to his sister written after the news of the expedition's fate had reached Sydney, he wrote (*L. & L.* i, 44): "A fine noble fellow poor Kennedy was too. . . . In fact we got on so well together that he wanted me much to accompany him and join the ship again at Cape York, and if the Service would have permitted of my absence I should certainly have done so. But it was well I did not. . . ."

[2]Two palms, Livistona and Seaforthia, are mentioned by MacGillivray.

of water. It was therefore considered expedient to return. Just ahead of us the river made a turn concealed by a point and no sooner was the boat's head put round than some twenty natives rushed round the point. The distance was too great to allow of our seeing whether they had spears or not, so every man took an involuntary look to his gun, but they approached without fear and empty-handed and we were soon engaged in lively conversation and barter of biscuit for armlets etc. These blacks differed from those at the settlement in being painted with black instead of red across the eyes. Some had their bodies marked with lines of white in a most hideous manner. They followed us down till we came to a clear spot in the forest where we anchored. Then some of us went ashore to shoot and they made signs that they would go further down and cross over. We shot some birds, returned and dined, but our friends did not approach, only in the distance we saw their fires smoking. After dinner getting under weigh, all the barrels which had remained loaded were discharged and suddenly out went the fires. Our black friends were evidently disgusted as we saw no more of them until we were clear out of the river when one or two made their appearance very cautiously upon the point.

June . [Blank in original.]

Moved to Frankland's Is.

June . [Blank in original.]

Moved to Fitzroy Is, Cape Grafton.

June 21st.

Towards noon a strange sail made her appearance to the southward. At first we imagined it must be the *Asp* but as the stranger drew nearer her different rig undeceived us and gave rise to an infinity of speculations. Some maintained that the stranger was a merchantman's longboat with a shipwrecked crew, some that she was a cruiser bringing us dispatches with immediate orders to move on to China; and speculation was

raised to its utmost pitch when somebody boldly asserted the
newcomer to be neither more or less than Want's yacht the
Will o' the Wisp. And old Want became transmogrified into
the Flying Dutchman? Or was he taking a mad cruise merely?
Had he probably as much champagne as usual on board? Or
was it Col. Barney coming to form a new indefinite settlement
somewhere? or—or—or——?

To solve all these queries the second galley was dispatched
to board the vessel. She returned speedily and raised us to a
pitch of excitement *"such as was not recollected by the oldest
inhabitant"* by a tale of natives and attacks and wounds and
distressed crews.

But what was said I do not well know as I was in the galley
in five minutes laden with lint and bandages, with thoughts of
amputation and fractures in my head, and pulling like mad
towards the vessel which in the meanwhile had anchored close
to us. On arrival I was speedily ushered below where I found
Roach, the skipper, lying half insensible with a very severe
wound of the head, plastered up as best might be.

And when I had attended to him I found that one of the
crew, a New Caledonian, had received even worse injuries in
the same quarter, but thanks to his good constitution or the
thickness of his scull, he seemed to be not in the slightest degree inconvenienced.

It appeared that the vessel had been dispatched from Sydney to search for sandal-wood among the Islands off the coast,
and that on the 22nd (Monday) she anchored under one of
the Palm Islands. The skipper and some of the crew went
ashore and fell in with many natives who appeared to be very
friendly. They brought off two and showed them the vessel.
It is noted in the Captain's log that they noticed only two
things—an accordion and some axes which latter they were
very desirous to possess. There can be little doubt that the
iron articles were in fact the cause of the subsequent attack.
However, the two natives were well treated and dismissed,
and the crew suspecting nothing went to rest. The middle
watch seems to have fallen to Sam, the black. He had gone
below for some purpose or other about half-past three in the
morning, when the vessel was surrounded by five or six canoes
containing about thirty natives, armed with waddies and

boomerangs and carrying pieces of lighted bark. They seem to have planned their attack well, for they stationed four of their party over the fore hatchway and two over the after one, ready to strike down anyone attempting to ascend, and then they threw some of the lighted bark down into the cabin —apparently for ferretting out the unfortunate occupants à la Pelissier. In the meanwhile the noise had aroused the skipper and Sam, both of whom were leaping up on deck when they were struck down by the boomerangs of the niggers above. But the mate had contrived to get hold of a cutlass and watching his opportunity he thrust one of them through the body, leaped on deck and commenced laying about him to some purpose. And he was speedily seconded by the crew, who by this time had ferretted out their pistols. One black-fellow fell back shot through the throat and in falling overturned his canoe and those who were in it. Of the rest some were killed, some wounded and the rest shoved overboard, and the decks once clear the crew got their little swivel gun loaded and let drive—into the midst of the fugitives. They had now time to attend to the Captain and Sam who lay helpless, and having plastered up their wounds as they best might they made sail, and stood on for Gould Island. Here, a similar fate seems to have awaited them. They were obliged to water and for this purpose the four available hands went ashore in their little whale-boat, armed to the teeth. They had hardly got their breakers ashore, before they saw a considerable body of natives putting off towards the vessel, this time in the ordinary small bark canoes. They were determined not to subject themselves to another attack so they immediately shoved off, pulled between the enemy and their vessel and then fired away. The gentlemen in black, unprepared for such a warm reception, vanished much faster than they came.

Cursing such inhospitable shores they once more made sail and on the Thursday morning fell in with our boats who directed them to us.

The whole cause of the attack at the Palm Islands seems to have been the iron which the natives saw in the vessel, for they contrived to carry away the pump spears [?], and a hatchet was found concealed in one of the canoes they left behind.

July 7th.

Anchored under Low Ids.[1]

Aug. 2nd.

At anchor under Lizard Island. Read through the first canto of the *Divina Commedia* this evening. Have not the impudence to say that I thoroughly understood all of it. Since I began Italian I have read, 1. the first part of Sforzi's *Storia Romana,* then, 2. *Il Cortegiano Questo,* then, 3. *L'Avare* & *Tartuffe* in Italian, then *Le Cerimonie,* then *L'Arta Poetica* of Metastasio (or rather of Horace) besides some of his Canzones and letters. Somehow or other Italian does not seem to come home to me as German does. The elegant smoothness seems cold compared to the glorious rugged "seelenvoll" old Saxon Deutsch.

Aug. 11th. Friday.

This afternoon I climbed up to a kind of shoulder about three-fifths of the way up to the top of Lizard Island. I would have gone up to the top but I feared that in that case I should have to descend after sunset, a journey not desirable when as in this case the ground consists of sharp lumps of granite partially covered by long grass. From the height I attained I could however very well see all I wished to see. Out to sea lay the white shining line of the breakers of the Great Barrier with here and there openings. To the westward again in the far distance one might discern the peak of the Australian coast marking the position of the Endeavour river. Between the island and these lay three large reefs, their white elliptical forms giving a singular aspect to the landscape. At the leeward end of the nearest might be seen the little Eagle Islet.

The natural beauty of the scene was heightened by the recollection that one stood on ground rendered classical by the footsteps of the great Cook, who from this height sought some exit from the dangers which had so nearly put an end to him and his glory. I say *"was* heightened". Truth requires

[1]All this part of the cruise is a perfect blank in my memory. Jany. '49 [written vertically up the page].

that I should substitute "ought to have been heightened", for in fact, the sun had been pouring on my back all the way up and my feelings more nearly approached sickness than sublimity when I reached the top.

On referring to *Cook's Voyages* I find curiously enough that it was on this very day 1770 that he visited Lizard Island and discovered the passage by which he subsequently took the *Endeavour* out to sea.

Aug. 14th. Monday.

Left Lizard Island and anchored under one of Howick's Ids.

[Here a gap of a page and a half.]

Sept. 30th.

Finished reading the *Inferno*. I began Dante with the *Paradiso* but after getting through some seven cantos I found that, what between the obscure reasonings and the difficulties of style, I made no great progress. So I turned to the *Inferno* which is indeed the natural commencement and read a canto every evening or thereabouts. Dante must employ a great variety of words for in the early cantos there were on an average about 30 words new to me in every canto; and the number did not sensibly diminish till I reached the 27th or 28th canto. I think I now understand all, except of course some of the historical allusions which could only be intelligible to one well up in the history of the times.

Certainly I understand it enough to enjoy it. All imperfect as my knowledge of the language is I can appreciate the wonderful graphic power of his descriptions.

He describes Hell like a practical *Times* reporter, sparing no detail however hideous and caring not how homely his comparisons may be so long as they are but apt. I think I never read anything so horribly distinct as his description of the Metamorphosis in Malebolge or those poor Popes with their writhing soles burning like "cose unte" and then Francesca da Rimini and the Count Ugolino with his "Anselmuccio mio" and that splendid sketch of a devil "sovrà il piè leggiero" in a verse of the 21st Canto. I don't wonder at the Italian women thinking that he had actually been down to Hell, for I have sometimes been half inclined to think the book not quite "canny" myself.

I have been getting very apathetic of late, and I think I never was so mortally sick of anything as of this wearisome monotonous cruise. I care for little else but sleep, and I have a great mind to coil myself up and hybernate until we get letters at Cape York. Another week, thank Heaven! must bring us there.

We are laying at present under Sunday Island, a kind of repetition in miniature of Lizard Island. I have not been ashore and don't care to go, what's more.

October 2nd. Bird Islands.

This is a group of islets more or less connected by reefs and at the northern end there is a shallow lagoon. It has been blowing fresh for some days past and the *Bramble* when she arrived here last evening found three natives on the island, two men and a boy, who had come over from the main and were unable to get back. As far as could be made out from their signs they had been five days on the group and for three days without water, so that they were half perished with thirst and drank with avidity the water with which the *Bramble* supplied them. They made signs that they had attempted to drink the sea water but that it had made them sick. So far as food went they were tolerably well supplied as I saw one of their large baskets half full of turtle eggs. These appeared to have been kept for some time, as they were much shrunken. The process of cooking was very simple, a small hole being made in the hot embers of their fire and a handful of the eggs thrown in. They were taken out and devoured before they were much more than hot through. The canoe of these natives was a very ramshackle affair, about fifteen feet long and apparently hollowed out [of] a tree. It was so narrow that it was with some difficulty they squeezed their hips down into the ordinary posture. It had an outrigger on each side, but there were seemingly no paddles.

The poor wretches appeared to be by no means satisfied of

the honesty of our intentions, and were greatly terrified when those who came ashore in the afternoon began pigeon shooting, moving over to the opposite side of the lagoon, canoe and all.

The one I conversed with was very desirous to know my name and when I told him "Tom", kept on repeating "Tom," "Tom" with great complacency, patting me and himself.

October 3rd.

Anchored under Cavin Cross Island this evening. This island is small but well wooded, the most conspicuous objects being the white naked Pisonia trees. But the island is chiefly remarkable as being the resort of immense numbers of Torres Strait pigeons which after feeding all day on the mainland return here, towards four o'clock in the afternoon, to roost. From this hour till dark there is a continued series of arrivals in flocks of from four to a dozen or more.

We had noticed the same occurrence at various small woody isles to the southward but never before on so large a scale. Of course such valuable prizes for the pot were not to be neglected, and some half a dozen guns were soon ashore. The poor birds were very tame and the shooting was simple butchery. I for my part not being fond of trouble took a very base method of gratifying my alimentiveness. I walked along the beach until I found a low wide-spreading tree, on which I perceived by unquestionable marks the pigeons were in the habit of roosting. Into the bosom of this sacred domestic hearth I intruded myself and as the guns of my neighbours sent the frightened birds from all sides to this well-frequented haunt I had nothing to do but to load and fire as fast as possible. In less than an hour I had shot sixteen and expended my ammunition, so I returned on board. The others who remained shot many more, so that, on reckoning up in the evening it appeared that not less than 160 had been brought off.

We remained at the island all the next day and that evening the tragedy was repeated, with no less success. The birds however as I heard had become a little more shy.

The number of pigeons in the habit of nightly resorting to

the island must be immense; they are fine birds, as large I think as our domestic pigeons.

October 5th.

Ran up opposite Albany Island and there anchored for the night. Next day after dinner we entered Port Albany, going round the north end of the island as the southern passage was declared unsafe (except with a good leading wind) on account of the tides.

Dec. 31st.

. . . and finally anchored off Evans Bay, Cape York. Three months passed and no journal. But here is the last day of the year and I must write something to satisfy my conscience. Besides, we have got into cold weather (30° South) and my energies, well nigh extinguished for some time after leaving Port Essington, are beginning to be restored. I shall leave a space for our doings then and since (for at present I can't for the life of me remember a single date) and proceed to page 124.

[Inserted later in the above-mentioned blank space:

We left Cape York on the 2nd November 1848 and reached Port Essington on the 9th. The land about the entrance is low and flat and except for the beacon on the eastern head it might easily have been missed. For some inexplicable reason the town or settlement is placed far up the inner harbour—quite out of reach of the fresh breeze which at night very generally blows at its mouth. We dropped anchor opposite a high cliff on the left bank of the harbour, on the top of which was perched a ruinous-looking block-house with a few pieces of cannon mounted on its top, the firing off of which would I verily believe have blown down the whole concern. A diagonal road ran down the side of the steep to a stone pier terminated by a crane, which as I afterwards found was decidedly the chef d'œuvre of the colony, having occupied the whole disposable force for some seven months. Beyond this on the other side of the road was the Hospital, a low building with a white face and wide verandah; behind, the various stores and huts of the marines peeped through the trees, though mostly hidden by the descent of the ground inland.

The place looked very deadly lively, and the unfavourable impression we had received from the accounts of others were by no means dispelled by its appearance. Presently the Commandant's gig came off bringing the sergeant-major of marines with a note from Capt. MacArthur apologising for the nonappearance of himself or the officer of the day on account of sickness. We further learnt from the sergeant-major that there were not more than ten healthy men in the settlement. The *John and Charlotte* had arrived a day or two before us and was anchored inshore unloading her cargo.

The next morning I went ashore with some others and wandered about to see what was to be seen and to call on Dr Crawford whom I had known in Sydney. The Doctor was away somewhere in the settlement and Tilstow, of whom I had heard in England, was down at Coral Bay and indeed did not return to the settlement during our stay, so that after all I did not see him.

In returning through the hot square, we fell in with Lambrick, the senior lieutenant, who courteously invited us to come and lunch with him. And a most acceptable business the said lunch was, to say nothing of the pineapples, which are here of very fine flavour and grow like weeds. In fact I must say one good word and only one for the settlement—it produces very good fruit, cocoanuts, pineapples, jack-fruit, etc.

As to the place itself it deserves all the abuse that has ever been heaped upon it. It is fit for neither man nor beast. Day and night there is the same fearful damp depressing heat, producing an unconquerable languour and rendering the unhappy resident a prey to ennui and cold brandy-and-water. Owing to the distance inland and the comparative shallowness of the water at the settlement, it is positively a *hot* salt-bath, the temperature of the sea varying from 87°–90°. From this circumstance as I suppose it is a hotbed for medusae and I obtained five or six species in great abundance; the sea seemed almost full of a species of Bougainvillia on some days.

Vile as the climate is, however, it does not seem positively unhealthy. That is to say there are very few endemic diseases, no predominant fever and not overmuch dysentery, yet many of the men had spent a third of their time on the sick list, and as I have said there were but ten out of the whole party fit for duty. Two causes seem to have produced this result, which might have been avoided by better management; these are overwork and bad food. Before Crawford put a stop to it the men had been worked eight or nine hours a day *through the mid-day heat,* and the diet was far worse than ordinary ship's food; the people at Sydney appear to have sent them things they could not get rid of elsewhere, bad peas, bad biscuit, bad everything, and though they had a good many cattle yet for months together they never tasted fresh meat. The cattle have to find their food at a considerable distance from the settlement, hands cannot be spared to look after them, and consequently they are half wild. They come into the settlement at night at some times of the year, but not always, and if they don't come bon gré, it requires a regular expedition to hunt them. Besides the commandant is very economical and unless some ship is there to divide the spoil he won't have a cow killed, because it's too much and a good deal spoils!!—so the oxen live and the men die.

Indeed the respected Captain MacArthur is with all reverence one of the most pragmatical old fogeys I ever met with, and contrives to keep the people under his command continually in hot water. There are just five officers in the place, to wit one captain and two lieuts. of marines, one surgeon and one asst. surgeon, and there is as much petty intrigue, caballing and mutual hatred as if it were the court of the Great Khan.

We had not been two days in the settlement before we were masters of all the scandal of the place. Each man seemed to hate the other with a most delightful cordiality and the only thing in which they were united was in the most unqualified abuse of the whole settlement.

I can't say more for Port Essington than that it is *worse than a ship,* and it is no small comfort to know that this is possible.[1]

[1]Compare a letter to his mother (*L. & L.* i, 43): "Port Essington . . . is about the most useless, miserable, ill-managed hole in Her Majesty's dominions", and more in the same strain.

There was one other point however in which the various officers were united and I ought not to forget it. That was in kindness and hospitality to all of us. I used to spend most of my time up at Crawford's quarters with all his doors and windows open, lying on his bed, sipping "cold without" and rummaging among his books, of which he had a very good little collection. Curiously enough I read *Candide* and *L'Huron* for the first time in this out-of-the-way corner of the world.

I read the first two volumes of *Wilhelm Meister* in the *Asp* as we took our memorable voyage from Brisbane to Port Curtis.

As for all the description of the town of Victoria is it not written in the Book of Jukes?

Several miles nearer the mouth of the harbour (below the red cliff) than Port Essington and on the opposite bank of the estuary, we passed in coming up a little low solitary house which we rightly judged to be the residence of Don Angelo the catholic missionary. When we arrived we learned that the poor man had died a short time before our arrival, of fever, under which he had laboured for a week before any one was acquainted with the circumstance. Indeed it was merely owing to Dunbar's going down in the boat of the settlement and accidentally calling upon him that his state was discovered. He was of course immediately brought to the hospital and treated with every attention, but he was too far gone. I was told that he manifested the most extreme horror of death—a curious circumstance enough for a man who must have known that he was at any time at the mercy of the wild savages by whom he was surrounded.

Don Angelo lived wholly by himself. He got the natives to build his house for him, and he lived wholly in their manner—rather priding himself upon so doing, though there can be little doubt that he thereby hastened his end. He continued to teach the blackfellows to say a few prayers, of whose meanings they had not the remotest notion: indeed I was told that they were occasionally to be heard repeating them in the square of the settlement with many gestures as rather a good joke than otherwise. And he took care of their children, for which the gins were doubtless much obliged to him. He hoped to make more impression upon the children than on the adults and he was doubtless right enough, but I fear he has done very little, and that little is a mere mechanical repetition of formulae.

Thinking upon the desolate life of the man, I said to Crawford (with whom Don Angelo used occasionally to come and spend a few weeks), "I suppose this man was a thorough enthusiast, for it is difficult to imagine what else could have supported him through such trials". Crawford told me that I quite deceived myself, that he had had much conversation with the priest, and that he seemed to be wholly without religious feeling, well acquainted with theology and a strong stickler for the doctrine of his church, but more like an advocate than a believer. Indeed he frequently gave occasion to doubt whether he himself gave credence to what he taught.

Indeed from all I could learn he was in an especial sense a *soldier of his church,* i.e. like most soldiers he did his duty religiously but cared not two straws for the quarrel in which he fought.

A ridiculous circumstance occurred with a package that was sent to him by the *John and Charlotte.* It had come from Italy and [on] one face of the large deal packing case there was an inscription in large letters with something about piano. The good folks at the settlement immediately concluded that it was a veritable piano forte sent to console Don Angelo's solitary hours and perhaps help his performance of the mass. And two or three credible witnesses averred that in shifting it into the boat, a distinct tinkle like that of jarred strings was heard inside. When we arrived we heard the story and much marvelled thereat, and Capt. Stanley who has an especial vocation for prying into all concerns, whether his own or other people's, determined to have a look at this travelled instrument. So the case was opened, when to his astonishment out came no rosewood grand—or cottage—but a quantity of priests' vestments and other baubles. Great was the wonder. But turning up the lid and looking a little more carefully at the inscription, it turned out to be *"Posa Piano"*—a bit of Italian equivalent to our "Glass, this side up".

We left Port Essington without regret on the 16th and on the 20th we saw Timor, and to our great disgust in consequence of a contrary wind which obliged us to beat between this island and the Sahul shoal we kept it in sight until the 3rd of December.

Timor is a magnificent island. We approached occasionally within a few miles and had a good view of its fertile plains and cloud-covered mountain tops, one of which I believe is 10 or 11,000 feet high, but as we weren't going there we saw rather too much of it.—Jan. 14th, 1849.]

[No date, but presumably *New Year's Eve* 1848.]

What has the year 1848 done for me? is a question I may well ask, and yet perhaps may not find the true answer these ten years. What have I done for it? All too little. I have spent time that should have been occupied with work in idleness, that should have been occupied with grateful recollections in foolish discontent at the present and still more foolish anticipation of the future, and yet as poor Gretchen sings:

> *Alles was dazu mich trieb*
> *Ach! war so schön,*
> *Ach! war so lieb . . .*

So true is it that the growth of our virtues involves that of our faults also, and the very circumstance that prompts my better actions is a source of discontent and vain regrets. Dearest Nettie, this time last year I had known you well but for one short week and I had received but one letter from you. Then as now I expected that two or three weeks would once more bring me to your side, then as now the fever of warm anticipation possessed me, but in one sense how much happier am I now. Then it seemed a dream, now I have a "sober certainty of waking bliss"; then I hoped you were what I wished you to be, now I know it. If time would but confirm as accurately all my instinctive beliefs I should make a famous seer.

CHAPTER 7

Huxley and the Savages

T HE fourth cruise of the *Rattlesnake* had, geographically speaking, the most interest. Setting out from Sydney, they for the third time called at Moreton Bay, near Brisbane, but then made straight across for Cape Deliverance, the easternmost point of the Louisiade archipelago. This consists of a chain of islands running out from the south-east extremity of New Guinea.[1] By Bougainville, who first bestowed the name of Louisiade, the archipelago was supposed to be continuous land, part of the great island of Papua. He was heading eastwards, and on account of contrary winds, found great difficulty in reaching and doubling the easternmost point: hence, when he at last succeeded, he christened it Cape Deliverance.

A few years later, in 1793, d'Entrecasteaux visited the region, discovered it to be an archipelago, and laid the real basis for our knowledge of it. But the *Rattlesnake* was the first expedition to chart most of the islands and their reefs in detail. Starting at Cape Deliverance, she proceeded slowly along the chain of islands and huge reefs until off the mainland; and thence along the south coast of New Guinea to Redscar Point, where they stopped for some days. Then, after making a little more west to Cape Reunion, they sailed for Cape York in Northern Queensland, which they had visited

---

[1] One of the smallest of the group was christened Huxley Island after the *Rattlesnake's* assistant-surgeon, and still bears that name. Characteristically, Huxley makes no mention of this fact, either in the Diary or elsewhere.

on the previous cruise. For over two months they explored
and surveyed the neighbouring islands, notably Mt. Ernest
Island and Darnley Island, and then again made for the New
Guinea coast. After a short time at Redscar Point, they re-
traced their previous course until beyond the mid point of
the Louisiade, then turned and made straight for Sydney.
After leaving Redscar on the homeward voyage they made no
further systematic observations.

It seems clear, from the pages of his Journal, that on this
voyage it was the natives who kindled Huxley's interest. All
but vanished is the depression and the introspection of the
previous cruise. There are hardly any long blanks in the Diary:
of the 80 days they spent in the Louisiade, 47 are the subject
of entries. For the 112 days comprising their voyage along
the New Guinea coast across to Cape York and back again,
until the date of leaving Redscar Point, there are but 32
references; but this includes the one large gap in the Diary,
from October 21st to December 3rd, when, as we shall see,
Huxley was immersed in zoological research. Discounting
this, we have almost one entry for every two days. Nor among
the pages do we find impressions of books, reflections on life
in general, records of internal struggle. There is no "literary"
entry for the whole cruise; there are but two or three that can
be styled subjective, and these mostly on dates when the ship
was out of sight of land.

Instead, there are long, vivid, and detailed accounts of the
natives, their houses, canoes, ornaments, language; of incidents that befell the landing parties, of the occasional "rows"
between the white men and the black. There are accounts of
sketching parties, reflections upon the conduct of the expeditions by Captain Stanley, entries evincing an interest in natural
history. All is objective, all is full of life. It is obvious that
during this period Huxley's faculties were keenly aroused and
often at full stretch.

Nor was pure zoology neglected. His scientific notebook
for May 1849 to March 1850 contains nearly 70 separate
entries, ranging from one to seven pages in length, and more
or less uniformly spaced from May to July, and from November to January with a few in the other months. There are 13
entires concerning Siphonophores, 22 on jellyfish and polyps,

4 on comb-jellies, 4 on annelid worms, 7 on crustacea (including two on the parasitic crustacea whose investigation he mentions (p. 9) as one of his scientific aims), 8 on Molluscs, one on a larval sea-urchin, and 6 on Ascidians. Among the latter are notes of extreme interest on the curious form Appendicularia (see p. 41). In addition, there are in his 1848 notebook numerous entries dating from this voyage, written on the blank pages opposite notes on similar animals previously examined.

Thus while Huxley was in the main checking up and amplifying his earlier observations, he was doing so with vigour, and in addition embarked upon valuable new work upon the Ascidians, both Appendicularians and Salps.

As I have recorded in an earlier chapter, the sea near Cape York was in November 1849 crowded by an innumerable multitude of Salps. Huxley's previous work on these animals, especially on their mode of reproduction, had been fragmentary. He took the opportunity here provided to settle down in good earnest and get to the bottom of the mystery. As regards the Salps, it was on this cruise that Huxley did his most intensive work and arrived at his important conclusions. Without doubt it was his immersion in this fascinating and difficult problem which accounts for the long gap in the Diary through the month of November.[1]

In general, however, it was not animal life which had kindled Huxley's interest, but human life. Even with his recovered animation, he paid no attention to corals, although the ship visited the most wonderful coral reefs and often anchored in huge coral lagoons. It was the natives that fascinated him.

We may here make a brief digression to explain the anthropology of the region. In this I have had the advantage of the help and advice of Dr. C. G. Seligman, F.R.S., who himself has made an exhaustive study of the inhabitants of south-eastern New Guinea. He has kindly read and annotated the relevant parts of the Diary in typescript, and has referred me to modern sources of information on the region.

In the districts visited by Huxley there existed and still exist several ethnically distinct types of human beings. First there

---

[1] Curiously enough, I can find no notes on this piece of work in the scientific notebooks: it may have merited a separate book to itself.

are the Australians, secondly the Papuans, and thirdly the Papuo-Melanesians. The Australians are confined to the continent of Australia and the small islands immediately adjacent to it. They constitute a very distinctive stock, by some authorities considered as one of the major divisions of the human species. In certain of their physical characters resembling the negro, in others, like the strong beard of the men, they recall the Caucasian or "white" subspecies, and in still others, such as the frequency of strong bony brow-ridges, they stand alone. Their nearest existing relatives appear to be the pre-Dravidian peoples of India, though these are now much mixed with other types. How they first reached Australia is still a mystery. Once there, however, they spread, albeit sparsely, over its whole extent, apparently supplanting a more primitive stock. The scattered remnants of this earlier population were forced, it seems, to take refuge in Tasmania and are known to anthropology as the Tasmanians. They were exterminated during the nineteenth century, and Huxley had no contacts with them.

The Australians exist at a very low level of culture. They were then, as they still are where uninfluenced by white contact, hunters and food-gatherers, with no knowledge of agriculture and no permanent settlements. They must have entered the continent from the north or north-east, but all living traces of them in other regions have been obliterated by later invaders of other types.

The Papuans constitute the inhabitants of the major part of the great islands of New Guinea. They have frizzy hair, which is often grown in a great mop, and brownish-black skins. They are usually taller, darker-skinned, and more strongly built than the Papuo-Melanesians; it is probable too that *en masse* they are longer-headed, though puzzling areas of round-headedness occur in the neighbourhood of the mouth of the Fly River and in Torres Straits. Their noses, usually broad, may present a curved or hooked outline, so that men of this type have been described as "Jewish-looking". They appear to be related, though not closely, to the Tasmanians.

In addition to them, New Guinea harbours some remarkable pigmy tribes, who have been forced up into the heights of the interior; but Huxley had no opportunity of seeing or even hearing tell of any of these.

The south-eastern portion of New Guinea, however, together with the Louisiade and the archipelagos to the north of it, is inhabited by people of another type, to which Seligman has given the name Papuo-Melanesian. They are a mixed group, consisting of elements from the true Melanesians, who in a succession of waves have invaded the region from the east, and from the original Papuan inhabitants, with whom the invaders interbred. A Melanesian type of culture and language has, broadly speaking, superseded the original Papuan within the area. Whereas, for instance, the Papuans have only numerals for 1 and 2, the Papuo-Melanesians have an elaborate numerical system. On the south coast, the western boundary between them and the true Papuans is quite sharp, running inland in an easterly direction from Cape Possession. The cultures and languages on either side of this line are very distinct.

The Papuo-Melanesians are in general lighter-coloured than the Papuans, but their mixed origin is revealed by their great variability in skin colour, from light coppery to almost black, while their hair (often dressed in a great mop) may be curly or even wavy.

The Papuo-Melanesians can further be subdivided into eastern and western groups. The eastern group inhabits the extreme eastern tip of New Guinea itself, together with the whole of the so-called Massim area, comprising the various groups of islands from the Trobriands in the north to the Louisiade in the south. The western group inhibits the remainder of the mainland area. In the eastern group, canoes built up with washboards are characteristic. Perhaps the most outstanding, certainly the most obvious difference between the eastern (Massim) and western groups is in their decorative art. The former have a highly developed and very beautiful zoomorphic art, in which spirals based on bird designs predominate (birds are the most important of their totems), whereas the art of the Western Papuo-Melanesians is almost entirely geometrical and is not as a rule related to living creatures. Although not very obvious in the illustrations, something of the character of Massim art is hinted in Huxley's drawings of canoes (Frontispiece, Pl. 9).

Both Papuans and Papuo-Melanesians are at a primitive

level of culture, though not so low as that of the Australians. When discovered by white men, culturally they were still in the Stone Age. Dr. Seligman tells me that in 1908, on the south coast of New Guinea, near Hood Point, he saw a fleet of dug-out canoes being constructed entirely with the aid of stone adzes! Huxley records two or three places where the people had still no idea of the value of iron, even when already worked up into tools.

They cultivate the land, growing bananas, yams, and other plants, and utilizing cocoanuts, but cereal agriculture is unknown. Their houses and their canoes are often of elaborate construction, and their decorative art may reach a high level.

.   .   .   .   .

Only those who have been privileged to see primitive peoples leading their own strange lives in their natural haunts can realize what a revelation of novelty, what a stimulus to interest and reflection, such a contact can provide. When to this is added, as was here the case, the fact that in many places the natives had never been visited by whites, and that in some cases their very land had not been explored or charted, we can begin to realize what the Louisiade meant to Huxley.

There can be little doubt that it provided the foundation in which, much later on in life, he built his great knowledge of anthropology. This intimate first-hand contact was essential: without it, his ethnological work would inevitably have suffered in some measure from the aridity and unreality of purely armchair studies.

At the time, however, there is little evidence that he realized what were the broad lines along which the main problems of anthropology might be attacked—nor indeed what these major problems were. In zoology, he knew that the classification of the lower forms of life was in chaos, and had realized that the concept of structural plan or archetype, rigorously applied, would clear up the chaos. But he had neither the training nor the experience to visualize the chaos in which the classification of man was plunged; nor to realize that here the concept of diversity arising from separate structural types would have to be supplemented by that of diversity arising from crossing;

nor furthermore that no real progress could be made until the concepts of structural type and cultural type were properly disentangled, and it was recognized that there need be no connection between the continuity of skin-colour or head-form via physical heredity and the continuity of language and material culture via the pseudo-heredity of tradition.

In respect of scientific anthropology, indeed, MacGillivray appears to have been ahead of Huxley. In his official account of the voyage, there is a very interesting discussion (vol. ii, pp. 3 *seq.*) of the main lines of differentiation which he deduces to have taken place in the area, especially in the region of Cape York and neighbouring islands. He bases his conclusions mainly on linguistic evidence; and Dr. Seligman tells me that both in his method and his results he is on surprisingly correct lines. For one thing, however, MacGillivray had been in the area before, with the *Fly;* and for another he had the same passion for collecting native vocabularies as for collecting natural history specimens and diagnosing species new to science.

Huxley instinctively perceived that there was much for science to do in studying these primitive peoples. But he had not the knowledge to make anything of their language. He had neither the equipment nor opportunity to study their ideas—indeed the modern technique of cultural anthropology whereby the scientist, living among the people, is enabled to investigate their culture psychologically and from the inside, was not even born until much later. Nor had the technique of physical anthropology been invented—the standardized and detailed measurements of head-form, stature, nose-form, skin-colour, and the rest which, taken in large numbers, permit a scientific description of an ethnic group to be given. There remained the possibility of straightforward record, without scientific refinement, of whatever seemed of interest in the people's appearance and in their objects of material culture. And to this, both in written description and still more with pencil and sketch-book, Huxley zealously applied himself. Huxley's sketch of a canoe in plan (Plate 9, facing p. 150), is a model of descriptive draughtsmanship. His account of the houses on Chaumont Island, recorded on p. 156 and supplemented by excellent drawings from his pencil in the official *Voyage,* is equally lucid and efficient. The sketches of ornaments, weapons, canoes, holy places, domestic utensils, with which Mac-Gillivray's book is supplied, and which give point and vividness to the verbal descriptions, are Huxley's.

In regard to his anthropological work on the *Rattlesnake*, Huxley may fittingly be described in the phrase he later used himself about the elder Gosse with reference to his accurate descriptions of sea-anemones and other creatures of the British coasts—"a useful hodman of science". It is indeed interesting to see how training and technique can act as limiting factors to achievement. Anthropology at the time of the *Rattlesnake's* voyage was still for the most part in an anecdotal, almost prescientific, stage: and Huxley had had no anthropological training. Zoology, on the other hand, was ripe for fundamental advance: and Huxley had a sufficiency of zoological knowledge and technique at his command. So it came about that the same young man who, for all his keenness, could do no more for anthropology than serve up a few scraps of fact, was during the same period able to transform the face of zoology.

This is perhaps the place to make a few notes, based on Dr. Seligman's friendly information, on matters of anthropological detail referred to in the Journal.

The most interesting single fact would appear to be Huxley's record (p. 187) of seeing natives with bows and arrows at Redscar Point. This represents an easterly extension of the use of the bow by some twenty miles, as compared with the present. When Seligman was in those parts, the bow was seriously used only from Cape Possession westwards; between Cape Possession and about twenty miles west of Redscar bows were to be seen, but were regarded rather as toys: and at Redscar itself they were wholly absent. It seems that this change is not so much an expression of further physical invasion by Melanesians, but rather due to a slowly predominating Melanesian influence, accompanied by a gradual loss of Papuan tradition. It seems an example of one of those slow ethnological changes which in time may produce definite and widespread effect.

Otherwise, both the people and the objects noted by Huxley

Plate 8

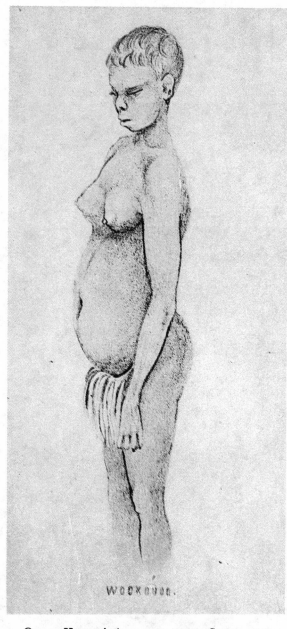

ONE OF HUXLEY'S ANTHROPOLOGICAL SKETCHES
An Australian woman, probably from the Cape York
region.   Pencil, unsigned, undated.

are, allowing for the influence of white contact, identical with
those to be seen in the same localities to-day, though Dr.
Seligman thinks that in some of his sketches of natives, both
those published in the official *Voyage* and the unpublished ones
in the sketch-book, Huxley tended to exaggerate the hooked
bridge of the nose: for although this "Jewish cast of countenance", common among Papuans, does occur among the
Papuo-Melanesians, it is by no means common.

On p. 148 Huxley is surprised at the marked difference
between the type of canoes used at Rossel Island and in the
region just to westward. "They can hardly have two fashions
of canoes in islands scarcely twenty miles apart?" His observations, however, were perfectly correct. He was a witness of
that curious obstinacy of cultural persistence which is so characteristic of many primitive peoples and so surprising to our
change-obsessed Western minds.

The Rossel islanders still sail the same type of canoe as they
did then, and it is still just as different from the canoes of
twenty miles away. Similarly the two types of houses, those on
piles and those like barrels cut in half, which he notes in the
Rossel area (pp. 139, 141), are still to be found side by side
to-day.

Huxley's quick observation is again evinced in his comments
on the earthenware cooking-pots which he saw at Chaumont
Island (pp. 157–8) : "How they contrive to make them of the
size (18 inches across), I don't know". Dr. Seligman tells me
that the natives of the Central District of British New Guinea
are wonderful potters, fashioning the bodies of more or less
spherical pots well over a foot in diameter, so that a cross-
section appears nicely circular, and this without the use of a
wheel. Some of the villages in this district are so famous for
their pots that they export them on a large scale to potless
areas further west.

Very characteristic are the wooden swords described by
Huxley, the bracelets made from human jaws (ceremonial
ornaments, associated with mourning), the waving of a green
branch as a sign of peace, and the behaviour of the "wag"
at Brumer Island (p. 169) with his performance as drummer
with an old tin.

Characteristic also was Huxley's involvement on Darnley Island in the natives' complex system of relationship, when he was offered a "wife" and found that this meant being pestered for gifts by all her relatives—"father, mother, brother, cousin, to the fiftieth degree". The system is, among other things, a system of mutual assistance, which often develops among the natives into a system we should be tempted to call sponging, distant relatives of the wife sometimes parking themselves for indefinite periods upon the husband and his hospitality. The assigning of a "wife" to Huxley was doubtless in part a gesture of friendship, in part a joke, but also a pretext for begging on the part of her relations (p. 202).

Of some interest is the shell-adorned screen or *"wowres"* mentioned on Mt. Earnest Island (p. 195). This is better written *waus,* and has been described in more detail by Dr. Haddon in vol. v. of the Reports of the Cambridge Expedition to Torres Straits. A *waus* is a place of initiation: the boys who are candidates stay for a month in the enclosure, undergoing a strict fast and being demonstrated the bull-roarer and other mysteries by the men. Huxley did not know this: all he could do was to recognize it as a sacred place. In the official *Voyage* (vol. ii, p. 14) MacGillivray speaks of a similar enclosure, on information provided by Mrs. Thompson, the white woman who had been living with the natives (p. 188). This is interesting, since the *waus* and all pertaining thereto is supposed to be kept entirely secret from women. Either the secret is not very well kept, or else Mrs. Thompson here as in other matters (p. 190) enjoyed favours not accorded by the blackfellows to their own womenfolk.

The temperament and attitude of the natives is interesting. For the most part they were friendly and even (p. 171) went out of their way to be helpful. But their suspicions were easily aroused, their cupidity often overreached itself, and misunderstanding on several occasions speedily brought on hostility.

    ·   ·   ·   ·   ·

The other chief interest in this part of the Journal is the light it throws upon Captain Stanley and his conduct of the expedition. Owen Stanley was a son of the Bishop of Norwich.

Huxley, in an unpublished sketch, depicts the crew of the *Rattlesnake* listening to the Bishop's parting sermon; and later (p. 174) finds a facial resemblance to him in the "fine venerable old man who appears to be a chief" who came off to the ship from the New Guinea coast and horrified Suckling by offering to rub noses. Another son later became celebrated as Dean of Westminster and biographer of Dr. Arnold of Rugby.

The family had strong intellectual traditions. The Bishop was a Fellow of the Royal Society, and it was through him that Captain Stanley transmitted Huxley's first important scientific communication. Owen Stanley himself had achieved the same distinction in reward for his services to hydrography and scientific exploration.

On this voyage, however, although he appears to have carried out the major task allotted to him—the survey of the Inner Passage—with care and in complete detail, he showed himself singularly unenterprising as regards any further exploration or the advancement of knowledge along any other channels. Again and again Huxley inveighs against his extreme caution, and finally comes out with a flat accusation of cowardice. Stanley, he confides at some length to the pages of his Journal, is afraid for his own skin, and this in spite of the fact that the natives, wherever they have been properly handled, are friendly and forthcoming.

The first sight of the New Guinea mountains, blue and mysterious in the distance, prompts Huxley to an outburst of strong feeling (pp. 165–6).

"Time was when I should have made this a red day in my calendar, at the time when I was young and a little enthusiastic myself and fondly imagined others must have somewhat similar feelings. There lies before us a grand continent, shut out from intercourse with the civilized world—more completely than China, and as rich if not richer in things rare and strange. The wide and noble rivers open wide their mouths inviting us to enter. All that is required is coolness, judgment, perseverance, to reap a rich harvest of knowledge and perhaps of more material profit. I beg pardon, that is not all that is required; a little risk is also needful. Investigators might get as many kicks as halfpence, and human life is so precious that investigators had better not investigate.

"These wounds and contusions are unpleasant and pay goes on just the same whether you have them or go without them. Discretion too is the better part of valour. And what is the advancement of knowledge and the opening of wide fields for future commerce to my comfort, my precious life, I should like to know? 'What's posterity done for me?' *A bas postérité*. No, no, it's all very well for young fools to talk about the duty of making the best use of the means lying in your power. You get no thanks for that and keeping to the letter of your instructions earns you pay just as well.

"Admirable reasoning! But Cortes did not reason thus when he won Mexico for Spain, nor the noble Brooke when he conquered a province in a yacht."

Again on August 31st their departure from Brumer Island stimulates him to similar reflections, but in a more sober vein. He realizes that any detailed exploration of the mainland itself might be difficult or dangerous. But not even a boat was sent to explore the mainland coastline or to look at what appeared to be the estuary of a large river not half a dozen miles from where they lay. Even so, the island might have provided them with rich stores of information about the animal and plant life and the natives and their habits, information valuable both in itself and as undoubtedly throwing light on the conditions prevailing in the adjacent land mass. But, though a fortnight was spent here, and the inhabitants of the island were extremely friendly, "we knew as much of its botany, similarly zoology, when we anchored as we do now". Visits to the shore numbered only two, of a mere couple of hours' duration. The natives' customs in their own homes have not been studied at all. And he ends up forcibly enough: "If this is surveying, if this is the process of English discovery, God defend me from any such elaborate waste of time and opportunity".

There is nothing of all this in MacGillivray's book. After all, it was written to order as a decorous official account. Or perhaps I should say that there is almost nothing. After access to Huxley's Journal, it is easy to read between the lines of a passage where with extreme brevity he notes (vol. 1, p. 265) that their first visit to Brumer Island was "a very short stay of a quarter of an hour"; and later (p. 283) that "during our

stay of thirteen days at this anchorage, . . . as our intercourse with the shore was limited to the two brief visits
already mentioned, I made no addition to the collection".

Nor is there anything in the hitherto published records of
Huxley's life. In the review he wrote of MacGillivray's book
he gives a half-humorous account of the difficulties inherent in
the cramped quarters and enforced contacts of the ship. But of
criticism of Stanley's leadership there is nothing, either in the
aforesaid review, or in the autobiographical sketch he wrote
late in life, or in my father's descriptive editing in the *Life
and Letters*. So long as he remained in the naval service, it
would have been mere foolishness on his part to jeopardize
his prospects by criticism, and in any case Stanley's sudden
death in March, 1850 forestalled any attack. And in later life
he doubtless felt that there was no point in reopening the old
grievance.

To-day, time has obliterated all immediacy of personal feelings, and the passages in the Journal can be printed without
giving offence as an interesting record of conditions aboard a
surveying ship of the British Navy.

It is interesting, if perhaps idle, to speculate on Stanley's
conduct. His death in Sydney but a few months later was
ascribed to the protracted strain and responsibilities of the
voyage. However that may be, it is at least possible that Stanley in 1849 was already a sick man, and that his excessive
caution and his reluctance to go beyond his minimum instructions were symptoms of his sickness.

It is true that if he had been more adventurous and had
displayed more of the spirit of Captain Cook, he might have
left a notable record as an explorer. His name to-day is affixed
to a mountain peak in the interior of a land which he was
content to leave untrodden, viewed only from the safe vantage
of his ship's deck. Let us, however, remember that the natives
of eastern New Guinea, though for the most part friendly
enough, include a number of cannibal tribes and have a certain
reputation for treachery. If he had decided on a bold policy
of exploration, it is on the cards that it might have ended in
disaster, and that the young assistant surgeon might have been
killed, and even eaten. In which case there would have been no
Thomas Henry Huxley dominating the Victorian scene, and

the only memorial to his genius would be the monograph on the Medusae.[1]

One other point deserves mention, and that is Huxley's attitude to the strained relations which now and then developed between white and black. He was often bitterly critical of his superior officers, and resentful at what he considered unjust treatment of the natives. He was not, however, irrationally or sentimentally "pro-native", and on several occasions stigmatizes their conduct as treacherous or unjustified. Even when the original fault seems to have lain with the Englishmen, he agrees that, in the circumstances which arose, strong measures were necessary.

He had none of the trained anthropologist's insight into the black man's mind, little conception of the alien ways of thought and feeling in which a primitive savage is enmeshed. His reactions were those of a generous-minded young man with plenty of common sense but a strong feeling for justice. He felt that there was some absolute standard of moral behaviour by which both the explorers and the natives could and should be judged. On the whole, he censured his white companions more hardly than the Papuans and Australian blacks.

But this commentary is long enough. Let us turn to the Journal itself, and see what Huxley has to say about the savages.

[1]In Stanley's sailing orders, quoted in MacGillivray's official account of the voyage, the following passage occurs: . . . "you must be constantly on your guard against the treacherous nature of the inhabitants; all barter for refreshments should be conducted under the eye of an officer and every pain be taken to avoid giving any just cause of offence to their prejudices. . . ."

CHAPTER 8

The Diary: Fourth Cruise, the Louisiade
MAY–AUG. 1849

O<small>NCE</small> more, no introduction is required for this section of the Diary. The map at the end of the volume gives the localities visited with the dates of the visits. They had enjoyed three-and-a-half months ashore—a time again unfortunately blank of record in the Diary—and did not set sail until May for what proved to be their longest cruise.

. . . . .

1849. May 8th.

We are off again on our cruise to New Guinea and the Louisiades. The wind has fallen light and we are dawdling about 9 or 10 miles from the Heads. Am I at sea or dreaming?

9th & 10th.

Ill.

17th.

Anchored in Cowan Cowan Roads, Moreton Bay, for the third time.

26th.

Sailed. Nothing of any importance occurred during our sojourn at Moreton Bay.

27th, 28th, 29th.

The worst gale of wind we have had yet. In consequence of the vicinity of the reefs we lay to with our heads to the southward for the greater part of the time.

Nothing could exceed the extreme discomfort of the ship—plunging and rolling in the heavy seas like a log.

To add to our disgusts she began to leak, owing to bad caulking they say, and consequently the after gun-room, gun-room and cabins thereto adjoining were all flooded, mine about the worst as I was to leeward.

Everybody felt qualmish and headachey and there was no sleep for any but the lucky possessors of hammocks.

On the afternoon of the 26th while the gale was at its height we nearly had a serious accident. The tiller rope gave way strand after strand and while the relieving tackles were got on we had to steer by our sails. All went on very well so far, but after they were on, being new they were stiff to work, and the quartermaster on deck not communicating with the quartermaster below quite soon enough to allow for their stiffness, the old ship broached to and received three heavyish seas, which however did no damage, and her head was soon got round again.

Had this happened at night it might have been awkward.

Apropos of the bad caulking one of the men said a good thing to-day: "If them —— had been 'tending to the ship, 'stead o' givin' pic-nics in Sydney harbour, we shouldn't 'a had this piece o' work". This was of course in an audible sotto voce merely.

Saturday, June 2nd.

Our previous discomfort enables us to appreciate with double force the exquisite weather we are now enjoying. Nothing can be more beautiful than this smooth sea, just sufficiently broken into waves to give an appearance of life to the deep blue waters; this deep infinite blue sky, with here and there a summer cloud floating dreamily along, or hanging like a hovering bird, realizing that exquisite simile of Joanna Baillie's:

As if an angel in his upward flight
Had left his garment floating in mid-air.

Even the old ship looks well with her pile of canvas just distended by the soft gentle breeze. At night she looks ghostly, the bright moon lights up the white sails, vague shadows from the rigging and spars play over their surface, and the darker outlines of the masts fade into the surrounding shade. The canvas looks like a self-supporting cloudy pyramid. At that time when the sleepy watch, weary of doing nothing, dozes away in imaginary wakefulness, I walk the deck. And I am not solitary for a thousand thousand thoughts chase one another through my brain. And strangely enough with whatever subject I commence, you, dear one, invariably become at last directly or indirectly the object of my meditation.

Or I lean over the gangway and look down into the dark shadow of the ship. The little waves plish-plash with a pleasant murmur against the side, and the light-sparkles dance and glimmer away for a brief moment and then are no more seen. Dreamy parables do these waves murmur in one's ears. That great sea is Time and the little waves are the changes and chances of life. The ship's side is Trouble, and it is only by meeting with this that the little creatures in the water shine and grow bright. They are men. If it were calm they would not be bright. See, there is a big one; he shines like a fiery globe. He is some great conqueror. He keeps on shining for full a minute—that is Fame—and then gives place to darkness like the rest. Oh brave! who would not be great!

SOMEBODY: "Well, what are you thinking about?"

SELF: "I was mereiy looking—to—to see what she is going——"

"Oh, two and four; bother it, I hate this lazy work."

SELF: "Hum: I rather like it." A pause.

SOMEBODY: "Well, aren't you going to have a walk?"

SELF: "No—a—thank you—a—I'm tired."

SOMEBODY: "Unsociable fellow that is." Exit.

SELF: "Thank God, that frump's gone."

If I had been Robinson Crusoe I certainly should never have been troubled with his yearnings after society, or else the mass of men are very different from those whom I have seen. And yet I believe they are as good as the mass and certainly quite as good as myself. The only reason why I prefer my own society to that of other people is, that—I am not obliged to regard my own follies as wisdom, or look as if I did, which is as bad. I can call myself a fool and believe it too, and offend no one.

Night. June 4th.

To-day we enter unknown seas, whereby care sits upon the brow of the Executive—a vision of reefs and wrecks haunting them on all sides. As for me, "cantabit vacuus"—it's no business of mine. Only as the ship rolls very much in consequence of being laid to I would that we might be going ahead.

8th.

The air is hot and damp, the sky cloudy and frequently it rains. My cabin resembles an orchis-house and I sit melting though half stripped. I have a sort of presentiment that this style of thing will endure for the next four months. Woe! Woe! to them that be fat [?]. Our course is peculiar. No longer we can see we go towards our goal, but at night we shorten sail and "revenons sur nos pas", till daylight, whereby our total progress is not the sum but the difference of our nocturnal and diurnal progression.

I am becoming a very morose animal, worse than I was last cruise I think. I feel inclined to avoid everybody, and to shut myself up in my own pursuits.

It annoys me at times to hear others talk, and I could sometimes bite anybody who speaks to me. Why this should be I can't tell, and I tell myself that it is very unreasonable—foolish—wrong, etc. All of which preachment has the usual effect of admonition.

I feel like a tiger fresh caught and put into a cage.[1]

[1]Compare with this a passage in his account of the voyage written in 1854 (*L. & L.* i, 50; the date is there given as August 1849): "Rain! rain! *encore et toujours*—I wonder if it is possible for the mind of man to conceive anything more degradingly offensive than the condition of us 150 men, shut up in this wooden box, being watered with hot water, as we are now. It is no exaggeration to say *hot*, for the temperature is that at which people at home commonly take a hot bath. . . . All energy is completely gone, and if I could help it I

9th.

Hot, wet, rainy, muggy. D'Urville was between Cape Deliverance and New Ireland and New Britain in 1827 in the months of June and July, and it rained almost incessantly. Are we to have the same pleasant weather during the whole of our three months cruise hereabouts? I fear yes.[1]

10th. Sunday.

Early this morning we sighted the Presqu'ile Condé (?) a point of land on one of the Islands to the southward and west-

ward of C. Deliverance. The land appears high and varied in outline. All day it has been overhung and obscured by dense clouds, frequently pouring down rain, sometimes one portion

would not think even; it's too hot . . . the lower and main decks are completely unventilated: a sort of solution of man in steam fills them from end to end, and surrounds the lights with a lurid halo. It's too hot to sleep, and my sole amusement consists in watching the cockroaches, which are in a state of intense excitement and happiness. . . ."

[1]It is interesting to append to Huxley's sketch of himself in his cabin, his description of that cabin written to his sister soon before sailing from England (*L. & L.* i, 26) ". . . upon the whole I really doubt whether Jonah was much worse accommodated, so far as room goes, than myself: my total length, as you are aware, is considerable, 5 feet 11 inches, possibly, but the height of the lower deck of the *Rattlesnake,* which will be my especial location, is at the

only being visible, sometimes another according as the cloudy canopy shifted. We have not been near enough to form any idea of the character of the country, though with this amount of heat and moisture it must be sand itself to be otherwise than fertile.

11th.

Saw the *Bramble* early this morning. This evening she was ordered to close and we spoke her. She arrived on Friday and lost her dinghy and flying jibboom in the gale.

It was discovered to-day that yesterday's Presqu'ile Condé was not the Presqu'ile Condé at all but some part of the S.W. islands [really Ile du Sud-Est: MacGillivray]. At midday yesterday we were abreast of Rossel Id. But we stood down to the W. and S. to look after *Bramble* and therefore were this morning much where we were yesterday morning. A long reef runs parallel to the land (of the S.W. island) at some miles distance from it but (*teste* Yule) does not reach as far as Rossel Id. We are now I believe to work round the N.E. end of Rossel Id. and get under the lee side of it, in hopes of finding a smooth anchorage.

N.B. Though cloudy it has been fine pleasant weather to-day.

12th.

A fine wind and lovely weather, occasionally almost calm, so that this evening we were only abreast of Adèle Island. This is a small islet lying off the N.E. end of Rossel Id. It is covered with thick low wood, high irregular trees projecting from among the underwood. The *Bramble* was sent inshore to find an anchorage for us.

Rossel Id. cannot be less than 2,000 ft high at its loftiest part, which all day was covered by a fleecy cloudy canopy. I

outside 4 feet 10 inches. What I am to do with the superfluous foot I cannot divine. Happily, however, there is a sort of skylight into the berth, so that I shall be able to sit with the body in it and my head out."

He first grew a beard during the Third Cruise, as we read in a letter to his sister (*L. & L.* i, 44): "I cultivated a peak in Charles I style, which imparted a remarkably peculiar and *triste* expression to my sunburnt phiz, heightened by the fact that the aforesaid beard was, I regret to say, of a very questionable auburn—my messmates called it red."

know nothing more beautiful than a cloud resting upon a mountain peak, like the head of a delicate girl resting on the broad shoulder of an old warrior. Each sets off the other's peculiar beauties.

13th.

To-day we stood in towards the land early in the morning and preceded by the *Bramble* made our way round the north end of Rossel Id. and thence along the Récif Rossel which stretches for some 30 miles to westward of the island, in the hope of finding a harbour on the W. side of the island and to the S. of the reef. But the sun set before we were very far round the end of the Récif Rossel and so we are hove to for the night. During the whole of the morning we were not more than two miles distance from the N. shore of Rossel Id, so that one could form some notion of the country. It is a beautiful island, with its surface diversified by numerous peaks and vallies, and clothed with verdure from the sea-shore to the top of the mountain peaks. And the verdure too is none of your green-brown Australian foliage, but a deep-coloured, rich, leafy mass, of all shades from indigo to grass green. Half a mile or so from the shore runs a narrow white line of surf marking the position of the fringing reef which, alas for our chances of finding a harbour, runs like a natural defense parallel to the coast. Within this is a space of deep blue water, contrasting beautifully with the sandy beach where such exists. But for the most part the shore was mangrovy.

Groves of cocoa-nut trees were to be seen here and there and "matted" among them, to quote a favourite expression of Brierly's, were usually one or more huts, usually in the shape of a barrel cut in half, i.e., low and arched and steep at each end. Not very far from the huts and cocoa-nut patches one might occasionally see a clear patch of land exhibiting many parallel rows of something or other, concerning which a great controversy has arisen, some maintaining them to be cleared and cultivated fields, planted in rows like any dibbled farm-ground, others, that it is a mere natural result, a sort of lusus naturae. But as the lusus-party don't allege *how* nature has played such tricks, in any feasible manner, and as I fear they are somewhat actuated by the spirit of opposition, I incline to the cultivation-party, and put it down as a fact: *"The Louisiadians cultivate the Ground"*.

We saw natives on the beach and parties of them engaged in fishing close to the reef, but they were too far off to make out their ugly mugs. Some of the canoes had large lateen sails. I hope we shall be nearer neighbours.

14*th.*

We drifted to leeward for some distance last night so that this morning it took us some time to regain our position of last night. Having done so we coasted along Rossel Reef, the *Bramble* close in and ourselves following at a cautious distance. But though one or two openings presented themselves in the reef they were not considered feasible and we stood on to Peron Island [Piron Island: MacGillivray] hoping to find shelter. Peron Island is low compared with Rossel Id. and comparatively clear of trees, its upper surface presenting more the appearance of a succession of downs. There were however plenty of cocoa-nut trees close to the beach. A fringing reef ran parallel with its coast as usual and prevented all access. A continuation of this reef stretches out a long way to the [left blank in MS.] ard so that we began almost to despair of finding shelter. However the *Bramble* coasted along, and finding a practicable looking break, about the middle of the day, stood off & on while Yule went in one of his boats to make a more minute examination. Between two and three o'clock a signal at the *Bramble's* mast had turned all eyes towards her and not without astonishment we read "A practicable opening if you are not busy". What our being busy had to do with the matter was not so clear, but presently they found out their mistake and hoisted the proper flags which were to the effect that the opening was practicable but narrow.

So we signalized to her to lead in and followed in her train. The opening is very narrow (a tenth of a mile nautical, about 200 yards), and it looks rather ticklish to see yourself passing within a stone's throw of roaring breakers on either hand, however loudly the leadsman may sing out his "Deep nine" or "By the mark fourteen."

But we passed in without let or hindrance and now are safely at anchor within a huge harbour formed by several high islands on the one side while to windward the reef which we have had so much trouble to thread defends us as a natural breakwater.

None of the islands about us appear so richly wooded or so beautiful as Rossel Id. The nearest is not very high and is pretty free from trees at its upper part. Halfway up the hillside five or six huts are perched and some of these appear to be of very singular construction—like convex-roofed sheds mounted on pillars. The others are somewhat like those seen on Rossel Id.

Natives are visible both on land and in canoes. The latter have not visited us and indeed hardly could as there is a fresh breeze dead against them.

After we came to an anchor, Capt. Stanley signalized to Yule inviting him to dinner. The answer was "plunging". But as the Lieutenant came, he must doubtless have meant something else.

N.B. It's much more satisfactory laying at anchor here than knocking about at sea in a dark night.

N.B.2. I have forgotten the most important thing of all. The skipper's black dog "Native", weary I suppose of leading a dog's life and among the middies, committed suicide last night, by walking into the sea out of the main chains.

The skipper and his dog had this in common, that they liked one another, and were disliked by every one else.

Nevertheless I could have wished the poor beast to die in some way less miserable, than paddling about so long as he had strength to and finally sucked down by some shark.

June 15th.

Boats out sounding to find us a new anchorage nearer the land. We saw seven or eight canoes with 8–10 men in each, but none of them would come near us. Several however went to the *Bramble*. I suppose they thought she was smaller and less able to do them harm.

They had some of them the large bushy heads of hair of the Papuans but others were without this distinctive mark and they varied considerably in colour. For the most part they were coppery. The canoes have a single outrigger and a good deal resemble those we saw at Cape York (see Frontispiece). The sail consists of three sheets of some fibrous substance, and shortening sail is performed by taking down each sheet separately and laying it along the gunnel. The upper end of each sheet has a great many little pennants streaming from it.

The paddles are something like the ace of spades with a long handle. They sail up near to the place they wish to reach, then strike sails, masts and all, and paddle up. The only articles of barter they brought to the *Bramble* were yams, cocoanuts and tortoiseshell. They were very greedy for iron and stole one of the crutches wh. happened to be lying loose on

the thwart of a boat astern. Like any dexterous London thieves they passed it from hand to hand and concealed it at the far end of their canoe, and when charged with the theft looked as innocent and impassive as M. de Talleyrand himself could have looked under similar circumstances.

But when from the threatening attitude the Brambles put on they saw it was "no go" they passed the crutch over again and paddled off as hard as they could paddle—more ashamed of the failure than the theft, I fancy.

16*th.*

At one o'clock Simpson was sent away in the cutter to look after a watering place and Henderson to open communications with the natives. I among others accompanied him.

A number of natives were fishing on the reef adjoining the small green island and thither we first betook ourselves. They were fishing, some with spears and others with a large sort of seine, but on our approach all their occupations were given up and in spite of the most enticing offer of red cloth etc. they betook themselves to their canoe and made off for the land waving towards it as if inviting us thither.

As a reef stretches between the small green island and the larger island on which are the huts, we could not follow them, but we landed very considerably more towards the ship. To use a paddyism we landed in the water, as the lumps of coral and rock would not allow of the boats grounding on the shore, thereby getting considerably damp and spoiling our shoes. Our fishing friends had in the meantime also landed and as soon as they saw us on this territory they advanced slowly towards us—one bright copper-coloured gentleman who appeared like Paul to be "the chief speaker" bearing a green branch in his hand which he frequently waved. We too gathered branches and waving for the dear life and making all sorts of unearthly noises, supposed to express our pacific disposition, went towards them.

At some forty yards distant however, our coppery friend halted and made very significant signs to us to be off about our business, and when we continued to advance, he and his people retreated. At last McGillivray, leaving his gun with us and taking a branch in each hand, went jumping and dancing with all sorts of antics towards them. They allowed him to come up but still seemed disinclined for our society.

Brierly then took upon himself to do the agreeable and advanced in the same way but with such wonderful antics that the niggers seemed irresistibly attracted and committed themselves to several acts of barter. After a little while, laying my gun aside I went to them, and had a very interesting and polite interview with friend coppery and two other gentlemen who were quite black and had large fuzzy heads of hair with combs a foot long, narrow and very long-pronged, stuck into the front of their very remarkable coiffure.

Brady had given me a red cap which was much coveted by all, but I made one of the fuzzy-headed gentry give me an ornamented chunam-gourd for it. Some waste paper procured me one of the long combs.

I made a hasty sketch of the most remarkable of the fuzzy heads, but in spite of all my attempts to be amusing he was off before I could finish it.

These men vary considerably in colour and appearance. Some of them are as black as the Australians and these appeared to me to be fuzzy-headed; others again were of various shades of copper colour and these appeared to have close short hair. Their only clothing was a long leaf curled up behind into a most absurd appendage like a bustle. Their teeth were stained red by the betel. They mostly carried baskets, containing various odds and ends, gourds containing chunam etc.

They had no arms of any description with them. The chief demand was for cloth, especially red cloth. Buttons were heavy on hand. Iron on the other hand at a great premium, to judge from the avidity with which they clutched at a penknife I accidentally took out. But I would not part with it as it was my only one, much to their disappointment.

Many wore circular ear-rings apparently made of the operculum of a Turbo ground flat and cut to the centre so as to allow of the pierced lobe of the ear being passed in. And the septum of the nose was ornamented—save the mark!—with a long white bone or some such thing stuck through it. They wanted us to go up to their village but the want of time obliged us to decline, and we betook ourselves along the beach in the opposite direction to look for water. The rock was slaty, and its fragments mingled with sharp and jaggy fragments of coral did not make a pleasant surface for walking, particularly considering the softened and pappy state of our shoes.

We passed several clumps of cocoa-nut trees and luxuriant brushes, the soil where bare of trees being covered with long silky grass, but we found water only at one place and there in small quantity. The cutter accompanied us along the shore and at the western point of the island we waded off again and got on board.

The only birds I saw were parrots, a white cockatoo and some kingfishers. There was a queer little leaping fish (Chironectes) with large pectorals, in the mud.

20th.

On the 17th (Sunday) Simpson and Heath went away in the cutter to examine the other (western) side of the island on which we landed on Saturday for the purpose of finding anchorage and watering place. McGillivray, Brierly and I accompanied them. We kept outside the small islet with the reef that stretches from it to the island and as we advanced towards the N.E. end of the island seeing natives (some of them with green branches) making their way over the hills and waving to us, we landed. The water shoaled so that the cutter was unable to approach within some fifty yards or so of the shore, so tucking up our duds, and looking well to our "ammunition of war", Simpson, McGillivray, Brierly and I waded to the beach. This was a narrow strip of sand behind which there was a steep grassy ascent, clothed abundantly with trees. By the time we had landed a number of the natives had arrived at the top of the ascent and were hullaballooing at a great rate.

We ascended to meet them and they incontinently retired, leading us over the tops of the hills, and through the luxuriant long grass, for about a quarter of a mile. Our coppery friend of the preceding day was of the company, but he did not seem much inclined to trust us, and the whole party went jogging on until they were joined by a good many more who came over the hills armed with their spears; by this time there were some 30 or 40 natives, almost all with their spears, and one had a carved and pointed wooden sword. This gentleman from his extreme blackness and ugliness and the peculiarity of his weapon was immediately named the "Jack of Clubs".

It was now our turn to be cautious, and without advancing any further we tried to do a little barter for their ornaments etc. But the market was decidedly dull. They seemed to have a very distinct notion of getting but no idea of giving, and they began to get round us (Brierly and I, Simpson and Mc-Gillivray keeping a look out as rear-guard), pulling and snatching at anything that took their fancy. Suddenly we heard a squeaking, and two blackfellows came over the hill at a great rate bearing an unfortunate pig slung over a pole. This they cast down at our feet, and taking a knife from me and a handkerchief from Brierly, seemed to wish us to understand that we had better be off at once. We were delighted to get the pig and immediately shouldered it and began to march off, chuckling immensely at our success, when I missed a pistol which I had stuck in my belt.

I did not at all like the idea of losing this, so I dropped the pig and went back making signs that I wanted it, as I had no doubt that it had been stolen by some of the blackguards. They pretended to look about in the grass for it, and when, disgusted at this sort of humbug, I looked big and blustered a little, they drew together and scowled, handling their spears. It was quite evident this game would not do, and so I pretended at last to be satisfied, and forming in battle-array, Simpson as advanced guard, Brierly and I carrying the pig, and McGillivray as rear-guard, off we marched, not without keeping a sharp look out on the gentry behind, who were evidently not [at] all well disposed. I was ready to die with laughing at the absurdity of the scene, more especially when we adopted the expedient of sliding down the high bank before mentioned, pig and all, as the quickest mode of reaching the boat. While piggy and his carriers, squealing and laughing, slid, Simpson and McGillivray kept a look-out at the top of the bank as some of the niggers were gliding off by twos and threes into the thick wood upon its side, and it would not have been a satisfactory place to have been attacked in. However we all got safe into the boat with our prize. The natives had pointed us out a deep ravine leading into a bay on the N.W. side of the Id., which they indicated to contain fresh water, and so we went round to examine it.

There was very good anchorage, but a reef stretched off so far from the shore that it would have been impossible to water the ship, as the boats would have been unable to get over it. The bay was very beautiful, with abundance of cocoa-nut trees, and towards one end there were several huts. We were not near enough to examine them clearly, but it appeared to us, with the glass, that the affairs on posts were really huts mounted up and not mere canopies.

After leaving the bay we stood over to a small thickly wooded island, where we anchored during the dinner hour. We landed and wandered over the island in quest of game. There were no inhabitants, and it altogether resembled one of the small Australian islets. There was the Casuarina, and a thick brush in which we found several Megapodius mounds. Mc-Gillivray shot a Megapodius identical with the Australian sp.

There seemed to be a clear passage out between the islands on this side.

When we returned to the boat we saw a canoe approaching under sail. There were eight or nine copper-coloured natives in it, and they steered straight for us, showing none of the distrust the others had manifested. We procured some very good cooked yams and a spear from them and they then went quietly to fish off the reef.

We returned to the ship by about half-past four.

18th.

The pinnace was got out. Five canoes came off to us to-day but would not approach very near. Two of them had not been seen before and had their prows carefully carved in a very singular manner, the carving being terminated by the figure of a bird. One fellow stood up and had a great deal to say, but unfortunately his oratory was lost upon us, though some of the more imaginative among us made out that some of the natives had hurt themselves with my pistol and then had come to bid us depart out of their coasts. However this may be, they went to the *Bramble* and then got under sail and took themselves off.

In the afternoon Yule came on board to announce that he had discovered a very fine watering place on South-West Island.

19th.

Pinnace sent away to work to windward as far as Peron Id. The same party as before accompanied Simpson (changing Heath for Staunton).

We had not been away from the ship four hours before it came on to rain like cats and dogs, and as there was no bottom to be got with I don't know how many fathoms we could not anchor—consequently could not spread the rain-awning, consekens got soaked through and through. It took us till evening to get dry and if it had not been for the admirable supply of eatables and drinkables which we had laid in it would have been rather uncomfortable. However as it turned out there was no passage to be found between Peron reef and South-West Island, a reef stretching right across from one to the other, and so today we returned.

N.B. The Pig was very good when cooked.

22nd.

Wading about on the reef near the ship in the middle of the day (yesterday) one of the galley's crew caught hold of a frog-fish. The beast wounded him in two places with the sharp spines of his dorsal fin. The wounds were mere punctures, but the man's hand and arm swelled up greatly. He suffered under the most intense pain, so great indeed as to cause sickness and almost fainting, with slow pulse and cool surface. Notwithstanding anodynes and warm fomentation the pain continued very severe the whole evening, and although much better today is not yet gone.

The hideousness of the brute might have deterred any one from touching it, one would think.

23rd.

Three canoes came off this afternoon to barter cocoa-nuts and bananas for our red cloth, knives etc. Two of them came from Pig Island and had the ordinary construction but the third we saw came from the direction of Rossel Id. this morning. It was white with a stage something like the Cape York canoes. It had a regular stand-up mast, supported by rope stays. And its sail was of matting, oval and neatly woven in one piece.

They can hardly have two fashions of canoes in islands scarcely twenty miles apart?

24th. Sunday.

We had four or five canoes off to barter with us this morning—such squealing and shouting and laughing and yelling was never heard! One of the niggers had a human jaw by way of a bracelet. There was one tooth in the jaw and the circlet was completed by a small bone apparently of some animal lashed to the coronoid process.

The old fellow would not part from it for love or money. Hatchets, looking-glasses, handkerchiefs, all were spurned and he seemed to think our attempts to get it rather absurd, turning to his fellows and jabbering, whereupon they all set up a great clamour, and laughed. Another jaw was seen soon in one of the canoes, so that it is possibly the custom there to ornament themselves with the memorials of friends or trophies of vanquished foes.

The blackies behaved very honestly with us, not attempting to take anything without giving a proper equivalent, but this afternoon a couple of canoes went off to the reef and purloined the stays of the tide-pole and some of the ballast, leaving the pole itself.

Some stranger canoes came off in the afternoon and in one of them one of the missing pigs of ballast was seen. We immediately claimed it and on the niggers refusing to give it up the jolly-boat was despatched after them. The poor blackies were in a great funk, more especially when a couple of musket shots were fired after them (over their heads), and threw over cocoa-nuts, fruit, and afterwards the ballast itself, when the chase being useless was given up.

The worst of it is that the strangers may possibly have been ignorant that the ballast was stolen, as it must have been given them by those who took it, who may not have thought it necessary to be explicit as to how they got it.

25th.

Several canoes came off this morning; one of them brought the figure-head which was so much wanted yesterday, and bartered it immediately. In one of the canoes was a man with a jaw bracelet. The jaw was in fine preservation and evidently belonged to a young person, every tooth being entire. They seemed to have no scruple in selling it. A jade hatchet was procured from them also.

In the middle of the day we weighed and stood over to our present anchorage, close to S.W. Island.

26th.

The master had found a watering place here previously and today I went up in one of the cutters. Passing over a bar you enter a narrow river bordered on each side by very high mangroves. As you go further up and the water becomes fresher these become less and less frequent, trees of all sorts arch overhead and spreading their branches across the stream impede your progress. Cutting and dodging and breaking boughs, putting the helm hard a-port to avoid this snag and hard a-starboard to get out of the way of that dead and fallen tree, you work your way up for about a mile, when suddenly turning a corner you see the water tumbling over a small rocky ridge which extends across the stream. The surrounding brush is very beautiful at this point. A dense dark mass of foliage stretches up into the sky in front, here and there relieved by the graceful bright feathery heads of palm trees or the fantastic shapes of the Pandanus, which here grow to the height of sixty feet or more, with its long pillar-like roots forming a pyramid 15–20 feet above the ground.

There were many tree-ferns about this spot too with beautiful finely-cut fronds and sculptured stems.

I tried to make a drawing of the place, but it disgusts me exceedingly compared with my remembrance of the reality.

We found a Megapodius mound and one was shot, and there were reports of traces of wild pigs.

Four or five canoes full of niggers, mostly old friends, came off to us today, from somewhere about Pig Id. Barter very active for iron. A thing like a kneading pan was procured. One old gentleman had lost his nose, which imparted an expression of soft and pleasing melancholy to his countenance.

July 1st.

I see I am getting out of my good habits but there has been nothing to write for the last few days. Various canoes have been to us every day, and the best understanding has been maintained. In some of the canoes they brought off some specimens of their ladies; they were ugly enough but not quite so bad as the Australians. They wear a girdle from which

Plate 9

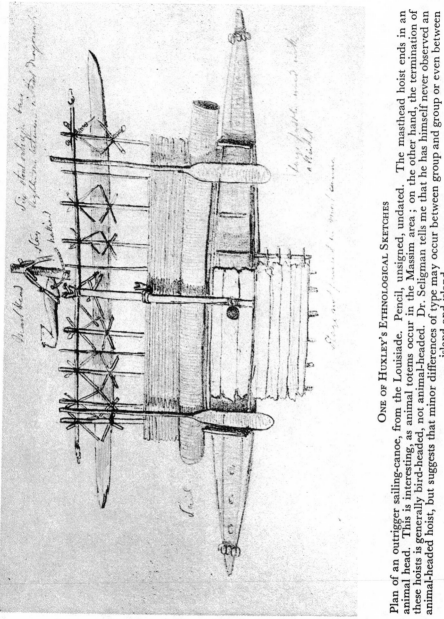

ONE OF HUXLEY'S ETHNOLOGICAL SKETCHES

Plan of an outrigger sailing-canoe, from the Louisiade. Pencil, unsigned, undated. The masthead hoist ends in an animal head. This is interesting, as animal totems occur in the Massim area ; on the other hand, the termination of these hoists is generally bird-headed, not animal-headed. Dr. Seligman tells me that he has himself never observed an animal-headed hoist, but suggests that minor differences of type may occur between group and group or even between island and island.

long grassy fibres depend as far as the knees so as to form a kind of petticoat. In this respect they exactly resemble the Darnley Islanders. They never stood up in the canoes as the men do but always kept sitting and sometimes shading themselves with a piece of matting.

One today had a child of which she took great care, shielding it from the sun with a light mat so that we could hardly get a sight of it.

Poor "Lighthouse" is lost. He strayed from the watering party yesterday and did not return. The jolly-boat was sent after him this morning but has not been successful. The ship's company, with whom he was a great favourite, are in despair.

We are unfortunate in our dogs, Lighthouse being the seventh or eighth that has disappeared since the ship was in commission. There is Denison's dog and Dayman's Billy and Pug and Native and another little beast of the skipper's, Brady's unfortunate kangaroo dog lost or as some opine shot at Cape Upstart, and Juno and the setter, left behind at Sydney this time.

That little skipper of ours is a greater ass than I thought. That he had neither smell nor hearing nor taste sufficiently refined to enable him to distinguish one sensation from another, sulphuretted hydrogen from Millefleurs, "God save the Queen" from "Old Dan Tucker", strawberries from mulberries—I knew long ago, but I now find that his eye is equally defective. The other day he and Brierly and I went across in the galley up the river, and each made a sketch of the same place. I finished mine in pencil and showed it him. He did me the honour (?) to approve, but said "Ah, wait till I get it out in colours". Thought I to myself we are going to have a Claude at least. The scene indeed was a beautiful one and a splendid subject, rich in colour and brilliant effects of light and shade. Last night the little man sent for me. I went and lo! the sketch, which with a look as much as to say "you don't see anything like that every day" he submitted to my inspection. I nearly burst out laughing. Words won't describe the absurdity of the thing. I was placed in a puzzling position, for I have a constitutional aversion to lying. So I said "Ah, exactly, sir. Yes, that's the Pandanus Tree and that's the water, and, ah, yes . . ." leaving him to form his own conclusions as to my opinion.

I am afraid his opinion of my taste is much diminished.

Evening.

"Lighthouse" has been recovered after all. About the middle of the day he came down to the beach opposite the ship through the mangroves, and wading out perched himself on the highest rock he could find so as to be as conspicuous as possible. A boat was immediately dispatched for him and when he came on board the Jacks nearly smothered him with their delicate (?) attentions.

July 2.

Got under way this morning and passing out between Pig Id., Joannet Id. and S.E. Id. anchored altogether to the S. of the archipelago under a small reef. The pinnace and the 2nd galley visited a small island to the N. of us which we passed in the morning, and had communication with the natives ashore. Some eight or ten of the women came within a short distance and they seemed altogether more friendly than on previous occasions.

Friday, July 6th.

I have been so much occupied for the last two days that I have really not had time to make any notes in my Journal, notwithstanding the vast numbers of events I have to record.

On Wednesday morning the Captain determined to visit the small island (supposed to be Chaumont Id.) which the galley visited on the 2nd, in order if possible to open up a communication with the natives. We formed a formidable party, the 1st galley and second cutter with their crews, the Captain, Thomson, Brady, McGillivray, Heath, the sergeant of marines, James the Captain's servant and myself.

The galley conveyed the skipper and surgeon; the rest of us went in the cutter.

We got over the reef which fringes the island and nearing its southern shore we saw several natives running along the shore and gesticulating. We stood in towards them but as we neared they retreated among the cocoa-nut trees that thickly wood the hill side, their dusky shapes showing here and there as they peeped from between the trees. We might have landed here but the water shoaled away much and as the tide was falling the boats would have been hardly able to remain near enough to the shore to afford us efficient protection, so we stood off again and pulled round a point to the westward, opening a little sandy bay with a long spit running out from the bushes and allowing the boats to remain pretty close. There could not have been a better place for our purpose as from several canoes being hauled up on the beach it was clear the natives were living near and at the same time the long bare space, on which a sandpiper would have been a capital mark to anyone in the boats, quite secured us when landed against any treachery.

The Captain landed, giving directions to Dr Thomson to remain in the galley and cover him with his gun. Several blacks came down, but each party was rather suspicious of the other, the skipper with his usual want of savoir-faire looking as stupid as a stockfish, and the niggers not knowing precisely what we wanted to be about. After a while it occurred to me in my presumption that this was not the way to do any good, so I said "I don't know that there are any orders about staying in the boats" and holding up my coat tails waded ashore. I began to dance and the niggers began to dance, and then we sat down and began to draw some of them, and then some more of the officers came ashore and we were very good friends. They offered us yams and cocoa-nuts for "Kalouma" and we gave them red cotton night-caps, bits of glaring cotton handkerchiefs and other articles of *virtù*, with which they were evidently delighted. By this time there were some twenty niggers down on the beach. At some distance in the background three or four ladies made their appearance in their peculiar dress, looking just like ballet girls, a resemblance not a little increased by the jumps and springs they occasionally took, but the men waved them off and would not let them approach.

Everything seemed to me to be going on rightly, and so I quietly wandered away and espying a path followed it up and in twenty steps found myself in an open area containing three houses, invisible from the sea by reason of a screen of bushes and cocoa-nut trees.

All the natives were down with the boats so there was no one to be seen but a stray woman or two who ran off on my approach and I had an excellent opportunity for examining the houses. I got a pretty clear understanding of their build and then, knowing the skipper's peculiar jealousy, I returned and told him that I could show him the houses if he would come quietly so as not to disturb the natives; so he and Brady and I went back, but when we came to the opening in the trees which led to the houses he turned back saying he thought it advisable to have somebody else with him.

Brady and I remained and he came presently with one of his boat's crew and the sergeant (?) and some of the natives.

The little man had his book and pencil in his hand but to my certain knowledge he neither made note nor sketch, and seemed rather anxious to get away, wandering about in a regular fidget and seemingly unhappy till he got away. I notice these things because today he said to B—— when he came on board, "Well, I have seen the houses and know all about them—got every particular". He seems to be much of Louis XIV's opinion—"La France, c'est moi".

After remaining on the island for about an hour and a half and getting on very good terms with the natives, we departed, the blackies accompanying us off to our boats; we returned to the ship about two o'clock.

In the evening over the customary cigar the skipper says to the first lieutenant, "Well Suckling, we have had a very satisfactory communication with the natives today, so much so indeed that though I mean to send the cutter tomorrow to barter for yams, *I don't think it necessary to go myself.*" "C'est moi" again.

So on the morning of the 5th, Thursday, the first cutter was manned, and Brady was dispatched with a supply of axes and knives to barter for the ship's company, the Master going in charge of this party and Robinson as Mid of the boat, while McGillivray, the Surgeon, James and I went as idlers and supernumeraries.

We landed at the same place as before and this time the

natives ran down prancing and gesticulating, as if to welcome
us, in a far more friendly manner than before. Many of them
had garlands of green leaves round their heads, knees and
ancles, some had long streamers depending from their arms
and ears and floating in the wind as they galloped along shaking their spears and prancing just as boys playing at horses do
at school.[1]

We soon were surrounded by them shouting "Kalooma,
Kalooma", their word for iron, and offering us all sorts of
things in exchange. One very fine athletic man, "Kai-oo-why-
who-ah" by name, was perfectly mad to get an axe and very
soon comprehended the arrangements that were made. Brady
drew ten lines on the sand and laid an axe down by them,
giving "Kai-oo-why-who-ah" who had hold of his arm to
understand that when there was a "bahar" (yam) on every
mark he should have the axe. He understood directly and
bolted off as fast as he could run, soon returning with his
hands full of yams which he deposited one by one on the
appropriate lines, then fearful lest some of the others should
cut him out of the axe, he caught hold of Brady by the arm
and would not let him go until he got yams enough from the
others to make up the number and the axe was given him. The
yell of delight the blackie gave! He jumped up in the air,
flourished it, passed it to his companions, tumbled down and
kicked up his heels in the air, and finally catching hold of me
we had a grand waltz with various poses plastiques for about
a quarter of a mile.

I dare say he was unsophisticated enough to imagine that I
was filled with sympathetic joy, but I was taking care all the
while to direct his steps towards the village, which I wished to
enter under Kai-oo-why-who-ah's respectable sanction. I think
he smelt a rat, for he looked at me rather dubiously when
I directed our steps towards the houses and wanted me to go
back, but I was urgent and he gave way and we both entered
the open space where we sat down and were joined by one or
two others. I got him to sit for his portrait and we ate cocoa-

[1]This and the succeeding two paragraphs were quoted by Huxley in his article
on the voyage of the *Rattlesnake* (see p. vi), and were later published in *L. & L.*
(vol. i, p. 50). There, however, the scene of the incident is wrongly given as
Bruny (Brumer) Island. This is the only passage in *L. & L.* giving a description
by Huxley of any incident on the fourth cruise.

nuts together and at last got on such good terms that he made me change names with him, calling himself "Tamoo", which I gave as my name, and giving me to understand that I was to be "Kai-oo-why-who-ah". When I called myself by the latter appelation and talked to him as "Tamoo" nothing could exceed their delight; they patted me and evidently said to one another "This is really a very intelligent white fellow". Like the Cape York natives they were immensely astonished at beholding one's naked legs, if one pulled up the trousers, spanning the calf with their hands and drawing in their breath and making big eyes. And once when my shirt was open and they saw the white skin of my chest, they set up a universal shout. I fancy that as they colour their faces black they imagined that we coloured ours white, and were surprised to see all our bodies of the same colour.

The women did not skurry away quite so fast as before except the very young ones; one old lady indeed passed from house to house upon her lawful occasions, but would not take any notice of me except by grinning when I held up some cotton print to her. They are not so hideous as the Australians, indeed, so far as I could judge at the distance, some of the young nymphs were comely enough. The old woman had a grass petticoat and a grass cape fitting round her neck and open at each side for the arms.

There were five or six houses, irregularly placed with clear spaces round them and at some distance, 30–40 yards, from one another. They were all of the same construction, about 30 feet long and fourteen high, supported by four stout posts about four feet above the ground, with a perfectly clear under space.

The posts are not more than twenty feet apart (in length) and some four-six feet distant (in breadth) so that the house which they support overlaps them on all sides. They are very stout and about 8–10 feet high, some 3 feet and a half from the ground, with an elliptical piece of wood like a shelf fitted on to them, and on the upper surface there were frequently roots laid out as if to dry; but these shelves must have had some other purpose, perhaps to keep animals—snakes, rats etc.—out. About six or seven inches above the shelf a strong stout cross-bar is lashed to the posts, forming the ends of a parallelogram whose sides are formed by two longer spars equally lashed to the posts above the cross-bars and supported by them. A third spar runs midway between these lateral ones and is lashed at each end to the cross-bar.

A number of thinner transverse bars are lashed across these again, immediately above them, and above these comes a layer of about a dozen longitudinal rafters; across these again is the proper floor formed of closely-set transverse narrow pieces, smooth on the surface and apparently split from some palm, so that the floor is formed of these layers besides the frame on which it is supported.

The roof is arched from side to side and rises in the middle to a height of 7–8 feet, but at the ends comes nearly down to the level of the floor; it is formed of a green thatch and outside this cocoa-nut leaves supported upon a frame of curved withes, like an Australian hut. The ends of the withes appear to be lashed to the cross-pieces.

As the fronts are 7–8 feet high and the floor not more than between four and five feet from the ground it follows that the upper ends of the posts stand out in the interior of the house, and a stout cross-piece is lashed to them and runs across as a sort of brace, supporting again at each end a longitudinal strengthening bar. These are all lashed together and to the withes of the roof. There are three other longitudinal spars similarly lashed to the withes, which run along, one in the centre of the roof and one on each side inside between the centre and the lateral bars before mentioned, so that altogether the roof is a very firm structure.

Several cross-bars run from one lateral strengthening bar to the others at distant intervals between the terminal ones. And the one half of their extent supports longitudinal sticks forming a sort of shelf, on which they keep root and chunam pots and other store matters.

A man may sit up but not stand in the interior of these huts. In one of the huts I saw the remains of a fire, but for the most part the fires with the cooking pots were on separate stages at some yards distance.

(The pots were of some kind of wood, and carved on the

outside.)[1] Not true—the pots are earthenware as I see by a fragment brought off to-day. How they contrive to make them of the size (18 inches across) I don't know.—July 31.

Behind the houses on one side they had formed a very curious inclosure, on the face of the hill. It must have been about ¾ acre in extent, but had not been cleared or apparently touched with any agricultural instrument, nor was anything, e.g. yams or the like, to be seen growing therein. The fence surrounding it was some 3 ft high and very strong, being formed of a double row of stakes, each pair being 18 inches apart. Each pair of stakes held the ends of a series of strong wooden bars one above the other and as the stakes were strongly lashed the whole formed a very strong fence. In one corner of the inclosure there was a sort of little shed of dry withered cocoa-nut leaves but it appeared to cover nothing.

As it is quite certain from what we saw in another part of the island that they don't take the trouble to enclose their yam and banana ground in this manner we imagined that the fence was for the purpose of keeping pigs. I walked all round it but could see nothing but trees; here and there were marks of grutting up. As I walked I could hear the women cutting about among the bushes near me, but of course I took no notice but quietly pursued my walk.

When some seventeen or eighteen hatchets had been disposed of—more yams being obtained for the later than the earlier ones—we had about 360 pounds of yams in the boat besides private supplies, and we shoved off, leaving our friends in the best of humours. We were no sooner away than we saw three or four women come capering down, with leaps that would have done honour to Taglioni.

We pulled round the point to the south side of the island and there all the officers except the Master landed.

This side of the island is very steep and is covered with cocoa-nut trees; at the top it is almost bare of trees but is clothed with the long luxuriant grass in which all the islands we have seen abound. From the boat we could see one patch of about half an acre covered with bananas, some of which were to be seen elsewhere, so that we concluded that this must

[1]In the MS. the sentence in parenthesis is crossed out, and the next two sentences have been added later.

be a cultivated spot. Anxious to ascertain if this were really the case, Brady and I ascended the hill, and found that this was in truth a rough sort of garden, not fenced in in any way but cleared of grass and of trees, the young slender trees being all cut down to within three feet of the ground. There were a great many yams which appeared to have been planted near these stumps so as to climb up them like so many hop plants.

There were a great many bananas, all young and without fruit, and these like the yams were planted quite irregularly. On returning to the beach I found that the natives had come round the point and from all I could hear I suppose that they must have imagined that we were taking French leave with their cocoa-nuts and yams. One of them who was in advance appeared very angry and scowling and poising his spear made up to Robinson. Robinson took it very coolly, just bringing his gun to his hand in readiness and looking at the fellow, who on coming closer thought better of it. As it was, it was as well there was no firing, though had I been in Robinson's place I should most undoubtedly have shot the man. I don't see the fun of waiting till you have a spear through you before you fire.

However, when they saw that we had been doing no mischief and were quite strong enough to take care of ourselves, they became very friendly again and bartered a few more cocoanuts etc.

Kai-oo-why-who-ah and one or two more were very desirous to understand the use of our guns and so James took aim at a swallow flying overhead and brought him down beautifully. Our friends were extremely astonished both at the report and the result, and at first would not so much as go near the bird, but when it was picked up and shown to them they seemed still more surprised to see the blood.

Some more shooting went on, rather unwisely as I thought, for the shots were not by any means successful, and then we parted, excellent friends. We hauled off for some distance from the shore to dine and the natives remained on the point looking at us.

We amused ourselves by firing at the bottles that were thrown overboard, taking care to fire in the opposite direction to the niggers. But the sergeant like a fool discharged his musket, not exactly at them, but sufficiently towards them to frighten them round the point. What should we have done had one of them thrown a spear within twenty yards of the boat?

July 8th.

Yesterday the pinnace and galley with Simpson, Cayman, Brierly and Staunton returned from their cruise to Joannet Id., and the islands to the W. They had had a row with the natives and brought back two wounded men—one (Backhouse) with a spear wound in the left arm, the other (Mitchener) with an axe cut on the head. The row happened on this wise.

On Wednesday night the two boats anchored under Johannet Id., both within a short distance of the shore and the galley some fifteen yards inshore of the pinnace. A thick belt of mangroves skirted the shore opposite to them and the land was high and hilly.

The night passed without interruptions, and as the day dawned, but before sunrise, the look-out man reported three canoes containing about thirty men to be coming towards them. As the officers in charge of the boats were instructed to have peaceable communication with the natives if possible, they rather favoured than opposed the approach of the canoes, the more as on their coming nearer many of the natives were recognized as having been off to the ship. Two of the canoes went to the pinnace and one to the galley, the natives calling out Kalooma! Kalooma! as usual and offering various articles for barter. The two canoes that were alongside the pinnace soon left her and went to the galley, and there was a great talking among the three. One of the natives who was in the canoe which had been alongside the galley from the first, now took hold of Shirley the coxswain, and would not leave his hold. Dayman seeing this imagined the man was skylarking and told him to leave off, and at the same time, as he saw the natives were getting troublesome, snatching etc., directed the anchor to be got up. Mitchener was in the act of hauling in the anchor, when a native quietly took hold of his arm and hit him with a stone axe on the head, and hauled him overboard. This seemed to be the signal for a general row, the natives striking with their axes and throwing their spears, some dropping into the water and trying to overturn the galley and drag her inshore. Dayman shouted to Simpson to get up his big gun and fired the only two muskets he could get at, wounding one man, and then the galley gave such a lurch that he slipped off the stern-grating on which he was sitting into the water.

The blackfellows did not care much for the firing up to this point, for it was after this that Backhouse got the spear wound; but now the pinnace got some muskets to bear upon them and they paddled away in all haste seeking for an opening among the mangroves.

The discomfited galleys got into their boat again and gave chase and the long gun from the pinnace opened fire upon them, first giving them a round shot which went close to one of the canoes, causing the unfortunate blackies to drop their paddles and jump out like smoke, and afterwards sending a charge of grape among them, doubtless to their infinite disgust. The crack and whistle of the shot and the sounding echoes of the report of the gun must have made them think the devil was among them. However, they got away among the mangroves at last, and left one canoe with all its spears and furniture as a trophy to our side. It was towed out into the stream, all the spears and paddles broken and turned adrift.

It was a very treacherous business altogether and I am only afraid they were not sufficiently punished.

After the row the boats went on with their work and as they sailed along inshore close to one of the villages, a number of natives came down dancing defiance to them and brandishing and sharpening their spears—as much as to say, "Come here and see what you'll get".

Brierly tells me that they saw several very large houses not less than five and twenty feet high at one village.

July 10*th*.

This morning got under weigh and moved some fifteen miles to seawards. *Bramble,* pinnace and 1st cutter despatched to the westward to survey.

July 17th.

Yesterday and to-day we have moved by short stages round the East and W. ends of Chaumont Island between it and Joannet Id. and are now anchored considerably to the W. of Chaumont Id. We passed the Bay where the attack took place on our way.

July 18th.

Got under way this morning and proceeded about fourteen miles to the W. Anchored in a most uncomfortable place, in mid-sea without shelter of any kind. Can't have scuttle out, miserably hot and uncomfortable. Weather damp and occasionally squally and rainy.

19th.

Raining hard all day. Rain awnings up and ship decidedly unpleasant. In the afternoons a canoe full of natives came alongside, with yams and plantains for barter. They were shivering with the wet and consequent chilliness. One of them had a very peculiar necklace, to wit a piece of their rude string on which several pieces of bark and a human odontoid vertebra were strung.

22nd. Sunday.

Got under weigh at six this morning and proceeded about 25 miles to the westward to a low woody island under which we are at present anchored.

The breeze has been very light all day and we consequently did not anchor until about five in the afternoon.

Two canoes came alongside soon after we anchored. They did not come from the island, which appears to be uninhabited, but from the distant islands to windward. One of the natives had picked up some English words (as I suppose from the *Bramble*), "Me very bad", "Me negar".

We spoke the *Bramble* and pinnace in the middle of the day and Yule and Simpson came on board for a short time.

28th.

Yesterday I went to the Middle Island where Dayman was observing, in hopes of having some communication with the natives of a couple of canoes who had landed there. Their landing caused a considerable panic in the ship. As we were fully half a mile from the shore with our 36-pounders, and Dayman had *only* 5 marines with their muskets to protect him, the first cutter was immediately dispatched by the Captain to lay off in readiness for anything that might occur.

All this might be very right, as doubtless the small numbers of those on the Island might have produced a collision had the natives been ill disposed, though I do not believe for a moment that they were so, as in one canoe there were two children— girls, not five years old, whom their fathers took with them ashore—very clear evidence they had no evil intention.

The children had their hair done up into long pipe-like ringlets with some adhesive stuff. It looked pretty enough to see these long ringlets hanging down their backs, at a distance. On close inspection there was too much dirt to my taste. One of the children was very pretty and its great black eyes rolled in wonderment upon me and such things as I offered it. Its father was a fine intelligent-looking man and seemed pleased with the notice I took of his child.

The natives did not remain long after the arrival of the cutter, but seeming in doubt of *our* intentions, moved off to the weather island.

To hear the Captain talking in the evening you would have imagined that a bloody battle had taken place at the least, or at any rate must have taken place had it not been for his extreme care and providence in sending the cutter. What a Sir Joshua Windbag the little man is!

The *Bramble* returned this evening. She has I believe found a new anchorage for us.

July 31st.

Another month gone. Gaudeamus igitur! No canoes have been near us for some days, and were it not for a few friendly "Buffons" I should be in a state of utter stagnation. I find that three months' sea is quite as much as suits me at once.

Aug. 2nd.

The carpenter who has been ill since our leaving Sydney died today. They buried him on Middle Island with all the honours, making a fire over his grave afterwards, to conceal it from the natives who might perhaps be disposed to make an armlet of his jaw-bone or a necklace of his vertebrae.

The traces of Death's hand at sea are soon obliterated; you die in the morning, and in half an hour your cabin is nailed up, and folks are speculating as to who will have your vacancy. You are buried or thrown overboard in the afternoon; the next day your traps are sold before the Captain, and the day after you are forgotten. There is hardly room for the living on board a ship, so that no wonder that the dead find no resting place in it.

Aug. 4th.

This morning early we made a flitting from the Iles Duchateau, intending to anchor anew at the Iles Duperré. Mais l'homme propose et Dieu dispose! After passing the Montemolin and Jomard, which like the Iles Duchateau and the Iles Duperré are low and woody, we arrived off the latter about mid-day, since which period (it is now about seven p.m.) we have been humbugging about in search of an anchorage. The bottom seems immensely irregular, sometimes we have had twenty fathoms and the orders were given to bring ship to an anchor, but at the next cast there were 60 or 80 fathoms, or perhaps no bottom.

About an hour ago we thought we had done it and the anchor was let go; 60 fathoms ran out like smoke and then it was found that it had not reached the bottom so there was nothing for it but to heave up again. A remarkably pleasant job for men who had been on deck all day. However it *was* got up and we are now standing off and on. The pinnace has been sent to one of the islets to make a beacon fire.

Aug. 5th.

Employed all the morning in beating up to the weather island where Yule had stated there was a good anchorage. The *Bramble* and pinnace in company astern of us.

Yule made straight for the opening he had mentioned, beat in and anchored in precisely the depth he had stated.

Even this was not demonstration enough for our chief. He sent the cutter away with Dayman to investigate this and another opening to leeward of the island.

Yule in the meantime came on board and offered to place boats as buoys so that there should be no mistake about our entering. However it was all no good. The little man's heart (if he had such a thing) failed him and instead of entering the lagoon and anchoring we hoisted in the pinnace and are now standing off and on the island waiting only for daylight to go to sea.

And all this discomfort, to avoid a little—very little risk! —I am sick of the brute. He has been like a little fiend all day, snubbing poor old Suckling in the most disgusting manner, and behaving like a perfect cub to all about him.

6th.

Worked up to leeward and passed out to sea by the passage between the Jomard and Duperrey [sic].

7th–8th.

Sailing along the outer edge of the great reef, passed De Jean Id. Lovely weather, and smooth water. . . .

Aug. 12th.

Yesterday and today we have been cruising on and off a set of islands which appear to answer, though not very accurately, to the Teste and Dumoulin Ids. of D'Urville. One of these (to the E.), which they propose to call the Bell Rock, is very remarkable from its steep conical form. The group we are off today consists of several small islands, high and very rocky. The highest has barren precipitous sides. On some of the others there are trees, some of them cocoa-nuts.

To-day for the first time we have seen the coast of New Guinea. It lies away to the westward, stretching along the horizon as a blue mountainous mass, several islands some large and some smaller lie between us and it.

Time was when I should have made this a red day in my calendar, at the time when I was young and a little enthusiastic myself and fondly imagined others must have somewhat similar feelings. There lies before us a grand continent—shut out from intercourse with the civilized world, more completely than China, and as rich if not richer in things rare and strange. The wide and noble rivers open wide their mouths inviting us to enter. All that is required is coolness, judgment, perseverance, to reap a rich harvest of knowledge and perhaps of more material profit. I beg pardon, that is not all that is required; a little risk is also needful. Investigators might get as many kicks as halfpence, and human life is so precious that investigators had better not investigate.

These wounds and contusions are unpleasant and pay goes on just the same whether you have them or go without them. Discretion too is the better part of valour. And what is the advancement of knowledge and the opening of wide fields for future commerce to my comfort, my precious life, I should like to know? "What's posterity done for me?" *A bas posterité!* No, no, it's all very well for young fools to talk about the duty of making the best use of the means lying in your power. You get no thanks for that and keeping to the letter of your instructions earns you pay just as well.

Admirable reasoning! but Cortes did not reason thus when he won Mexico for Spain, nor the noble Brooke when he conquered a province in a yacht.[1]

The *Bramble* has worked up her way parallel to us inside the reef (which ceases a little to the E. of our present position) and this afternoon signalized a good anchorage under one of the islands. She was directed to go in and anchor and has done so accordingly about half a mile from the shore. We are standing off—why, God knows.

13*th.*

This morning at daylight we found ourselves out of sight of land altogether. In fact I don't think anybody knew very

[1]Compare a letter to his sister written immediately after his appointment to the *Rattlesnake* on May 24, 1846 (*L. & L.* i, 25): "New Guinea, as you may be aware, is a place almost unknown, and our object is to bring back a full account of its Geography, Geology, and Natural History".

clearly where we were. However, after a while we made the land, about 15 miles to leeward of yesterday's position, the Dumoulin Id. being out of sight altogether. Old Yule must have been rather nonplussed when he did not see us this morning as we were to have spoken with him; by sunset we had worked up in sight of the Dumoulin Ids again but of course at dark began the old game of standing on and off. Here is a whole day clean lost.

The islands we saw today are believed to be the Brumer Ids.[1] They are high as is the mainland behind them, but we were too far off to make them out well.

The weather is cool, but overcast and hazy, and there seems to be much rain along the coast.

16th.

We have had a good deal of rain and squally weather for the last day or two. Our occupation has been to work up within sight of Brumer Id during the day by about four o'clock P.M. and then to get into a great pother and stand off for the night; next morning we usually found ourselves twenty or thirty miles to leeward. Mysterious currents and the like appear to have been in operation.

This afternoon we got up rather earlier and the *Bramble* coming out to lead us we took heart of grace, stood in (under her guidance) and are now anchored safely. We did not come to an anchor until dark.

17th.

This Brumer Id. is one of the most beautiful we have seen, remarkable at once for its singular form, its greenness and the immense number of the cocoa-nut trees; they literally crown the island. The upper regions are free from trees here and there, and with a glass we can see hurdled inclosures apparently for the cultivation of yams etc.

The natives have been off to us today in considerable numbers although it has been blowing hard with occasional sharp

---

[1]So far as can be deciphered, Huxley appears to write this *Bruinie* consistently: I have, however, employed the true name as printed by MacGillivray.

squalls. Only one set came in a canoe and this differed from those we have seen before in having no raised gunwale and in the outrigger pole being more horizontal. We saw no mast or sails. The paddles are longer (over six feet), more slender and far better made than any we have seen yet. They are of some hard but light wood, and the head of the slender handle is very neatly carved.

The most of the natives came off in catamarans composed of three or four logs (usually three) lashed together by cords of rattan which though doubtless strong appeared very slight. These catamarans varied much in size, from nine to 30 feet long and bearing one to a dozen men. That they are permanent constructions and of common use appears from the elaborate carving bestowed upon the pointed ends of the middle logs—the outer logs are shorter than the middle one and though not carved are smooth and pointed at each end.

It is amusing to watch the careful dexterous manner in which the natives balance themselves on their queer-looking structures over which the sea continually washes, and how they prevent their cocoa-nuts and yams from washing off, or dive after any stray part of their cargo.

They resemble the other Louisiadians perfectly in appearance, but do not understand the words we have elsewhere collected, nor do they use the same word for iron etc. They have some ludicrous signs which appear to be meant for symbols of friendship and whose repetition by us produced extravagant signs of delight and amusement among them.

This afternoon one fellow who appeared to be a great wag —perhaps the intense blackening of his face might be a sign of his being a wit—having obtained a tin-pot, began to make use of it as a drum, putting it under his left arm and tapping on the bottom or lid as the case might be with the fingers of his disengaged hand. He had three white cowries in a necklace, and he prepared himself for his performance by putting the string of his necklace in his mouth so as to have the shells in strong contrast with his black face.

To show them that we could do a little in this way too, the skipper ordered the drummer into the chains and marvellous was their amazement when he beat off a roll. They seemed a little frightened at first, particularly as the whole ship's company, attracted by the noise, rushed to the side and shrouds to see what was going on, but soon recovering. The "wag" appeared to be intensely delighted. In the meantime the fiddler and fife had joined the drummer and the two struck up a lively tune.

The wag was like to go out of his senses, prancing about on his unstable foundation, listening to catch the time and putting in a touch on his own drum here and there. We were all convulsed with laughter. Even when it was time to be off, the wag would take his paddle and work away vehemently for a moment or two, then the music became too much for his feelings and he would start up, drop his paddle and drum; then paddle again and drum again until the drumming was over.

18th.

Today we have been visited by many natives coming off by relays in their catamarans and canoes. A number came on board when invited, without any hesitation. They were shown all the wonders of the ship and loaded with presents and then dismissed in the highest good humour. These are the first who have ventured on board us, although they have frequently visited the *Bramble* at other places.

In the afternoon a catamaran came off from the large island towards the mainland with six or seven very good-looking young men. She was made of three spars lashed together, the middle one elaborately carved at its ends and painted in red and black. The spars were regularly smoothed off and flattened above as if with an adze. They had built up a little stage to hold their goods (yams, cocos, and cocoa-nuts) and prevent them from being washed off by the sea, which occasionally made a clean breach over the bow-man.

They hauled on to a line from the cabin windows and afterwards by a stout rope let down from the jolly-boat, and on being invited two or three "shinned" up the aforesaid rope and came on board. I offered my services as guide to one gentleman, and he accepted them, seeming to believe that by keeping tight hold of my hand he should be protected from any harm. I took him down into the wardroom where they happened to be sitting over their wine. They invited him to take a glass and he sat down in the arm-chair, not without some persuasion, however, as for some time he regarded the chair with very suspicious eyes—I think he looked upon it as a kind of trap. He admired the wine and wanted to give his companions some, but when we got on deck he found they had gone back to the catamaran. He wanted sadly to keep the glass, but in the present state of the butler's department that was wholly impossible.

19th. *Sunday.*

Today at one o'clock the first and second cutters were despatched ashore under Simpson's orders to enter into communication with the natives and ascertain if possible whether water was to be obtained. Several of the natives (among them the "wag" or "dancing master", for he delights in both soubriquets) had been on board and we persuaded the "wag" and another without difficulty to accompany us. They seemed indeed rather delighted at being transported ashore like gentlemen, and examined very curiously the different parts of the boat. She had been up for some time and consequently took in a good deal of water, whereupon the wag fished out the balers and set to work in right earnest to clean the well. As usual, however, with savages he soon tired of his work.

A nasty little reef of rocks runs along the beach at a short distance, and we got well ducked in going ashore. A number of natives, both men and women, had come down to the beach and seated themselves on the centre piece of a large catamaran hauled up there. As we landed, the women withdrew to a little distance but the men advanced and taking hold of our hands and making their ordinary remarkable signs of friendship, led us to the log, where we all sat down for a short time.

They then proposed that we should go to their village, and as they had no arms, and we were a strong party (Simpson, Thomson, Brady, McGillivray and myself) we saw no difficulty in accepting their invitation. A special friend or chum attached himself to each of us and we marched up the steep and craggy path which leads over the lowest part of the central ridge of the island, hand in hand. The view from the top

of the ridge is lovely in the extreme. Right before you is the
wide ocean with a tremendous line of rollers as it breaks over
the rocky shallows near the beach. At your feet in a valley
between high precipitous hills on each side is a clear level
space, thickly planted with cocoa-nut trees, and peeping among
these lie the curious gables of the native houses. Descending
by a very picturesque but somewhat inconvenient path we soon
reached the village where we found all the feminine population
and a good share of the masculine up in arms to receive us.
They got out their drums and raised the most hideous uproar
imaginable on our arrival. We were soon great friends, and I
went prying about to examine the houses. They are raised on
posts in just the same fashion as those at Chaumont Id., and
the general structure is much the same, but their shape is very
different inasmuch as the roof is raised at each end into two
very high triangular gables, its ridge sweeping into a concave
curve. The gables are formed by two long poles lashed together, the space left between them below being filled by a sort
of thin wall made of flattened cane or some such material.
The floor does not come out so far on the gable nor does the
thin wall of the gable reach down to the level of the floor so
that there is a sort of door lift, which is reached by a wooden
stair, or rather step, of the simplest construction such as we
saw at Chaumont Id.

Besides looking at the houses I obtained one or two sketches
of the women who, though diminutive (as indeed both men
and women are), are by no means so bad looking, and by that
time Simpson wanted to be off again, and we marched back
attended by the whole population of the village.

We had made them a great many presents both on board
the ship and during our visit to the village, and on our return
to the beach, in order as I suppose not to be outdone in generosity, each of our chums went and cut a lot of cocoa-nuts,
which were speedily deposited in the boats without the donors
accepting any further payment for them.

More than this, the second cutter's anchor had somehow or
other become foul and two natives seeing what was the matter
pushed off in a catamaran. On reaching the boat one of the
two, an old man, dived down and after three or four attempts
(during each of which he remained under water for what

seemed to all of us a most astonishing time) succeeded in clearing it. He was going away without asking for anything but we called him back and gave him an axe.

We were all so pleased with the primitive simplicity and kind-heartedness of these people that we gave them three cheers on our departure, a proceeding which astonished them not a little.

During our whole visit we saw no arms of any kind in the hands of any of the males.

20th.

Our yesterday's visit had been so successful that the Captain determined on going himself this morning, with the purser, to visit the village and barter for yams etc. However just before starting he changed his mind and sent Simpson in his stead. As the boats approached the shore we saw no signs of any such numerous assemblage of men as yesterday. There were but a few women, and one or two young men and boys, sitting down, who retreated up the narrow path on our landing. The young men and boys came down to us and "fraternized". But as no others made their appearance we proposed to our friends to visit the village, to which they made no manner of objection. So we, i.e. Simpson, Brierly, McGillivray, and myself, marched off leaving Brady and the Captain's steward behind with their wares until we should return with some customers. We halted for a while on the top of the ridge to get some sketches and then proceeded to the village where we found nobody to receive us but a parcel of women with our friend the "dandy", looking at once friendly and martial, the former feeling being expressed in his countenance and gesture, the latter by means of a large wooden sword, with which on his shoulder he strutted about. He had a young girl on each arm, one of them my friend of the previous day, and these he gave us to understand were his wives.

Although very civil, however, he was evidently not at his ease, and seeing this we did not stop, but turned to go back, expounding to them by signs that we had plenty of "lopooroopa" and other grand things if they would come with us. Our determination to return, too, was somewhat excited by certain distant shoutings we heard in the brush as though people were hastening towards us. The Dandy and his feminine train accompanied us on our way back, keeping last between us and the ladies, and as we went he explained to me some very long story in a private and confidential manner. What it might mean of course I can't pretend to say but it appeared to be something to this effect. "Really my dear friend, I am very sorry to be obliged to treat you in this inhospitable manner, but you see, our acquaintance is so *very* slight, and the ladies are so unprotected here, that the other gentlemen would be angry if they found you here."

I had given him an axe-head for old acquaintance sake, and when we arrived at the beach, he and one of his wives took a different direction to the rest, beckoning to me to follow. I went and we came at length to a group of cocoa-nut trees. He went up one of them, while I staid below and sketched his wife. She took care to keep a very respectable distance between us, hardly allowing me to put her in proper position. After a while the Dandy descended with a bunch of green cocoa-nuts which he explained were for me and then (I regret to state it) gave them to his wife to carry down to the boats for me.

When we arrived at the boats there was a great noise and confusion. Some strangers had arrived and were by no means so well behaved as the islanders themselves. In the midst of the noise I sat down on a log and began to draw the Dandy's other wife (who had come to ask me to do so) a reddish-brown-haired girl with the hair in thrums and by no means so good looking as the other. I had almost completed my sketch, when I heard Simpson call me and saw that all our folks were retreating to the boats. I thought there was going to be some row and walked into the cutter with very short leave-taking of my friends. When we had shoved off I managed to make out that there had been some snatching at the barter articles, that the women had been observed bringing down axes with which the men provided themselves, and that one fellow, so far from fraternizing when Brierly made the usual signs, spit over his shoulder with a very contemptuous gesture. That so far as I can collect was the sum and substance of what happened.

22nd.

Today and yesterday we have had a great number of canoes and catamarans alongside, making no small noise. In fact their visits have become so troublesome that none are admitted on board, greatly to the disgust of the Dancing Master who did not at first at all understand the prohibition. Today four or five of the women came off in a canoe, among them the two wives of the Dancing Master, but no persuasion or temptation would induce them to come up. They had some men with them when they came and these did the paddling for the most part, but going back again when they were half way over to the Island, the men jumped into a passing catamaran, leaving the poor women to stem the current as they best might, and a long time it was before they reached the shore.

A very large canoe came to us from the New Guinea side, the largest that has been seen. It had a large oval sail like the Rossel Id. canoes, and a crew of 27 stout natives. We gave them a rope over the stern, by which they held on while a fine venerable old man who appeared to be a sort of chief, embarked on board one of the small canoes and came to us. I spoke to the first lieutenant and got him on board, when we showed him over the ship and made him some presents. Old Suckling was horrified when the old fellow offered to rub noses —imagining he was going to kiss him. The old man was not unlike the Bishop of Norwich, only taller. By dint of dogging him about and getting a line here and a line there I contrived to get a likeness of him.

The natives here have a great variety of vegetable products —cocoa-nuts, bananas, guavas (unripe), breadfruit (unripe), yams, sweet potatoes, cocos, betelnut and betel pepper leaf, and for some days past they have brought off large hanks of very strong flax with a very long fibre (6–9 feet in length).

They must have a considerable mechanical turn, for besides their carving, and the careful way in which the large beams of the catamarans are adzed flat on their upper surface, they make admirable ropes. And they have several varieties of musical instruments—drums of various sizes, hollow bamboos through which they roar and bellow, pans-pipes of seven reeds, and a kind of large Jew's harp.

The people seem happy, the means of subsistence are abundant, the air warm and balmy, they are untroubled with "the malady of thought", and so far as I see civilization as we call it would be rather a curse than a blessing to them. I could little admire the mistaken goodness of the "Stigginses" of Exeter Hall, who would send missionaries to these men to tell them that they will all infallibly be damned.

The niggers have been having a grand corobbory ashore tonight, lights have been dancing and winding among the trees and their drums have been heard. Not to be outdone we burnt a blue light and sent up two or three rockets, which must have astonished them considerably if they saw them. I know nothing that has so strange a ghostly spectral look as a ship lighted up by a blue light.

23rd.

The usual crowd of natives and canoes from all quarters. In consequence of some cheating that has been going on by some of the ship's company, orders were given this morning that none but the officers and their servants and a man from each mess should be allowed to barter. It is a very good thing that this regulation has been made, for the natives have been imposed upon in the most shameful manner. For instance, one of our people would hold up a fine piece of iron and make signs that he would give it for certain yams etc. The native hands up his yams unsuspectingly, and "Honest Jack", shoving a piece of worthless tin into his hand, walks off leaving the native to express his astonishment and disgust as he thinks fit.

It must be confessed however that the natives paid the sailors in kind occasionally, getting the "loporopo" beforehand, and then looking up with a vacant stare into the face of the expectant Jack, who all indignant at the cheat was probably pouring forth torrents of choice Billingsgate. This would happen occasionally, but it was by no means the rule and I do not know that any of our islanders have been guilty of such dishonesty.

The canoes had left us for the greater part of the afternoon, but about half-past four I heard a great noise on deck and going up found it to proceed from a canoe coming off from the island with an old woman, a boy, four or five men and a fine live pig securely lashed and slung over a pole after the manner of the Pig Island porker. The old woman was dancing, shouting and flourishing an axe in the most frantic manner upon the outrigger. And the sternmost man was winding forth the most dolourous noises upon a large shell, while the others added to the concert by shouting and yelling at the top of their voices. Directly I espied "ye pigge" I sent for two axes and exhibited them, whereupon our friends paddled up alongside in double quick time and handed up the porker, not before one native, however, had taken his spear and, making a grand flourish, stuck it into piggy, transfixing the unfortunate brute so that we were obliged to kill him forthwith.

The captain had in the meantime come on deck and he ordered one of the natives (the transfixer and chief man to all appearance) to be admitted. When he came on deck he had in his hand a wooden sword, and he immediately commenced a long oration, first casting the sword on the deck, then making signs to us to go ashore and finally going through the motions of sticking himself or being stuck with a spear. These motions and the energy with which he performed his part attracted a good deal of attention and some very marvellous theories were raised to explain them. The most elaborate hypothesis maintained by the orthodox was this. The other tribes, jealous of our favouring them, had been ashore, insulted the women and speared the pigs; a general row had ensued and the invaders been beaten (according to some—according to others it was a drawn battle) and the present visit was to be considered as an ambassadorial message (the old woman being probably minister plenipotentiary) propitiating us with a pig and demanding our aid. And furthermore Dayman averred that in his belief it was all connected with the row with the boats.

For my own part, I am as usual inclined to put a rationalistic explanation upon the mystery. To my mind the killing a pig among these people is considered a great occasion, a sort of grand feast in their church. They therefore brought this off with all ceremony and finally wish to inform us that if we will go ashore like jolly fellows, they will kill one for us, and have a grand corobbory. There is nothing I should like better.

After a while a large catamaran came from the shore, but as she was pulling up, the canoe filled by being caught on the side steps as the ship rolled. She did not sink, however, and the old lady kept her seat with the utmost coolness, canoe and all drifting down with the current. The large catamaran (on board which was our friend the Dandy) went to the canoe's assistance and we gave the end of the deep-sea lead line to a small catamaran alongside with directions to carry it to their companions in order that they might not drift out to sea while righting their canoe. The large catamaran and canoe must have been a good quarter of a mile away by the time the line reached them. They immediately made fast and made signs to us that they had done so, when we got the line over the winch and wound them up.

They were greatly pleased at this bit of assistance and the old woman was persuaded to come on board at last when she saw the Dandy and others so well received. The Dandy as usual brought a present for the Doctor in the shape of an uncooked yam.

The old lady was rather nervous, but became considerably reassured by our respectful treatment and the presents she received on all hands. Going away they were greatly delighted at getting possession of a cask of damaged flour, several of which were being thrown overboard. They seemed perfectly to understand its use, making some into a paste with a little sea water in order to show us what they would do with it.

26th.

Yesterday afternoon catamarans and some canoes from the island came alongside. The natives brought four or five of their women with them and these were without very much difficulty persuaded to come up. We did the honours and dressed the ladies up to their infinite satisfaction. Afterwards two of the men got their own native drums (wh. we had on board) and performed a dance for our amusement. A very singular affair the dance is too, consisting of a series of not ungraceful leaps and jumps, in a sort of cat-like manner, the body bent, the chin raised high up, and a sort of absurd half-humourous half-conceited expression on the countenance. The steps are accompanied in most accurate time by taps with the hand upon the drum, and the dance is always concluded with several short taps one after the other. Occasionally the two performers poussetted together up in a corner but for the most part they leapt along the length of the quarter deck and back again.

The girls were very merry and unconstrained though perfectly modest in their behaviour. They seemed half inclined to have a dance too but had not the courage. It amused me very much to see how perfectly women are women all the world over. There was the same incessant flow of small talk among themselves, the same caressing and putting their arms round one another, as would have been seen in *any* other group of women in any other place from London to Sydney. And to complete the resemblance they all persisted in kissing and hugging an impudent young varlet of a ship's boy who went down on the catamaran as they were going away. One of these damsels, who had disfigured her face by a copious coat of black pigment, was more affectionate than any of the others and seemed to take a most roguish delight in inspecting the traces of her kindness, left very visible upon the boy's white face.

One of the dancers (the same man who came off with the pig) very unceremoniously gave us to understand that he meant to stay on board by composing himself into a slumbering attitude upon the deck. By first grunting and going through the motion of sticking himself, and then howling, and pretending to hit something very vehemently over the head, he gave us to understand that if we would go ashore he would have a pig and a dog (!) killed for us, accompanying these assurances with many declarations about plenty of "quatai" or yams. He made up his mind that we would go ashore in the evening and have a jolly corobbory but he was wofully disappointed, for manifold as were the hints the skipper received he neither went himself nor offered to let anybody else go.

In the evening however he got up some amusement for the native by showing him his magic lantern. The chromatic colours and some of the strange apparitions of men swallowing rats etc. produced great exclamations from our savage friend, "dem! dem!" Afterwards he was taken up on the poop and a rocket fired, which astonished him still more. He was dressed up in a complete suit of coat, shirt and trousers, and hat. He seemed very temperate, would not touch our grog or wine and water, and preferred drinking his water out of one of their own vessels rather than from a tumbler.

We made him up a bed under the half deck but he found that too hot and went on to the poop, where he went to sleep in the midst of hot discussion that was going on among a party of us.

About half-past two in the morning he woke up and immediately began walking about and singing in no very low tones. He had to be informed that this was not quite *comme il faut* but gave the usual "ben! ben!" to all hints that he had better compose himself again.

The next morning (Sunday) he was very anxious to go ashore and that we should come with him, but the skipper for some reason or no reason did not choose to lower a boat and so the poor blackfellow remained, his spirits gradually ebbing in spite of all we could do to cheer him, till at last in the afternoon the poor fellow was fairly crying.

As no canoes came or appeared likely to come the Captain at last late in the afternoon sent him ashore in the cutter. He was well loaded with presents of various descriptions.

27th.

No canoes off, though there is no obvious obstacle to their coming.

CHAPTER 9

The Diary: Fourth Cruise, New Guinea and Cape York

AUG. 1849–JAN. 1850

ALTHOUGH the third cruise only lasted a few weeks less than the fourth, Huxley's gloom on the former and his delight in recording every detail of his contacts with native life during the latter have led to a great disparity in the two relevant sections of the Diary. Indeed the entries for the fourth cruise take up more than three times as much space as those for the third. I have therefore divided the material in this section of the Diary into two chapters, putting the break between them at the point where the *Rattlesnake* left the Louisiade for New Guinea and the Torres Straits.

.   .   .   .   .

August 31st.

We left Brumer Id. on the 29th. We had plenty of visitors from the island on the 28th and I fancy must have left a very good reputation behind us, unless indeed our non-acceptance of their numerous and hospitable invitations has given them the idea that we are not very sociable. We spent a fortnight at Brumer Island, and have been allowed to touch the shore twice, and our visit on each occasion did not exceed a couple of hours. Although the natives have shown us the friendliest possible disposition, those who would gladly have done so have not been permitted to take the slightest advantage of the opportunities afforded them. The island has a very similar appearance to the mainland and a careful investigation of its natural products might have given us some idea of what is to be expected on the main, where examination must always be so much more difficult and dangerous. But we knew as much of its botany, similarly zoology, when we anchored, as we do now. The domestic life and habits of the natives, so interesting from their near relation to the unknown New Guinea men, after the fairest opportunities remain only known to us through their behaviour as visitors—when probably so much is constrained and artificial.

The mainland was not half a dozen miles off and there appeared to be some promise of a large river. Not a boat was sent to explore the coast. For anything we can say to the contrary, the land we saw may have been a succession of islands.

If this is surveying, if this is the process of English Discovery, God defend me from any such elaborate waste of time and opportunity.

At present we are knocking about at sea with a repetition of the old game. We were forty miles off the land at daybreak this morning and have had a westerly wind all day so that we might as well be at Cape York.

Yesterday we got into 12 fathoms suddenly, then into six, and then 150 and no bottom, and the master who was up aloft at the time avers that he saw our wake discoloured as if we had stirred up the mud on some shoal. Suppose it had been two fathoms instead of six? I should perhaps just now be one of a snug party of a score stowed away among pork casks and bread bags in the second cutter.

A wonderful history has arisen—a regular Mährchen—about a volcano, on this wise:

Some days ago the Captain showed me a piece of glassy substance which the natives had brought off and with which according to him they shaved themselves. I said I thought it was obsidian and he looked the thing up in his cyclopaedia and chemical ready reckoner and found out that it really was such. Furthermore he passed the information that obsidian is only found in the neighbourhood of active volcanoes.

Whereupon the little man goes and tells everybody with an air of great importance that he expects to see an active—fiery

—smoking—Vesuvius somewhere along the coast. And people come up on deck and ask where the volcano is!

On much the same grounds a burnt stump should indicate a burning forest, or a bit of glass bottle a near glass house, or an old Roman coin the existence of the emperor who struck it.

Sept. 1.

Light wind from the S.E. Hardly enough to stem the current which has been setting us to the E. all day. The coast of New Guinea hereabouts is very rich and bold, and from the heavy clouds which rest upon it seems to be watered by continual rains.

Sept. 4th.

We have been coquetting with the shore for several days past—as usual—the weather having been thick and cloudy. This afternoon we found ourselves opposite the "Cul de Sac de l'Orangerie" of Bougainville and saw the *Bramble.* She stood out to us and signalized that she had found good anchorage, then standing in we followed. But with our usual luck darkness came on as we approached our goal, and after following at a cautious distance for a while, we are now (7 p.m.) standing off again.

A most delicious scent was borne to us on the breeze from the land, something like the odour of a lilac bush after heavy rain.

5th.

We anchored after all last night, but in a spot pretty exposed to all the swell and about a mile and a half from the *Bramble* which is close in shore.

The latter has been playing off some brilliant achievements since we parted company. I carefully gathered the following particulars from three of her officers. On the 31st of last month, she was standing along shore as usual when it fell calm and many canoes came off. Their number gradually increased until there were not fewer than sixty surrounding her and as they usually contain seven or eight men there were probably not fewer than four hundred natives present. This was altogether too many to be pleasant, as their apparent strength might have induced the niggers to attempt an attack, though they would have been wofully astonished when the grape began to tear holes among them.

Yule beat to quarter and made every preparation but no attempt was made and a breeze springing up let him off with a fright.

On the following day, the *Bramble* had as I understood anchored opposite some spot further down the coast (I am sure as to her being at anchor) when a canoe came off, unarmed but without having any article for barter on board. One of the Brumer Islanders was recognized by Moss as an old friend; Yule's permission was asked to have him on board, which was granted; and he brought up with him a friend to whom he wished to show the wonders with which he was familiar.

In the meanwhile three canoes joined the one already alongside, all perfectly friendly, and all, to all appearances, unarmed. Nine or ten others were seen inshore, at a very considerable distance, apparently coming to the ship.

Suddenly Yule came up and ordered the native down into his canoe and then waived to all the four to be off. They did not quite understand all this and hung on astern making their usual friendly signs. Yule then became excited and called for his gun, which was loaded with small shot. He waived to the natives again to be off and called out "Now I give you fair warning, I give you fair warning", and finally fired right among them. So little did the natives understand him, that while some looked astonished others laughed as though it had been something done for their amusement. Yule hereupon fired again and at first (so excited was he) snapped his already fired barrel, complaining that the cap would not go off. This time there was no mistake, the natives felt that if a joke it was a very queer one, looked one moment as if in utter astonishment (so my informant described it) then seized their paddles and paddled away as if the devils were behind them. One man took up water in the palm of his hand and cast it towards the *Bramble* as if "casting the dust from off his feet" at such a treacherous set. Not content with this Yule ordered one of the marines to take his musket and fire close to the unfortunate devils. The man obeyed and the bullet dropped within a few yards of the canoe. The gallant lieutenant then ordered another to fire close to but not to hit the canoe. This man is a great blackguard and as I was told took deliberate aim with every appearance of intending to fire in earnest, and as it turned out the bullet passed under the outrigger. After that this gallant and humane commander "piped down", and wrote a long despatch about the "engagement" to Capt. Stanley.

Suppose we landed at a village, the natives received us with every appearance of friendship, took one or two of our number up to their houses, and then as we were shoving off treated us to a shower of spears? What should we say? When should we have held forth sufficiently about their treachery?

And yet some day or other a big book will appear with a statement to the effect that "every effort was made to conciliate the natives and treat them kindly."

6th.

It rains continually; heavy clouds hang over the land in bands almost down to the shore, their white fleece shewing beautifully against the blue side of the mountains.

We catch quantities of rain water and have to drink it. It's what a wine merchant would call a "full-bodied" drink by the time we get it.

10th.

Left our anchorage at Dufaure Id. and stood out about thirty miles to sea.

[Here a page left blank.]

16th.

Saw Cape Rodney. The land has become lower and the smoke of vast fires is seen along the coast. We have had no rain for some time and the weather is very hot with continual calms. Our old friend the monsoon seems to have altogether ceased, so that we make but slow progress. We keep at a distance of from seven to thirty miles from the land, so that we have but a very distant view of our Pisgah and float along the blue sea idly and lazily with nothing to divert the routine of our occupations.

Redscar Point. 20*th*.

Saw *Bramble,* coming up from the eastward. Closed and *Bramble* going ahead, stood in to the land—anchored about 2½ miles from shore. *Bramble* had finished her work as far as Grange Id, and then had a row with the natives. The land off which we are at present laying is low and flat with occasional low red cliffs and hillocks here and there.

21*st*.

Cutter sent away, found good anchorage and smooth water close in shore. There appears to be a considerable river flowing through the low land and debouching here.

24*th*.

The third anniversary of our commissioning. I have said that the land about here is low but this is only partially true, for an immense mountain ridge, which can be hardly less than 10,000 feet high, rises up thirty or forty miles inland. During the day it is concealed by the vapours and clouds, but just before sunrise it is very visible. I have rarely seen a more beautiful sight than the sun-rise behind the hills on Sunday morning.

The *Bramble* was sent away 5 or 6 miles last evening to get a base so as to ascertain the height of the mountains. But this morning it was unfortunately cloudy and thick so that the tops of the peaks were invisible.

There appears to be little doubt that two men were shot on the occasion of the last row (one by Yule himself, who however it should be stated won't admit the fact) and one by one of the marines—Lord—who *does* admit it.

The facts of the case from all I have been able to learn from the *Bramble's* people are shortly these. Natives came off to the number of forty or thereabouts with several women and children. In one canoe was a pig, which they offered to the *Bramble's* men who were standing in the chains ready to barter. The blacksmith received the pig, contrary to Inskip's orders who directed that there should be no barter. Inskip imagining that something had been given for the pig ordered the man to come out of the chains and bring the pig aft. One of the natives then snatched the cap from the sentry who was looking over the side. The sentry reported the fact to Yule who ordered one of the gigs to be lowered. As the men went to lower the gig the natives appeared to take an alarm and one man snatched his spears and with every appearance of rage directed them towards Yule and Inskip who were aft, vibrating them and exciting his companions by his words and gestures. They began to pick up their spears. Yule took one of the two muskets which were kept loaded, and fired. The man who was shaking his spears dropped *backwards* into the water, the others dived over the side of the canoe. Yule ordered the sentry to fire the other musket, which he did and as he himself states hit the man who took his cap. In the mean time they beat to quarters and loaded a six-pounder with a round shot. The unfortunate natives scrambled into the canoes, seized such of their paddles as had not floated away and paddled off as they best might. The six-pounder was fired close over them to their great consternation.

These are the facts as I gathered them from the eye witnesses (Inskip, Smith, &c.). That Yule did rightly in firing cannot I think admit of doubt. But it is to be lamented that the taking of the pig without a fair exchange should have put our people in the position of aggressors. That the natives intended any hostilities when they came is wholly absurd, as the fact of bringing their women and children shows.

There appear to be plenty of natives about here and we can make out a village at no great distance, but they do not come off. To-day a canoe ventured within a few hundred yards of us but would not come close. They shouted and beckoned that we should go ashore. They and their canoe closely resembled the Louisiadians.

Sept. 25th.

Got under way this afternoon and proceeded about six miles, anchored at sunset.

Sept. 26th.

Several canoes came off to us. The natives differ very little from those we have previously seen except that they have a peculiar way of binding up their hair behind into a huge top-knot with a long thin pigtail hanging therefrom down their backs. One had the end of his pigtail adorned with a rosette of dogs' teeth. They were mostly small men but fat and in good condition. They had plenty of bows and arrows (the first we have seen thus armed). The bows are apparently made of the hard cocoa-nut wood and about five or six feet long. The string is a flat band of rattan or some such stuff.

The arrows are of two or three different kinds. Short light reeds, others with heavy carved ends and long light reed shafts not less than 5 or 6 feet. A third kind had the ends pointed and flattened like a spear but without barbs. The fellows were

[Here a small sketch of an arrow-head.]

civil enough and wanted us to go ashore. They did not know anything about iron, but coveted coloured cloth etc.

We sailed in the afternoon about 30 miles along the coast and anchored right out at sea off a deep inlet and island which the Captain called Yule Id. A thick heavy cloud hung over the land concealing Mount Victoria, which however became very visible early next morning. Mount Victoria has a very curious shape—its highest peak is not unlike "Lord Hood's Nose" at Rio.

Cape Possession bore from our anchorage about N.N.W. 30 miles.

27th.

Sailed for Cape York, ran on during the night with the exception of a few hours' standing back etc.

28th.

About six p.m. anchored off Bramble Key, about 2 miles to N.W.

29th.

From Bramble Key to Marsden Island.

30th.

From Marsden Id. to Cocoa-nut Island. The latter is inhabited, we can see plenty of cocoa-nut trees, and a village towards the N. point of the Island.

Oct. 1st.

From Cocoa-nut Island to Cape York. Anchored about half past four p.m. in our old position in Evans Bay. No provision ship, no letters. I won't swear. . . . The provision ship arrived on the 2nd and sailed on the 16th.

16th.

The most remarkable occurrence that has yet befallen us happened yesterday. A large party of natives came on from the islands and shortly after their arrival Scott (the Capt's Cox[n]) and several seamen wandering about fell in with a party of them—gins—among whom was a white woman disfigured by dirt and the effect of the sun on her almost uncovered body; her face was nevertheless clean enough, and before the men had time to recover from their astonishment she advanced towards them and in hesitating broken language cried "I am a Christian—I am ashamed". The men immediately escorted her down to Heath's party, ashore watering, who of course immediately took her under their protection, and the cutter arriving very shortly to take the party on board, she found herself once more safe among her own people. Three natives accompanied her off in the canoe whom she called her brothers and who appeared much interested in her.

This is her story, told in half Scotch, half native dialect, for she has been so long among these people as nearly to forget her mother tongue.

Her name is Thompson and her maiden name was Crawford. She was born in Aberdeen and her father was a tinsmith who emigrated when she was about eight years old to Australia. From her account he appears to have been at first in very good business in Sydney but latterly became unsteady and consequently descending lower in the scale, was, when she left him, only a journeyman.

When between fifteen and sixteen she left her father's house without his knowledge or consent and making her way up to Moreton Bay with a lover of hers was there married to him. She wrote to her father to tell him that she was happy and doing well but has never since heard anything of him. The husband was a sailor and appears to have been a very handy sort of man, according to her account he could make everything for himself from the shoes on his feet to the hat on his head and furthermore fitted up very well a small cutter rather larger than our *Asp*.

She tells me he was a great favourite with Capt. Wickham and might have done very well at Moreton Bay. However the tempter came, in the shape of an old sailor who had been wrecked in a large ship, well laden, on an island in Torres Straits, and he gave Thompson such brilliant ideas of the profit to be obtained by any one who should take the trouble to visit the wreck and walk off with "jetsam and flotsam" that the latter resolved to go in his cutter and either return to Moreton Bay or go on to Port Essington (at which place he seems to have had some idea of settling). About this time Dr Leichhardt was starting on his overland expedition and it appears that he wished Thompson to join him, but the latter, the worse for him, preferred his own exploration, only promising on his arrival at Port Essington to inform the people of the coming expedition and induce them to send a party to meet it.

After living, then, about 18 months at Brisbane, Thompson with his wife and three men, started in the cutter on their ill-omened journey. They had nearly reached the desired island when a heavy squall came on, and their little vessel was utterly wrecked upon a reef running out from the island.

Two native canoes which were out turtle-fishing were similarly distressed by the squall but the natives easily reached the shore. Not so with the unfortunate tenants of the cutter: the three men were drowned, and Mrs. Thompson was drowning when one of the blackfellows (Aliki[1] who came on board with

---

[1] It was not Aliki but Toma-gogi who swam out. Aliki only assisted in helping her on board the canoe. [Note, added later.]

her) swam out, and seizing her arm brought her safely to land.

They treated her very kindly, fed her and protected her from insult. One of the old chiefs, who had lately lost a daughter, persisted, according to their common belief that white people are the ghosts of black, that she was this very daughter "jump alive again" and she seems to have been regularly adopted among them, so that she talks of her brothers, nephews etc. Years rolled on, and by degrees she approximated towards her friends, adopting their language so that she speaks it fluently and at present evidently thinks in it, having in talking to you to translate her native thoughts into plain English, sometimes a matter of considerable difficulty, and at the same time adopting their ways so that her manners present a most ludicrous graft of the gin upon the white woman.

For the first twelvemonth she kept some account of time but afterwards lost it, so that she has no idea of dates at present, and indeed, as she says herself she would have forgotten her own language had she not been accustomed to sing to herself at night all the old fragments of songs and ballads she could remember.

The natives appear to have treated her quite as a pet; she never shared in the labours of the women but stayed in the camp to look after the children while they went out on "hospitable cares intent". Of the kindness and good disposition of the men she speaks in the highest terms, and of the women too she speaks well but says that some of them were not so kind.

Year after year she saw the English ships sail by on their way to China but never had any opportunity of communicating with them, and sometimes she says she was very sorrowful and despairing.

Last year she knew of our being here but the natives would not let her come, and when the canoes were setting out from the islands to visit us for the purpose of getting tobacco etc. the women were very unwilling to let her come, and it was only partly by promises to return, partly by the influence of "Toma-gogi", one of her brothers, a gentleman about 6 ft. 2 and doubtless proportionately respected, that she got away.

So far as we can judge she has been five years among these people, and is therefore even now a very young woman; and indeed notwithstanding the hard life she must have led, she looks young, and I have no doubt when she is appropriately dressed, and gets rid of her inflamed eyes, she will be not bad-looking.

Poor creature! we have all great compassion for her and I am sure there is no one who would not do anything to make her comfortable. Capt. Stanley gives her his workshop for a cabin, and as soon as she recovers herself sufficiently to understand the use of a needle, she can have as much calico and flannel as she wants, to make mysterious feminine toggery.

She must be content to take a long cruise with us, but it will be at any rate, I should think, preferable to her late circumstances.

I inquired of her if she knew anything about poor Kennedy's murder; she told me that "Baki" (an old friend of ours) had told her all about it; that the people here had nothing to do with it, but a bad tribe to the southward; and that they killed him for nothing but his clothes.

18th.

It appears from further inquiry that Mrs Thompson was wrecked on Possession Island and that the natives carried her over to the Southern Prince of Wales Island, where she subsequently lived. And until we arrived she never left the Prince of Wales Islands. Curiously enough the complete identification of the island on which she lived was afforded by the fact that as she stated, on one point there was a cairn or heap of stones which the natives told her had been built by the white men. Now Mr Yule had built a cairn in the very position she indicated, some four or five years ago.

She has already given us a great deal of curious information about the habits of these people, with an air of the most perfect truth and sincerity, and no little intelligence. One story was rather startling. She says that a little to the N. and W. of us there is a tribe of very bad natives, and that one night they lighted a very large fire on their beach as a challenge to the P. of Wales Id. blacks, to come over and fight them. Her friends, no wise backward, lighted a fire on their side to show that the challenge had been accepted, and one night embarking all their disposable force in six canoes landed very secretly on the main. They stole up to an encampment of their enemies and falling upon them suddenly killed two men, a woman and a child. They cut off the heads of these and returned in great triumph, making a hideous noise upon a conch, to the island. A great corobbory was celebrated and the four heads having been placed on one of their rude ovens they ate the eyes and pieces of the cheeks of their enemies "to make them brave" as they said.

The women were excluded from all share in this recherché repast.

We asked if the mainlanders made no reprisals, but it appears that they had no canoes. However, our friends were not altogether secure, for some natives from the northward landed secretly on the island on one occasion and cut off the heads of a man and an old woman with which they decamped. The fellows have a special apparatus for cutting and carrying heads, consisting of a bamboo knife with a long loop. They do not make this, any more than their arrows, but get them from the natives to the northward.

Mrs Thompson gives us a rather unfavourable idea of the morals of these people. She says that they have no idea of a Supreme Being and that they always laughed at her if she talked of anything of the kind. But they believe in all sorts of varieties of ghosts. When the heavy squall of these latitudes gathers and the clouds topple over one another in huge fantastic masses they say the "marki" (ghosts) are looking out for turtle and they profess that one comes down and fetches a supply for the rest. So again they believe that porpoises and sharks are a sort of enchanted beings and they never injure them.

The natives have no idea of moral or legal obligation. No fixed punishments are annexed to any crimes. Theft usually produces a scolding match between the aggressor and the aggrieved, in which the filthiest language is made use of. Murder she told us never occurred (among members of the same tribe) to her knowledge, and the men never use personal violence to one another although the women do. Unchastity before marriage is thought nothing of. Afterwards, its punishment depends pretty much upon the temper of the husband. He would be considered quite justified, however, in spearing both parties if taken *flagrante delicto*. Otherwise Mrs. T. very naively told us that the husband's wrath would be very likely regulated by the state of the *quisdilli* [?]. If that were kept full of yams he would probably shut his eyes. It is astonishing how similar man is to man from "China to Peru". Child-murder prevails to the most fearful extent. All illegitimate children are destroyed by burying them in a hole in the sand immediately on their birth unless the father intends to marry the girl, when he can if he likes order the offspring to be saved. The children of the married owe their life entirely to the caprice of the husband. If he says they are to live, they live. If he orders them to die, they are all buried at once. It is very common for a man to order all his male children to be kept and all the females to be killed and Mrs T. gave us by name several natives whom she *knew* to have destroyed child after child.

The mothers pay their children very little attention and take care to see "their own bellies filled first". The old and infirm share the fate of the children and live altogether *par hasard*.

The affections appear to be at the very lowest ebb—worse than on board ship.

A man's importance and the number of his wives go together; they have sometimes as many as five, but the first and last are the only recognized wives, the others appearing more in the light of concubines. Girls are married as early as 10–11 years of age.

Two great occasions occur in the course of a man's existence —his induction to the privilege of manhood (assuming the toga virilis one might call it if they had any pretence for a toga at all) and his burial. The women have no observances of the former kind, and unless they happen to be young and favourite gins, are very often tossed into a hole without ceremony.

When a man dies the whole camp goes into mourning, men, boys and women smear themselves with clay and casting themselves down with great lamentation pass the time in mourning.

In the meanwhile the corpse is straightened and the eyes closed and it is placed upon a sort of bier formed of two long poles with a number of cross-sticks placed on them, bark is placed over the body and the whole bound together into a secure mummy-like package. On the afternoon of the day succeeding the death two men take the corpse on the bier and convey it to some already appointed place where it is set upon a sort of trestle formed by two poles crossing one another and support-ing the bier, at each end. Here it is left, but the mourning continues for a month or six weeks and no corroborrys are held in the camp. By this time the head of the corpse has usually rotted very nearly off and when this is the case a day is appointed for its removal.

October 21*st*.

Went away in the *Asp* with *Bramble* and pinnace to the Badoo Islands.

Returned *November* 18*th*.

Left Cape York *Dec. 3rd*.

Anchored the same day about 3 P.M. under Mount Ernest Id. or Tragé.

In the afternoon a boat sent ashore with a party to land on the island and I took the opportunity of going. As we ap-proached in the ship we had seen three or four natives sitting on a sandy beach near a long hut but some of them were women and had disappeared before we landed.

We saw only one oldish man, standing at the edge of the brush which bounds the flat plain on which you land, on one side, and he did not seem very desirous to have anything to do with us. However we gathered branches and shouting Poud! Poud! Colaiga! etc. at the top of our voices we con-trived to get near enough to scratch hands, an operation which the old gentleman performed with great energy, giving you three distinct tugs. We went through the usual formalities of inquiring one another's names etc. and gradually established a friendly footing. The old man made great inquiries for "Sagouba", "Tooree", "Aga", "Taparra" etc., offering tortoiseshell in exchange, but we had nothing but biscuit with us. We gave him plenty and soon set him in good humour. He was greatly alarmed at first hearing the noise of the guns, but being shown that we only killed "Worroi" he became reassured and at our request readily conducted us to the village.

On our way thither we had a peep at what looked like a very singular inclosure but our guide did not wish us to go nearer, making signs that it was a place to be feared. The houses are enclosed in a low fence of bamboo about five feet high, and are built of square or penthouse-shaped frames not higher, and thatched with coarse grass. They are a sort of combination of the Darnley Id. fence with the Cape York hut.

One or two cocoa-nut trees were growing near the huts. The trunk of one was ornamented with red paint. On our wishing to procure some of the tempting green cocoa-nuts our friend gave us to understand that the tree belonged to some other person (whom he named) and that *therefore* "his legs were sore" and he could not climb to get them. However if we would bring plenty of "Aga" and "Tooree" tomorrow we could have as many as we liked.

The cooking places were on little low stages before the huts.

Seeing a native path leading into the brush I began poking my nose into it and as the brush looked pretty we proposed to our guide to take us by it. He willingly acceded and passing through a low arched opening, we came at once into a most beautiful opening in the brush arched over by magnificent trees and so shaded and cool, with such a "dim religious light" pervading it, that it looked quite like a chapel, and indeed the name would not be wholly inappropriate, for there was a strange fantastic sort of monument in this savage sanctuary. Suppose a great screen of posts five or six feet high supporting vertically a long wall-like plaited mat, cut at each end so that the upper ends overhung the lower, and their ends fringed with long hanging strips of grass. The tops and offshoots of the posts were covered with huge reddened Fusus shells. The front of the screen was set with regular series of the spider shell, also reddened, and stuck up against the foot of the screen were a number of flat stones of all shapes carved and painted with hideous human faces.

Panooda (that was our friend's name) gave us to understand that this was a sort of tomb and he named to us some half a dozen individuals whose effigies were depicted upon the stones. Panooda plainly considered the thing a considerable work of art and was considerably pleased by our sketching it. After a little while, seeing that we were good peaceable folks, he let us go up close and handle this redoubtable affair. He was greatly amused at our looking to see if there were anything behind the screen, and very soon lost all the awe with which he had at first affected that the place inspired him.

Panooda subsequently took us to a native well, to plantations of yams and tobacco (exactly resembling those I had seen at Double Id.), and to a very singular grave of which I hope to see more tomorrow. By canoe off to the ship at sunset.

Dec. 5th.

Brierly and I spent the greater part of yesterday on the island, on a regular sketching expedition. Old Panooda was down at the beach before we landed, according to appointment, and had brought with him some tortoiseshell and a cocoa-nut wh. he offered to us. Capt. Stanley gave him a knife with wh. he seemed much delighted, but nevertheless he attached himself to us as if he considered himself our regular "cotaiga".

We waited until the skipper had got sights as he wanted to see the wonders, and then visited the houses, the "Wowres" and the plantation, after which to our great relief the little man took his departure and then we and our cotaiga went and sat down in the beautiful "chapel", studying lights and shades in most artistic fashion, as we proceeded with our drawings. Panooda would occasionally request a look and then with a grin of satisfaction and a sort of grunt relapse into a most patiently quiescent state. He was a first-rate fellow in this respect, never fidgetting or bothering us for biscuit or sagouba, but where we were he seemed content to be and he was grateful for all he got, great or small.

There we sat like three Chinese Josses squatted down. We knew the hot sun was pouring down a flood of light and heat outside—the chirp-chirping chords of the cicadas and the glare of the sand at the end of the long avenues told us that—how it enhanced the coolness of that dim green shade! The silence and the gloom heightened the strange appearance of the fantastic savage monument. You might have fancied it a temple for the performance of strange and horrible savage rites, had it not looked so utterly peaceful. Now and then a stray pigeon would perch over our heads, or a pair of the beautiful ground-doves would begin their soft cooing, or a pair of ant-thrushes would be heard answering one another's loud calls from either side of the wood.

I never shall forget the beauty of the place; while in it I felt as if listening to beautiful music.

When we had finished our sketches and measurements we migrated over to the other "wowre", which though not so beautifully placed is prettier in its structure as there is a sort of Gothic arch formed by two high crossing poles in its centre. Instead of being made of grass thatch too, it is formed of cocoa-nut leaves plaited together.

After this we bethought ourselves of the corporeal man and descended to lunching, and under the influence of the meal we "snaked" old Panooda into taking us to see his wife and children who were hidden away in the bush. *Why* he consented was curious.

The Goodangarkagi (Cape York) blacks had called Brierly "Antarke", believing him to be the "marki" or ghost of a Mount Ernest man of that name who had lately died. Now it so happened that Panooda had taken to wife a certain daughter of Antarke's, Domani by name, and when this came out in the course of conversation Brierly thought it would be a capital pretext for seeing the women, and gravely tried the pathetic with Panooda, insisting that it would be very unkind not to let a father see his daughter and grandchildren. Panooda admitted the plea fully but still hesitated, when the scale was turned by my giving him a piece of finely variegated and marbled paper out of my drawing book, while Brierly promised Domani a shirt. He came to us very confidentially and told us that he had no objection to take us two but we must have no "kalaki" or guns and on no account must any of the other "markis" know anything about the matter. Of course we agreed and off we started. He took us right away into the bush for some distance off the native tracks and then told us to sit down while he went away. We sat very patiently for about half an hour, occasionally speculating on our foolish looks if he did not come back, till at last we saw him return. He made signs to us to be quiet and led us up the side of the hill for a short distance, where we came upon his family seated ready to receive us under the trees. There was the wife Domani, a good-looking clean native with a child at the breast; "Dowai", a pretty grown-up daughter; and a third younger child, also a daughter. Poor Domani had the "dopo" or ague. A most friendly recognition took place between Brierly and his daughter, we were all introduced to one another and then commenced a grand palaver. Everything was new and delightful to them, and Dowai gave me a most enchanting smile in return for another piece of marbled paper and was not a little vain when I made a sketch of her. I was much pleased with the cheerful quiet ways of these people and most agreeably surprised at the contrast they presented to the Goodangar-kagis in point of cleanliness. After half an hour's chat we departed, "scratching hands" very cordially.

On our way back we passed some yam and tobacco plantations more extensive than we had hitherto seen. Some of the yam plantations had their stakes united by horizontal cross-bars of bamboo and some had fish-shaped red smeared scare-crows suspended in them, which turned and twisted in the wind. There were eight of these plantations, each containing on an average 30 yam plants, covering a space of about ¼ acre.

Panooda explained to us that they belonged to 18 people, counting them up by name first on his fingers, then on the wrist, arm and shoulder joints and top of the chest. (Brady told me in the evening that he had seen a great deal more cultivated ground.)

We went back to the well and drank with avidity out of an extemporaneous leaf cup some most filthy water, and then betook ourselves to the ten-skull grave. This was very curious. In a little recess of the brush close to the beach was a tringular heap of turtle and dugong skulls lying nearly East and W., the pointed end being westward. At this end there was a flat stone placed vertically; at the other end or base of the triangle there were two stones, one at each corner, and supported upon them a flat board (apparently from a wreck) on which were arranged ten whitened and weather-worn skulls. At each end three little turtle heads were placed under the end of the board. In front of the skulls lay a flattened-conical big stone painted with red and black, and white feathers stuck round it. At one end of the skull board there was a long thin stick with three large fruits of some palm strung on it and a quantity of feathers at the end of long switches sticking out from the uppermost.

Panooda told us that these were all Coolcalagas or Mount Ernest people.

At the present time it appears that there are only two men besides Panooda's own family on the island; the mass of people are away in canoes, as indeed Teoma[1] had previously told us was frequently the case.

What little we have seen unquestionably justifies her opinion that the Coolcalagas are "very good blacks".

We have been waiting all day for *Bramble*. No boat ashore. Off to Darnley Id. *morgen*—dead beat all the way, wind being about E.

6th.

Got under way and beat up to the Three Sisters. Anchored at sunset about two miles to W. of Sue. Large villages and plenty of natives on Sue. They came off the next morning in a very wide canoe cut off in the middle as it were but otherwise resembling those we had seen. They understood "bitchket" and "water" and brought off a quantity of very good tortoiseshell, which they eagerly bartered for biscuit, iron etc.

7th.

Under way all day from 9 a.m., anchored about 7 miles S.W. of Cocoa-nut Id. Tide very strong.

8th.

Passed Cocoa-nut Id. Plenty of houses and natives. Anchored under Arden Island. A seining party is to go away in

[1] Mrs. Thompson's native name.

the morning, as we shall not get under way till 9 or 10 o'clock on account of the tides.

9th.

The seining party got no fish as it was a coral beach. Got under way about 11½ a.m., had a lucky slant of wind and anchored 7 p.m. about 10 miles from Darnley Id. in the open sea which is as smooth as a mill pond.

10th.

Light wind and strong tide against us in the morning. Did not get under way till 11½ a.m. Before this time a canoe full of natives had come off to us from Oonga, a little id. at no great distance. In it were two Darnley Islanders, Dzoum and a boy. Dzoum was one of those who shot at Capt. Blackwood when the *Fly* was at Darnley Id. He immediately recognized McGillivray.

We took the canoe in tow and the whole party except a "boat-keeper" came on board to see all the wonders. They had none of them the peculiar prominent abdomen and broken back of the Australians, and several had the peculiar Jewish cast of countenance. They had all great holes in the septum of the nose, and the hair in thrums. Several had their wigs on, the hair being cropped close beneath. One man who belonged to the little id., Oonga, and whom I sketched, had his beard rolled into two long pendant cords.

Towards sunset as we passed Oonga they left us to sleep thither, trying hard to persuade us that we had better do the same.

11th.

Anchored at Darnley Island in Treacherous Bay about noon. In the afternoon the Captain went away (with the two cutters and having given special directions to Simpson to look out and fire a round shot in case of necessity) with McGillivray, and others. He visited Mogoor, a village on the opposite side of the island, and found the natives very friendly and desirous of barter.

There was but little water and that difficult to be procured.

He brought off with him old Sewai, a native of whom Jukes speaks, and three sons, Do-outou, Quarp and Cowai, the last a youngster of whom he seemed very fond. The old man was quite feeble, but his sons—especially Do-outou—were fine athletic young men.

We heard that Meammoos [Mamus: MacGillivray] and a great many others had been killed at Dowdee.[1]

These people remained on board all night, and I established an especial friendship with Do-outou, with whom according to custom I changed names. He promised me a "coskeer" (wife) and all sorts of fine things when I came ashore.

In the evening Brierly and I got up a project to go to Mogoor in the morning and see a grand canoe, but on consulting the commanding officer much to our disgust we were put off with being told it would be much better to go a day or two hence, when the marines were landed, or as I understood it at the Greek Kalends.

12th.

Raining hard all night after twelve p.m. so that Sewai and company were obliged to retreat to the main-deck. Directions had been given that a boat should early this morning visit the regular watering place in Treacherous Bay. But in the morning the rain still came down and the wind had shifted round to the N.W. so that there was a heavy surf running right into the Bay and I, who had made up my mind to take my chance of seeing what was to be seen, walked about in huge disgust. Somewhere about nine o'clock however the weather mended, and we shoved off, got intolerably wet wading ashore, found no water, waded back and came on board again, a regular King of France's cruise.

> *The King of France marched up a hill*
> *With twenty thousand men,*
> *The King of France marched round that hill*
> *And then marched down again.*

In the afternoon however there was a promise of better things. The skipper determined to go and barter for yams etc.

[1] The native name for the mainland of New Guinea.

for the ship's company at one of the villages. He told me I should have a good chance of getting lots of sketches, enlarged upon the beauties of the valley behind Mogoor, etc. so that I was quite delighted and took a good supply of drawing material, deluded animal that I was! We pulled round to Mogoor in the cutter, the second, well armed, accompanying us to lay off and protect us. A long shallow beach with the water smooth as glass ran off towards us. The natives came crowding round of all sexes and ages, men, boys, women, children, bringing everything they had for barter. We anchored and I and others stood up in the boat all ready, when our "brave Captain" took the lead, to rush into the water. But all in vain did we chafe. All in vain did one or two suggest to him gently that we had better go ashore if we were going. He said "No hurry, presently", etc. etc. And there we stood.

Do-otou, to whom I had been discoursing eloquently about going ashore, did not at all understand this delay and unfortunately I could not explain to him, so I have no doubt that he thought me either a fool or a poltroon, perhaps both.

The natives were kicking up a tremendous shindy round us —yelling, shouting, jumping. I sat down to get a sketch of the village, in the bows of the boat, and soon had a little conversazione to myself. Do-outou took great care of me, acting as interpreter and in a most amusing manner endeavouring to cajole me into buying (extravagantly) anything his companions brought. I must not forget too that he introduced me to a very good-looking girl who was to be my "coskeer". I felt rather flattered at first but soon found my error. It was all very fine giving a knife or so to the coskeer herself and getting a brilliant smile from her black eyes and ivory-toothed mouth in return. But there were those cursed wife's relations. All the scoundrels came round me who could claim any degree of affinity with "Kaeta", father, mother, brother, cousins to the fiftieth degree, begging for the smallest trifle. I sent them all off, but I was greatly puzzled how to silence the "gentle" Kaeta herself, who with all a woman's vanity, bothered me incessantly for "walli" (red cloth). At last I observed that, like a careful body, she had only put one petticoat on to come into the water, so whenever she begged for walli, I asked for the "messoon". This was not to be had at any price and my ruse caused a great laugh among the bystanders.

Eventually we took our way back to the ship without a single soul setting foot on the shore.

Old Sewai was of great use in the boat in keeping the people in order.

The site of this village of Mogoor is exceedingly beautiful, more resembling the Louisiade country than anything we had seen in Australia. Gently sloping hills, bare of trees but covered with verdure, deep dark green vallies thickly wooded, groups of the delicate looking shimmering bamboos, formed the background, a thick belt of trees, mostly cocoa-nuts, skirted the bright white beach, and among them were scattered the whimsical-looking beehive-shaped and palisaded native huts.

In the evening Capt. Stanley, the Doctor, and I were sitting on the poop. In the course of conversation, willing to give the skipper a gentle rub I said "So after all, sir, we did not see the fine canoe nor the splendid valley we heard of". He answered, "Ah, why did you not go ashore—you could have done so very well". I thought this rather too good, and so expounded that I did not think it at all correct to go when he himself showed no intention of so doing. "Oh," he said, "you might have gone if you liked. I told two or three of them to go." This to my knowledge by the bye was a flat downright falsehood, but of course I could only look demure and give him more rope. As I expected, I got at the real motive. "You know, in fact, I could see from the boat various little things I did not like; straws show wh. way the wind blows among these people." So *that* was it, my little Trojan, thought I. Funk after all. What does the man want? I suppose nothing would satisfy him of the security of his little body but seeing all the bows and arrows in the boat and all the men bound on the beach. I doubt then the old women, if at all shrewishly inclined, might scare him off.

13*th.*

Rained heavily in the night, and for the greater part of the morning.

At one o'clock p.m. the boats were sent under Simpson's charge to Kiriam to barter for yams etc. for the ship's company. Orders were given to permit officers to land.

I went with the party and this time we *did really* land. Do-outou was there and took charge of me, giving up all attempts at barter to be my escort. I sketched the houses inside and out, saw the dead-houses but could not get a peep inside for love or axes. Nevertheless Do-outou had no objection to pilfer his ancestors' sculls and basely sell them. I got three. My coskeer Kaeta met me too, all smiles, but not forgetting to beg incessantly for "walli". It was somewhat amusing to see the "fair" dame coolly walk up a cocoa-nut tree, precisely like an ape or rather monkey, to which latter animal her pendant petticoat gave her no small resemblance.

I might have been seen seated on a log with Kaeta on one side holding my pencils, on the other a little black boy who had taken an affection for me and was cuddling me most energetically, and a party of natives of all ages and sizes watching my pencil, as it delineated the outline of their houses, with vast approbation.

With all their savagery these people are very gentle and polite, never incommoding you if you once explain what you would do. While drawing, for instance, I might have at first to request them to stand out of the way of the object, but if subsequently any newcomer accidentally placed himself so as to interfere with my view, half a dozen voices would warn him off. I have noticed this gentleness to one another and to their friends among all the natives we have seen.

By way of a joke I explained to Kaeta that as she had demanded and received so much "walli" on the strength of being my coskeer she must prove herself to be such and go off to the "ow shippo". This caused a great laugh and I thought no more of it. But when we were going off, I was told that she had been down to the boat and stoutly demanded to be taken off, making use of "Tamoo's" name as her authority. How astonished the Sydney folks would have been at my introducing Kaeta as Mrs Huxley! if she really had come off.

The old game was played about the "barreet". On McGillivray's inquiring for it, it was explained that D. would bring it off, and in effect he did so about five o'clock in the afternoon.

It was nothing but a cuscus[1] such as we had seen on the coast
of New Guinea, but a different variety. It was in a very nice
bamboo spindle-shaped cage, and Dzoum brought a quantity
of yams and cocoa-nuts for it, promising to bring some more
in the morning. McGillivray gave a big axe, a little axe, a
knife, several bottles, some tobacco and a piece of white cloth
for the beast; even then D. was not satisfied, but on McGillivray's gently hinting that he might take his barreet to the ——
if he so pleased, and offering to take away his own goods,
Dzoum was but too glad to get off with his booty. Mrs
Thompson told me, however, that they grumbled a good deal
to one another as they went away.

14*th*.

Sailed early this morning for Bramble Key. Did not get
more than 5 or 6 miles from Darnley Id. owing to the light
winds and strong tides.

15*th*.

Had to anchor (for the same reasons) midway between
Darnley Id. and Bramble Key.

16*th*.

Got a breeze and anchored under Bramble Key about 11 a.m.
Boat went ashore in the afternoon to break all the Terns' and
Boobies' eggs, bringing off any that looked good, to look out
for turtle tracks and to bring off a supply of spinach.
Plenty of turtle tracks were reported, and a turtling party
being sent away, one was taken (280 lbs) during the night.
Terns eggs not so bad—about one in 3 eatable.

17*th*.

Magnetic observations going on the reef. Turtling party
sent away in the evening. They got 17, of wh. 14 were fine
Green Turtles, and 3 Hawksbills. The spinach to my mind is
filth; others like it however.
The weather has been very curious for several days past. In

[1] A marsupial mammal, one of the phalangers.

the morning we got a N.W. breeze. This dies away about
noon. It is nearly calm during the afternoon, clouds gradually
gathering. Then in the evening we get a heavy squall or two,
sometimes from the N.W. sometimes from S.E., with thunder
and lightning and heavy rain. It's hot, damp, muggy, rheu-
matic, disgusting, and abominable.

19th.

Left Bramble Key, ostensibly for Cape Possession. But on
getting near the latter Capt. Stanley thought it advisable to
send the *Bramble* thither, going on to Redscar Point himself.

21st.

Anchored at Redscar, but in a new position close to the little
islands between there and the point. The westerly monsoon
appears to have set in but the weather is still thick and thun-
dery. The mainland is much clearer than when we came here
before so that we see many mountains in the interior which
are quite new to us. One is a very curious double-peaked concern like the Mammelles at Mauritius.

It looks a magnificent country.

22nd.

Natives came off in two canoes, and several others passed
near the ship in the course of the day. There was a woman in
each of the canoes which came in the morning and the people
were very friendly. They brought a few cocoa-nuts and bows
and arrows for sale which they were very ready to exchange
for glass bottles, but they did not seem to understand the use
of iron. In dress they resembled the people we had seen before
to the westward. The women had their heads shaved and were
a great deal tattooed. One was of a light copper colour. Their
petticoats more resembled those we had seen at Mt. Ernest
than the regular New Guinea ones.

Jany. 2nd, 1849. [*Sic.* Really 1850.]

We left Redscar on the 29th Dec. Many natives came off to
us but shewed very little confidence and none could be per-

suaded to go below. To the last they could not comprehend the use of iron, but would give anything for bottles.

Redscar is a bad anchorage. We rolled incessantly with a ground swell and on one occasion when a very heavy squall came down we had to let go a second anchor. The *Bramble* joined us while there. She has instructions to do a great deal that we have left undone and will therefore be considerably later in Sydney.

Since leaving Redscar we have had light variable winds, with very oppressive damp weather. Last night there was a strong breeze from S.E. During yesterday and the previous day the sick list has been increased from half a dozen to 23, with a febrile diarrhœa which however readily yields to treatment. Had not the weather today completely altered (a fine dry breeze from N.W.-W.S.W.) I doubt not we should have had many more.

The air was very clear today. In the forenoon Mount Victoria was plainly visible 120 miles distant and Mount d'Urville was clear and cloudless.

Jan. 6th.

Anchored under Duchateau Isles at ½ past four this afternoon. The sky is much clearer than on our previous visit. We can see the tops of St. Aignon Id. and the distant peaks of Joannet.

8th.

Sailed from Duchateau this morning. We are fairly off— blessed be all the Gods therefor.

Today finishes eight months since we have been in harbour —I mean of course a civilized place.

A month hence we must be in Sydney. I dare not think about it.

Several canoes full of natives came alongside this morning early (confound them—for they disturbed my slumbers). They had not much to barter. The canoes were like the large one we saw at Brumer.

[Here a sketch of canoe.]

24th.

This day year we returned to Sydney. *Now* we are beating about off this vile "Ship Frederick" reef with a strong S.E. wind right in our teeth.

We have made about 600 miles in the last fortnight; we are about 800 miles from Sydney, and might be there in a week. But so we might a week ago. Uncertainty and suspense seem my lot. Patience! Patience!

[Blank page here.]

Sydney, April 6th, 1850.

Here is the end of a "History of Four Years", dearest. It tells of the wanderings of a man among all varieties of human life and character, from the ball-room among the elegancies and soft nothings of society to the hut of the savage and the grand untrodden forest. It should tell more. It should tell of the wider and stranger wanderings of a human soul, now proud and confident, now sunk in bitter despondency—now so raised above its own coarser nature by the influence of a pure and devoted love as to dare to feel almost worthy of being so loved.

Could the history of the soul be written for that time it would be fuller of change and struggle than that of the outward man, but who shall write it? I, the only possible historian, am too much implicated, too interested, to tell such a story fairly.

I have besides no talent for writing on any such subject. I no sooner take the pen in my hand than I begin thinking of all things in heaven and earth relevant and irrelevant to the matter under consideration. I am not of a "subjective" disposition and unless I have some tangible object for my thoughts they all go woolgathering.

Just now indeed I can with difficulty keep them fixed on any subject. One feeling hangs like an incubus over me. When I go to sleep and when I wake in the morning, whenever I am not actively engaged during the day there it is like a weight, or a sense of evil hanging over me.

Can you guess, dearest, what this feeling is? I fear so, for

I see the same in your patience and weakness and the clouds that sometimes—too often—pass over a face incapable of concealment or dissimulation.

We are to part—dearest—the thought seems ever present to me.

And though I am sure that two or three years at the outside must bring us together again, to be parted, as I fervently hope, no more, and though I chide myself for allowing these feelings to arise when I ought to have strength and cheerfulness enough for us both, yet there they are and remain, and I fear will remain until the dreaded separation is over, and Hope has again become the only possible comforter.

CHAPTER 10

Miss Heathorn and Her Journal
MAY 1849–APRIL 1850

THIS will be, I think, the place at which I may best insert some passages from the Journal kept by my grandmother. When the time came, in May 1849, for the young couple to be once more separated, she promised to keep a record of her doings at home to parallel the record kept aboard ship by him. The resultant journal, which covers the period from the day after the *Rattlesnake* left on her last cruise to the day before she sailed for home almost a year later, fills an ample leather-bound notebook of 200 pages and overflows on to some loose sheets. The total bulk amounts to something over 50,000 words, written in a tidy but flowing old-fashioned handwriting.

Much of it is small beer—a record of domestic incidents, visits to and from friends, picnics, shopping excursions into Sydney, and the like. But a good deal is of lasting interest. There are pictures of Australian life in the middle of last century which make entertaining and vivid footnotes to history. There are revelations of personal tastes and character which are interesting and charming in the young girl Henrietta Heathorn, and doubly interesting when we remember that Henrietta Heathorn was destined, as Henrietta Huxley, to play hostess to some of the most brilliant figures of the late Victorian period. And above all interesting to us in this volume, there are her impressions of her young lover, her outpourings of her intense and abiding love for him, her despair at the prospect of parting, which help us to understand the complex of deep desires and feelings in which the young couple

210

were plunged, the paralysis of emotional conflict in which Huxley seems for a time to have been enveloped, and his final extrication of himself from this on to a new plane of assurance. Until his death, forty-five years later, their mutual love remained both a constant centre and a directive force in their lives. In the journals kept by the two lovers we can see the tumultuous and passionate beginnings of this later depth of central certitude.

Here I may quote Huxley's own description of his fiancée, written to his mother in February 1849 (*L. & L.* i, 39).

". . . as to age, Nettie is about three months younger than myself—that is the difference in *our years,* but she is *in fact* as much younger than her years as I am older than mine. Next, as to complexion she is exceedingly fair, with the Saxon yellow hair and blue eyes. Then as to face, I really don't know whether she is pretty or not. I have never been able to decide the matter in my own mind. Sometimes I think she is, and sometimes I wonder how the idea ever came into my head. Whether or not, her personal appearance has nothing whatever to do with the hold she has upon my mind, for I have seen hundreds of prettier women. But I never met with so sweet a temper, so self-sacrificing and affectionate a disposition, or so pure and womanly a mind, and from the perfectly intimate footing on which I stand with her family I have plenty of opportunities of judging. As I tell her, the only great folly I am aware of her being guilty of was the leaving her happiness in the hands of a man like myself, struggling upwards and certain of nothing."

.   .   .   .   .

Her journal opens thus:

"I have promised to keep a journal and this promise made to one inexpressibly dear shall be faithfully kept—a journal not only of daily occurrences but thoughts which bad or good shall be registered, even tho' intended for his perusal, for should he not see me as I am? I will hide nothing from him.

" 'Tis the third time in my life I have begun a journal— may I persevere more in writing this than I have done with the others. Surely I shall, for I know it will cheer Hal when he again starts on another long voyage to learn how the previous year was spent at Holmwood."

The fact that her journal is to conceal nothing from her lover makes her all the more anxious to conceal it from everyone else. On July 18th she ends her entry:

"It is very difficult to write up my journal now Isy [her half-sister] is here as I wish no one to know of it—I only seize opportunities to do so when alone and a week elapsed ere I could write a word, which makes me almost inclined to give it up, but my promise prevents me."

Let us first see something of the background of Miss Heathorn's life. Helping her married half-sister Oriana, wife of William Fanning, to keep house only a few miles outside Sydney, she had a busy time enough, the domestic round being broken almost daily by some visit paid or returned, and at no infrequent intervals by dinner parties, picnics, balls, or other festivities.

On May 10th, 1849, they went to a ball:

"the best party outside Govt. House that I was ever at . . . the Band alone was imperfect—at least they did not play good dancing tunes.

"I felt so disinclined to go to the Ball, for the one in whose eyes alone I cared to look well would not be there, and it was most provoking to be told by Will and Ory that I looked very nice and hear a quiet whisper of conscious assent from within and he the dear one not there."

There she met a gentleman who had previously pressed his suit upon her, Dr. Turnbull, whom she is pleased to call *Monsieur Taureau-qui-tourne*:

"I like Dr Turnbull all the more, that finding his first advances misplaced he with true gentlemanly feeling has not abruptly ended our acquaintance but is uniformly most kind and attentive. Mr Payne and I had a merry chat in the supper-room, that I think had I not been engaged it might have been almost called flirtation. Could Miss Lamb have seen me she would have doubtless esteemed me heartless, because, under a happy exterior I hid the regret that was aching within. Dr Turnbull said he was glad to see I considered such feelings too sacred for display—and unlike Miss Lamb had not stayed away from the party. God knows my heart was with you, dear one. How I considered what you would be doing—you would know how we were occupied and would picture the dance and the dear ones in it till you were there in the midst of us. My likeness too would be before you."

On the 14th she goes into town with her sister, being deterred from shopping by "overpowering wind and dust", and pays a call upon Mrs. Joshua Young:

"Mrs Joshua Young is a very kind-hearted person and industriously managing but I sh^d like to suggest a clean collar and a less expensive but cleaner dress. They have not very great means and I fancied myself in her position and hoped to goodness I would never pursue a dirty economy—I inwardly vowed if needs were I would wear nothing but cotton dresses that they might be susceptible of washing."

On the 16th they go to the races:

"The French consul was there, looking like a huge black slug. Also Mr D., who had failed in his candidature for the speakership. . . . I am glad Mr D. has not got it or his organ of self-esteem would have so prodigiously increased that fears might have been entertained for his sanity.
"Sunday next a fortnight will have passed away, another and then remains but 8 months.

> *Would I kept the watch of Time—*
> *Oh how fast I'd keep it going*
> *Sweet revenge w^d then be mine*
> *For all the grudges that I owe him*
>
> *On the hands I'd hurry ever*
> *They obedient to my will*
> *Ah the world sh^d then see whether*
> *Time could possibly stand still.*

This only in your absence, dearest."

On the 18th she was reading Emerson's *Lectures on the Times*, "which is the most musical fairy-like production I ever read on such subjects. Later I became so sad and cried bitterly that dear Hal was so far away—and worse, that when he did come it would be again to go, and oh—for what a weary time."

On the 25th she writes:

"Three such days of excitement one way and another! What with my incessant stitch-stitch, the Ball, and the Picture Exhibition I am almost worn out, having only had 10 hours sleep since Monday morning."

She sat up till four one night and three the next, only to go to the Public Ball on the third:

"About 700 persons—a much less number than usually attends on this public occasion. Of course being a public affair there were as usual some odd characters there. The Aldermen's wives and some others. One in particular who had three immense white feathers in her head, and quaint dress. A tall gipsy-like looking person gave one the idea of one of Cinderella's wicked sisters."

But all is not gaiety. Next day she writes:

"The day passed as Mondays generally do, very busy all the morning in household matters and all the afternoon at work. I am getting quite sick of it but there is no use feeling so as there will be enough to do in getting ready for the voyage [the Fannings were preparing to return to England]. It is absurd of Hal to bid me read and practise regularly—what with making my own things, helping Ory with the children and looking after things in the house I have full employment. And yet I am sure I cannot do enough for all dear Will's kindness. I am indebted to him for so much kindness and there are few who would have behaved so generously as he has done."

And again on the 31st:

"Kept close at work the whole day and have done so much this last fortnight that I am quite astonished. A dress for

Plate 10

Henrietta Heathorn, a few years after her marriage
to T. H. Huxley. *From a photograph in the
possession of The Hon. Mrs. John Collier.*

myself, two spencers and a frock for the children and the body
of a dress for Ory. Until the winter things are made one cannot begin cutting out for the voyage and Ory is so dreamlike
about it she will certainly be behindhand if I do not urge her."

And on June 7th, after spending a morning making up accounts and an evening (till one o'clock) sitting up reading
("a new *Blackwoods* and Theodore Hook's novels are a great
temptation"), she is looking forward to a day of marmalade-
making.

On the 10th she went over to stay a couple of days at
Tempé with her friend Alice Radford, who was also engaged
to be married, and the two of them, as is the way with engaged
girls, spent much of their time in talk about their respective
fiancés. On the 16th she went riding, and records that it was
"a pleasant ride, unattended by heat, wind or dust, the three
comfort-destroyers of Australia". In the evening she reads a
review of *Vanity Fair*. "There is an originality and a life-like
reality about Thackeray's writings which gives them great
force: at the same time, to judge from the few extracts, want
of refinement in his characters."

On the 18th they were expecting a visit from Marmaduke
Ramsay, a wealthy young man. Mr. Fanning "is anticipating
with a feeling of oppression the deprivation of his evenings'
sleep when he comes". Henrietta recalls that he told a friend
that she was "the only young lady in the colony he would like
to make his wife", and confesses that "my vanity was pleased
that the one who, to use Miss Donaldson's worldly term, was
beside her brother the only 'eligible' in Sydney should seem to
prefer me to others", then immediately adding "Neither he
nor any one I know or ever knew is such a nice creature as
dear Hal."

On June 23rd they were entertaining a Miss Breillat:

"We tried to teach her the schottische which she persisted
in doing by herself. . . . She would not dance it with Will
because she considered that having a gentleman's arm round
her waist was not quite correct. I like her much yet can often
scarcely forbear smiling at her excessive simplicity."

On June 25th they went for an all-day picnic in the heavy boats:

"The gentlemen were very tired, having rowed 36 miles— much too far in my opinion and had it not been for the continual application to a bottle of port wine we should not have so soon reached home."

The Servant Problem is ever with us, nor was the Fanning household exempt. The entry of May 21st begins:

"Of all the minor miseries of life there is of a truth one transcending all, that of being dependent on your cook for a certain amount of happiness—I shall not as yesterday forget to order bread sauce with wild turkey in a hurry. Will bore it however most philosophically for an excitable man—but to-day the cook's carelessness called forth a stronger amount of anger and most deservedly too, but as there are none to be now had in Sydney I suppose we must e'en brook it. It would be well if cooks like milliners were apprenticed before they were let loose upon society and many a fireside would be the happier for it. Dear Will is now so changed that such things only annoy him for the moment and I really think that by the time he is 50 he may possibly become a philosopher."

On June 20th she writes:

"Domestic troubles—a new housemaid arrived the night before, sent word before breakfast—she didn't think she'd like the place and forthwith left—all the other servants believing her crazed. Really I never knew such a discontented race."

Again, June 28th, 1849:

"It was my first wonder and annoyance on coming to Australia to hear servants the prevailing theme of conversation and, tho' knowing as I do now how much discomfort they cause by their general bad behaviour, it still provokes me to hear them dwelt upon for an hour together."

However, the servants sometimes gave their employers plenty to talk about:

"*Oct. 23rd.* We returned about six o'clock and never shall I forget the scene which presented itself that evening. The house all open, no butler to be found. Cook tipsy, hardly able to give me an answer to my questions. I ran to the nursery— 'twas deserted by the nurse. Alice and Willie were busy washing their arms in a pail of soap-suds, Baby alone on a bed playing with an egg which he had contrived to crush, the rooms in disorder and confusion. The nurse came running in with hanging hair and rumpled dress, and her appearance told me that she too was tipsy. Angrily I enquired what all this meant. She gave me a tolerably consistent reply, but as I knew, told a falsehood. Agitated beyond measure I ordered her away and with Alice's help put the children to bed. This done I sought the butler. What c^d mean the horse saddled and bridled tied up in the yard? The gardener came at length and solved it. George was lying down in the road tipsy too. The horse had escaped and only thro' a neighbour did the gardener hear of it and succeeded in catching him in the Waterloo paddocks. There was fresh distress for me. He told me that on going into the kitchen it was with difficulty he prevented the women setting themselves or the house on fire. He found George shortly and got him to bed. A young man whom we all thought most staid and trustworthy. Unfortunately Mary Anne on whom we can so firmly rely had gone into town for the day but I had never suspected the nurse altho' her husband had left us for that same offence. Alice and I shut up the house and after vainly trying to keep the nurse out of the kitchen we went to the drawing room to wait for tea till the housemaid sh^d come home. A door opened and a rap was heard. I sprang up and opening the door confronted the nurse with whom I had had very angry words. She began to abuse me, I ordering her away—everything she c^d say and call the Almighty to witness she did, abusing me in most unmeasur'd terms. I sent for the gardener to sleep in the house and shut up immediately that I might get them off to bed and after very quiet and firm measures restored the house to peace. Once tho' I was so angry that I quite astonished Alice by my way of speaking to the insolent creature. She (Alice) affirmed she w^d not like to rouse my temper. I c^d not sleep all night from excitement and in the morning sent for them all separately, heard their tales and talked of immediately discharging them. George had had no knowledge of the others having got tipsy and had it seemed been tempted by an old shipmate to go into a public house. The women had procured some spirit thro' some one who came here and they were one and all especially George heartily ashamed of themselves so as it w^d have seriously inconvenienced me to lose them, they being penitent and we resolved that we w^d never both leave the house again together, I forgave them after very serious lectures. Will's riding whip was lost but fortunately the horse was not hurt. So ends this dreadful scene, which like a nightmare haunts me yet."

And only a few days later the nurse took the children to the local inn to get a few drinks for herself.

Shopping too is a recurrent *corvè:*

"*April* 27*th,* 1849. Intense shopping, rendered pleasant to me by the recollection of a very pretty muslin dress."

"*June* 28*th,* 1849. We executed our shopping, always a disagreeable employment despite gentlemen's assertions to the contrary."

"*Dec.* 26 *and* 27, 1849. Shopping days, consequently unpleasant."

"*Jan.* 10*th,* 1850. Shopping all day—quel [*sic*] horreur!"

So the record continues. She learns "La Grace", that charming game for two, played with a little hoop propelled and caught on a pair of sticks. She takes part in games of Pope Joan and Speculation and Whist—although she says "I never find any amusement in cards". She plays chess with her brother-in-law. She teaches her friends the correct method of dancing the Schottische and the Polka. She helps to entertain visitors, some of whom come for a stay of two or three weeks. She reads in her favourite German authors: "not feeling very well, so I sat and worked and with some of Schiller's volumes open before me relearnt a long piece of the *Bürgschaft,* which made me think of the happy days I spent in old Deutschland".

"Tis so delightful to read the plays again. I am now going through Don Carlos, a great favourite with me, and then I shall read Wilhelm Tell."

She enjoys rowing and riding, and when the summer comes, goes down every morning to swim, in spite of it making her feel tired. She goes to balls whenever the opportunity offers, and dances all the evening. She attends Church every Sunday, and regularly comments on the sermon. She makes marmalade, cuts out dresses, goes mushroom-hunting, looks after the children.

She and her friend Alice Radford take every opportunity of talking about their absent *fiancés,* although, as she once records, "We had so much to talk of Hal and Archie that we made each other most impatient and discontented that we could not see them—a general result of our chats". She and Alice "practice our duetts, which are especially for Hal's hearing". Almost every Sunday she plays sacred music to the family.

On July 8th they made up a "rowing party" to visit the sugar works. "We went over them and a very dirty sticky business it was, only compensated by the knowledge gained and, as the boys thought, by the large lumps of candy we carried off."

A little later she was riding the new hunter her brother-in-law has bought, "and liked him much. He is rather spirited. The hounds now meeting twice a week and Will attends regularly, rising at five in the morning. Last time a deer, poor wretch, was hunted and unfortunately killed. This morning only a 'dingo' which however seems to afford more sport."

On August 8th there is a record of rain and robbery:

"We have had rain nearly every day in such quantities as to render the roads almost impassable and consequently we have been unable to go into town. We had had an early luncheon to-day intending to have gone in and had already gone a short distance when a few drops of rain and threatening clouds made us deem it more prudent to return. Luckily for us, as the bright morning has suddenly changed into a tempest of rain and wind, and I have just taken off my cloak and bonnet in great disappointment and turned to my Journal for consolation. Such daring robberies have lately been committed that Will has of late paid extreme attention to fastening up the house and seeing that his gun and pistols were in proper order. Six armed men entered a house at Wooloomooloo at dusk and whilst two kept guard over the family seated in the dining-room the rest ransacked the house and threatened to torture the children if the lady did not make known where every valuable was kept, the wretches—I hope we may escape."

These anxieties about the ex-convicts sometimes came very near home. On September 11th:

"Will discovered this day that our new butler, an excellent servant, was a runaway from his district—had twice recd. 50 lashes—had since been sent to an iron gang and had been suspected of two robberies. He was to be arrested on the morrow and sent back to his district. I always had an instinctive dread of the man, much as he pleased us otherwise and often thought I sh^d not much like to have him in the house when Will and Ory went up the country, yet I am very sorry for him.

"*Friday, 14th.* The constables not having arrived to take Richard the butler.—Will not liking to see the unfortunate man and know he was about to be pounced upon—told he all he had learnt and advised him to go and surrender himself, offering if he did to speak on his behalf, which he afterwards did and got Richard completely out of the scrape. The poor man much taken aback instantly left and we lost the best servant we had ever had."

On Sunday (August 5th):

"We had a sermon from Mr Wood who is to succeed Mr Hassal here, he being appointed to Bungonia—I do not like the appearance of the new clergyman. He resembles in shape of head and expression a romish priest (—for I do believe they have an appearance in common) and I do not think he will prove so agreeable a neighbour as Mr Hassal."

On the 9th she was walking with her sister and her friend Alice Radford:

"We had not gone far in the bush when Alice screamed 'A snake', seizing hold of Ory who immediately sprang to the other side. I looked round for a stick and killed the creature, breaking two or three very brittle ones over him. It was of a lead colour and about 3 feet long, a deadly one, but very thin, and I must own as I was about to strike it I felt very strange from the idea that I was about to kill. Mr. Hamilton said I was very brave and I looked upon myself as a miniature heroine."

On the 18th:

"The evening's paper brings news from Europe—War, nothing but war: the French in Italy to effect the Pope's restoration, the Prussians uniting with Austria"—a contrast with her domestic troubles: "an hour's disputation with the laundress requiring the utmost amount of patience as she can neither count, read nor write and couldn't be made to understand she was fully paid".

Later, on October 7th, comes further news which stimulates her anti-French bias:

"Last Monday English news reached us. Rome had been sacked by the miscreant French and all the beautiful works of art destroyed. It will be Rome's eternal loss—and France's lasting shame. I feel quite angry on thinking of it, often had I hoped that I might some day see them, if I never had it would have been pleasant to know they existed. I could exclaim with Will 'Now I haven't the least prejudice about me, but I do hate a Frenchman'."

"*Aug. 17th.* A bright and warm morning heralding summer which I shall welcome with pleasure. Even its excessive heat is to me preferable to the mild winter of this climate."

On August 26th "The opera of 'Maritana' was performed and very well too for Sydney, but I admired neither the music

nor the plot". The Australian programmes of those days must
have been of formidable length, for "Next came a be-negroed
man who sang three comic songs and made a most odd ac-
compt. with pieces of bone"—the original nigger minstrel, in
fact—and "after this was a farce called 'Twice Killed' which
made everyone laugh excessively".

On September 29th they sat through the same programme
of opera, "negro songs with bone accompaniment", and a
farce; and this time she was "very much affected" by the
opera, which was *La Sonnambula*.

A few days later "the influenza is very general" and she has
it "most severely", which does not prevent her going out into
the garden with "Ory, Will, Dr. Shanks and Mr. Donaldson
(I put him last as he always puts himself first)", to see her
brother-in-law trying a new horse—"'tis not a fit employment
for Sunday, methinks".

On August 27th Mr. Fanning has to go to Paramatta "to
see after some sheep from Nauima, which had come just too
late to be profitable"—which inspires the reflection, "First
page of the Pleasures of Sheep-farming, which may be justly
entitled 'the Pleasures of Hope' ".

On September 5th there was another ball, where an acquaintance introduced her to the Baron de Millebien,

"Having begged I would reserve myself for a formidable-
looking partner—which indeed with beard, moustaches, large
black eyes and long black hair he certainly was. . . . He
danced the Polka differently from us, now and then urging
you suddenly backwards and forwards so that people stopped
to look at him. . . . I afterwards had a *deux temps* valse
with the Frenchman, with whose dancing I was quite enchanted."

She had to tell one young man that "I made it a rule never
to dance more than thrice with anyone and that was even monstrous". But he "would not take any hint, altho' whenever he
came near or sat down I pretended not to see him—he was as
obstinate as a mosquito and as disagreeable". And then she

Plate 11

A SCENE OF UP-COUNTRY AUSTRALIAN LIFE

Pencil, unsigned, undated. This sketch was probably made by Huxley on his ride to Darling Downs (p. **67**)

meets someone who knew Huxley, "so I had a slight vision of the dear absent one. I look at all and see none like him: There is not one who has such a mind and heart and whom I ever c^d have loved so dearly as I do him."

But I must not take up too much space with this pleasant artless record of colonial life. Let me turn the Journal's pages more quickly:

"*Sept. 17th.* Poor Mrs Broughton has died from erisypelas [*sic*], a complaint that has of late seized many and terminated fatally." "*Sept. 18th.* Nothing but stitch-stitch—two workwomen, myself and Ory, and so much to do it seems an endless task." "*Sept. 25th.* More emigrant ships in, which will make up for the number going to California I I am seated in my room warming my feet upon a hot brick—and am just looking with deep melancholy upon my cold-looking white frock which il faut que je put on." *Sept. 29th.* Her neighbour at a Government House dinner-party was "so taken up with Miss Bradley that he only now and then dropped a pearly compliment—no real gem tho', only an imitation". "*Oct. 22nd.* A Mr and Mrs John Nicholas Beit came down to see the house having read the advertisement Will had put in about letting it. Such folks I they decidedly come under the denomination of 'Snob'. I did the polite and agreeable too, showing them the house which also they seemed to be charmed with. If Will lets the house to them their 14 children will break the gardener's heart."

On November 5th she interviewed an applicant for the post of companion to her sister on the voyage home. "Spoke like a little book bound in gold, but I have made up my mind in favour of the first applicant, being like Lavater a true believer in physiognomy."

On November 11th letters from the Fannings, who were on a journey up-country, provide the occasion for a vivid record of Australian travel in those days:

"Their journey from Mrs. Hood's at Wellington was grossly unpleasant. The horses went 56 miles that day, only halting after the first twelve. Late in the evening they reached a public house called the Black Rock, a miserable dwelling where 5 or 6 drunken and ruffianly looking men rushed out each seizing some article from the carriage and conveying it within, the host meanwhile opening a door to Ory, which discovered several more of this horrid brotherhood stretched on a sofa. Drawing back in alarm she retreated to the carriage, and Will collecting the things they had carried off told Smith to drive on or they must sleep in the Bush. Smith turned sulky, said the horses would drop and by his driving so contrived to increase the difficulties of the way already very bad from the incessant rain that Will jumped on the box and threatening to send him back to Sydney if he didn't do better restored him to his senses. At length they reached another inn where from a different but scarcely less disagreeable reason they could not at first sleep. Fatigue however overpowered numbers."

"*November* 18*th*. The *on dit* is that the Asiatic cholera has broken out in town and several have died. I truly hope it is not true."

In spite of ill-health she will take part in whatever gaieties are going on. On November 26th they had a picnic—"a party of 20 on horseback and two carriages' full"—and ended the day with dancing.

"We had ridden 27 miles and had now the prospect of being up till past 2 o'clock. Had I not taken so much to support me I could not have done it. The quantity of ale I am ordered and obliged to take [for her health] seems quite monstrous. I had a glass at home before I set out—then one at luncheon —then a glass of wine—another of ale on reaching Tempe— and more wine—and wine and water in the evening, and had I taken only water it could not have had less effect on me. At length with Alice's assistance, for I was too weak to do the least thing for myself, we got into the carriage."

Not unnaturally, she fainted at the ball, and next day spent the afternoon on the sofa, where "for two hours was at intervals in violent hysterics from excessive weakness". However, on the day following she was well enough for "much irksome shopping".

"*Dec. 9th.* A sad accident happened in the Harbour this week. Several men were bathing when one was seized by a shark and so severely torn that though after great difficulty rescued he died. Numbers of sharks are thronging the Harbour in consequence of a whale having been brought in. I do hope dear Hal will be careful against these monsters."

"*Dec. 17th.* Scarcely a minute can I snatch to read a new *Blackwoods*—in it another number of my favourite book, *The Caxtons,* amused me on Saturday night. Never was anything written that so points out the Right. It does honour to the mind and heart of the writer, whoever he may be."

"*Nov. 27th.* At 3 o'clock, quite tired, I lay down for an hour and read Carlyle's review of the life of Jean Paul. I rose a better creature, more cheerful and happy. He struggled thro' deepest poverty and pain. Mind conquered the infirmities of the body and the evils of life. He had under foot the giant Self and was rewarded in the mastery. And shall not I whose troubles are but faint and miniature shadows of his, strive against and subdue them? Henceforth I will, if I feel weak and ill, I will at least be cheerful, thankfully comparing my state with others—if I am sad, I will think on others' woes. All sorrow is selfish. I will become better and God help me in my intentions that they be deeds not words. I returned to the drawing-room happier and in better spirits than I had been for a long while."

In December there is a question of her "being daguerrotyped". There are great festivities at Christmas, and "the evenings are very merry", though at one party she has to sit next to a Mr T. who "is my aversion—He has coarse jokes and hoarse laughter, neither good by itself but combined quite unbearable".

On December 29th she records:

"The night before Will said at dinner time 'Do you know, Menen, you were within two minutes of dying and I saw you tho' I did not then know it—since you have been with us too'. Much astonished I at last gained from him that he had in the morning accompanied Mr Ramsey to Mr Belisario the dentist who, speaking of chloroform, said that he now never administered it from the great danger of death from its inhalation and that he never was more alarmed than when I inhaled it. Another two minutes and had I not recovered, an apoplectic fit must have ensued and the doctor present anxiously expecting it. Thank God that it passed over. How often do our steps unwittingly near the yawning and dread gulph of Death. To die in the course of nature is a fearful thing but to be suddenly snatched away is a thousandfold more appalling. Well may we pray 'From battle and murder and from sudden death Good Lord deliver us'."

"*Jan. 3rd,* 1850. I have just sat down to write at 11 o'clock, p.m., after a somewhat vain attempt to wash off some burnt cork moustaches and eyebrows from my face. Ory, Mrs Green and I having dressed up in jackets and opossum cloaks and thereby become most hideous figures. Will was laughing heartily, little dreaming that whilst he was asleep we had adorned his own face. At which when we told him he was not a little discomfited. We have been veritable children this evening and I feel all the better for it."

"*Jan. 9th* at one o'clock (a.m). Bush fires are blazing in the distance, one a very large one which was very grand."

"*Jan. 20th.* I was quite charmed with Margaret Thacker's excellent playing on the piano, and thought with a sigh (and a resolution to amend) of all I had lost by want of practice."

On a date in January, her sister and brother-in-law left Holmwood for England—a journey which we hear was expected to endure for 16 weeks! For a long time previous to this there had been great activity in the household, making clothes for the journey, packing up, arranging the house. On January 22nd (or 23rd) she records the final rush:

"Such a week as we have had at Holmwood packing and arranging. The last two days were overpowering. Will worked hard to get everything finished and on Monday evening we drove away from the dismantled home with tearful eyes and aching hearts. Poor Ory was very weak and I felt that now all motive for exertion was over I c^d really give up. Nurse and the wee things were already at Mrs Griffiths having been despatched thither in the morning. When we arrived there, poor Ory cried bitterly, as indeed she had done all day."

Meanwhile the return of the *Rattlesnake* was daily expected, and it was her constant prayer that Huxley should be back before her brother-in-law left, for he was one of the few who counselled an immediate marriage.

The *Rattlesnake* returned on January 24th, only three days after Holmwood, the Fannings' friendly house, had been abandoned. Possibly Huxley saw the Fannings before they actually sailed, but of this there is no record, for there is no entry in his Diary for the whole period during which the ship was at Sydney, and her entries do not begin again until March 10th. That she had the intention to fill the gap is evidenced by her leaving seven pages blank—but the record was never made.

To this final section of the Diary I will return. Meanwhile let me say something of the character and temperament of the girl (she was but twenty-three) as revealed in these pages.

The Diary records much gaiety, and, as she herself says (January 11th), after an evening of "playing, singing, dancing and merrymaking, Will doing Carandini, I a pupil in dancing and singing and Ory the mistress, Mr and Mrs Cornish being the audience", "I am always better for a little fun, although I may have come to years of discretion". But this was set against a background of constant work in the supervision of her sister's household, and, like her love of riding and swimming and the open air, was part of the natural overflow of a vital and varied youthful nature.

She had also a serious side, much preoccupied with morals and religion:

"*May* 18th, 1849. I more than ever see my own faults and deficiencies and strive, but not enough, against them. My prayers for advancement in good (whose aim, Perfection, like the ladder in Jacob's vision, may begin on earth but is only attained in Heaven) are indeed earnest—but this dreadful lethargy that oppresses me seems to deprive me of all power over myself and I am borne onwards in a dream and my will cannot wake me—Tomorrow is today or today becomes yesterday without any renewal of heart—I purpose but cannot fulfil.

"I ought to have a thankful heart and a cheerful spirit and gather the flowers and not the nettles of life—there are enough wild without nursing any. I do think I could more fully do this if I were permitted to be always with dear Hal— this dreadful absence does certainly excite repining feelings more especially as I know not when the end lieth—but God knows what is best for me—and I would not mind what tribulation I endured in this world (I say it in all hope that I may not be uttering what I could not do and oh may He avert it) could I but be certain of our meeting in Heaven."

On January 20th, 1850, just before her sister's and brother-in-law's departure, she writes: "Night—night indeed both without and within: I am wretched—altho' I have to-day taken the sacrament, which generally makes me peacefully-minded—the last time, perhaps for ever, that I may take it in company with Will and Ory".

On June 3, 1849, she is upset about Huxley's irreligion:

"Tonight I have been reading about the accordance of the times with prophecy—It seems to be well borne out—I mean the prophecy of Daniel referring as is supposed to the end of the Papal Power—but in most cases I think 'tis beyond man to explain—nor as we know that our own end is so near, need we concern ourselves about the actual time of that greater event so certain but so hidden. Oh if I only, together with all I love so much, felt assured that Death would be to us but the dark gate which led us to eternal happiness, what peace would possess me—Alas I feel that I have so transgressed, unless the Saviour beckon I may not thus look upon it. And my friends—my Father, my Mother, the one believes not and the other believing is not so mindful of heavenly things as I would she were—and he, dear Hal—God guide him to the perfect light for I am often very unhappy about his sentiments—I have so much need of leading unto holy things, am so dilatory luke-warm and dreamlike myself that I fondly hoped he would have been the guide and instructor unto more perfect ways—

but here my hopes have borne bitter fruit. Something has come over me of late; I cannot pray as fervently as I did."

Passages such as these I read with a shock of surprise, for when I knew my grandmother best, as an old lady in her eighties, deeply interested in life, benign, humorous, and happy, she had fully adopted the agnostic position, expected no personal survival after death, and was facing this antici-pated extinction with complete equanimity. However, until she was past fifty, she went regularly to Church and insisted on her children accompanying her.

It is perhaps worth while amplifying my recollections a lit-tle, for the evolution of the grandmother from the girl was indeed an interesting one. The ailing young woman, whom Huxley married in spite of a warning from an eminent physi-cian that she could not be expected to live out another twelve months, survived her husband by 19 years and died at the ripe age of 89.

Nor was it mere longevity which she displayed: her vitality remained undimmed. Writing, poetry and improvising on the piano were diversions she always enjoyed, and she continued both until her last brief illness. The *Spectator* published some verses which she had written during the last six months of her life.

Her intellect too remained fully awake. In fact, I remember her saying to me—she was 83 or 84 at the time—"You know, it is only in the last few years that I have been able to develop my intellectual interests properly". A little startled, I asked her what she meant. She explained that she had been a frivo-lous young girl (a self-accusation not wholly borne out by the present Journal) ; that a year or so after her engagement she had become very ill; that when she recovered and married, her time was fully taken up with household duties (a claim to which we can give every credence, when we remember that she bore Huxley eight children, of whom seven survived to marry and have children themselves, that they entertained a great deal, and that for most of their married life they were poor, and she had to do with the minimum of domestic help) ; and that after Huxley's death she was again ill for some years— "so you see, I really never had a chance before".

In her old age, she read *Nature* regularly, and the various scientific books that colleagues of her husband used to send her; she used to pump her doctor-son about medicine, me about biology, and another grandson, who was working as a technical adviser in wireless, about the mysteries of that then infant science.

With it all, she was wonderful company, a mine of stories about the past, but really much more interested in young people and the present, and especially in the personal lives of her big crop of grandchildren; she was always fond of a joke, even at the expense of her own infirmities, always fond too of poetry and of music. I can see her now in my mind's eye, a small figure in black, with lace cap on her head, making her way to the piano to sing to us boys, or, leaning on her stick, showing us the beauties of her garden, when we came down to stay.

She provided in her own person a lesson in how to grow old, serene in spite of her infirmity and her lack of what is usually called faith. Indeed, the mellow age of the grandmother is in strong contrast with the troubled soul of the young woman.

But it is time to return to Henrietta Heathorn as she was in 1849.

Her emotions were strongly developed, and she was capable of the deepest attachment to family and friends. Scattered throughout the Diary are references to her love of her sister and of her brother-in-law, "dear Will", even when he has been teasing her in an outrageous manner. She has a great love for her little niece Alice:

"Wednesday Sep. 12, darling Alice's birthday, in consequence of which she was allowed to breakfast with us. She is four years old—and a dear wilful intelligent little creature, her temper is very violent, but then she has no sulkiness whatever and is most forgiving and I hope that firm managing may subdue her—I do love her so much and shall bitterly feel parting with her. 'Tis very strange that altho' I acknowledge little Will's amiability and gentleness I cannot love him nearly so well, perhaps 'tis because he is already such a pet with his Father and Mother; indeed I love Baby better who tho' better tempered much resembles dear Alice in his lively independent

disposition. Moreover he is dear Hal's godson and therefore claims some love. If dear Alice were only my own to do as I liked with how I should love her now. I almost check it knowing she will soon be taken from me—perhaps—I don't like to imagine it—forget me. The love that one has for a child is such a tender holy love, it seems to expand the heart and make one better and so does my heart overflow with this feeling to dear Alice that I could fold it round and round her as a garment. As the time draws near when I might lose her she becomes yet dearer and I hoard her as a miser w^d his treasures.

"We dine alone, when the dear children join us, I having previously taught little Alice reading for an hour at which my darling is very quick. Dearly as I love her I do not spoil her but have her in perfect obedience. And they sit at dinner like two dear little dogs—watching my looks to know what they are to do and perfectly silent—a most difficult habit for them to acquire."

The child returned her aunt's love in full measure:

"Darling Alice, she is so changed, so tractable, that both Will and Ory [after an absence from their house] are delighted with her and she loves me more and more. When we go into the garden 'tis to me she runs first—for me she gathers the buttercups, every morning she creeps in to my bed and with her arm round my neck and cheek against mine now and then kissing me. I teach her little poems which on Sunday morning she repeats to Papa. The prospect of telling him a new one is her great ambition. Every day too I teach her reading and she is getting on nicely—how my heart will ache when I fold her for the last time in my arms."

Her health gave her a great deal of anxiety. She is constantly complaining of faintness and weakness and of faceache. It is difficult to be sure exactly what was the matter with her, but certain that she did suffer a great deal, and that, on her return to England in 1855 to be married, she was in a really serious state, largely as the result of mistaken treatment by an Australian doctor. In later life, however, she got over her troubles, and in the end survived until nearly ninety.

Finally there is the record of her love for Huxley—a love as deep as it was strong, as strong as it proved lasting. Not a week goes by without her confiding some expression of it to the pages of her Journal, happy in the knowledge that it will later be read by her lover.

The first page of the Journal testifies to her anguish on separation:

"It is the 7th May 1849—late in the evening. This morning I woke to sorrow. Scarcely could I believe in dear Hal's departure yet the bitter parting of the previous night was too vivid to let me doubt about it. So much did I struggle to suppress my grief that when he was gone I almost feared my parting had not evinced sufficient feeling, but I dared not trust myself to say much and he I know will understand and appreciate my endeavours (almost ineffectual) to control my agony of grief that possessed me but which after he had gone I could no longer repress—it burst forth in all the vehemence of despair—such anguish inexpressible convulsed me.

"I took a solitary walk to look after a required servant and thought the whole way of all dear Hal had done or spoken yesterday. Still his last dear words murmured in my ear— 'God help you Menen dear'. I felt his arm round me as he patted poor Snap and bade me pet him for his sake—his last dear kiss ere he sprang upon his horse and was (oh how soon) out of sight. Returning home I sat down in the Bush and calling Snap beside me talked to him as if he were able to understand me—indeed I fancy the dear brute did for he looked quite wistful and dropped his tail most sadly. I shall love him much—he was the last thing caressed by Hal. I hoped when Will returned at evening he might bring me a note from the dear one—and to my joy so he did: the dear words, how I read and treasured up their meaning. I cd not help crying long and bitterly. May God bless and restore him to me."

Let us remember that their engagement lasted eight years, and that during that formidable lapse of time they were together only on five occasions, during the times which he spent at Sydney between cruises. These periods totalled not more than eleven months, and during them of course he was only free to visit her off and on. Little wonder that she as well as he felt the strain of absence so deeply.

"*May* 13*th.* This afternoon I again read the packet of letters Hal sent me on leaving, but written on his last cruise. They are never-failing sources of comfort. Let me peruse them ever so often I find new meanings in each oft-read line and realize the feelings which prompted each fond word—Ah how I love him—with my whole soul—with all the truth and devotion that ever urged a woman's heart. My desire is to become good and excellent as the being he imagines me—my happiest dreams are of a peaceful home with him to love and care for —my hopes, his advancement in temporal and eternal blessings. We live in other times than those which often required some great sacrifice at the hands of the loving for the loved, so in this way no proof of my strong affection can I offer— only the smaller ones of patience and endurance under sorrow, adversity and separation can I give, and my happiness is in their performance. So after all—there is no sacrifice."

"*May* 18*th.* To-morrow I will begin a letter to dear Henry —what a pleasure. It will seem as if I spoke to him—alas that I can hear no answer! He has thought of me a thousand times and looked at my picture and kissed it too, I am sure. I wish it had been myself."

"*May* 25*th.* [A letter from him has referred to a book she lent him.] I am so glad he has read the sweet tale of *Midsummer Night* that we may have more thoughts and feelings alike. He objects to Mrs Hale's having made Eva surprisingly beautiful, that 'such a soul needs no such clothing'. I disagree with him—she may not need it but it makes her lovelier still. A sly thought crept into my mind as I read that part—that if I were a stranger reading it my impressions wd be '*his* lady-love is evidently deficient in beauty'; not that I believe he would love me better if I were [*sic*], altho' he might admire more. Who wants more than to be loved?"

"*May* 29*th.* His likeness (so unlike) is beside me and I shall as I always do put it under my pillow that I may have his spiritual if not his real presence."

"*June* 13*th*. Alice Authile declared that she quite loved Mr Huxley but she knew she was safe in doing so. I am delighted and like her ten thousandfold better for her confession. I would that everyone should love him as long as he loved only me. There is no selfishness at all in this! Were such a thing likely that he should ever love another I do think my heart would break—or if as I'm told this rarely happens there would be the more bitter fact of living on—in utter hopelessness—uncared for and alone."

"*June* 14*th*. [Apropos of the arrival of a second letter from Huxley.] It is like him, kind frank and affectionate and makes me more than ever prize and love him. I have read it many times, some few parts again and again and it will now take the place of the last one as coming more recently from the dear one, and it is more fondly regarded—indeed it almost seems as if it had borne away part of himself so does it stir my heart. Bless you my own dear Henry for the never failing love you have bestowed upon me—the spring of happy thoughts—bright hopes and blissful memories—the source from whence in every grief or vexation I draw sweet consolation—the fount of all good feelings—the incentive to right resolves and their fulfilment—my earthly ark from which unlike the dove I would never never wander. 'Tis a happy thing to love and be loved again—almost a mystery how this joy is ours."

"*June* 15*th*. Little Alice . . . asked me if I had seen Mr Huxley, as I was laughing."

"*Sunday July* 1*st*. This day I have completed my 24th year. I can scarcely believe it, so fast the years come round. Such a mixture of joy and sadness I never felt, for after breakfast dear Will led me to his room and handing me a parcel bid me open it. I imagined it a present from him and had ere it was half unclosed begun to thank him when he said 'Look again, 'tis not from me'. Whereupon twelve volumes of Schiller's works discovered themselves together with a note from dearest Hal. So surprised and overcome was I that I wept for many minutes. This unexpected proof of his thoughtful love on this my birthday was deeply felt and warmly appreciated and I longed that he were by to thank and tell him how much how very much I loved him."

On July 5th, after listening to her half-sister singing, she writes: "I envy her the gift denied to me—especially as Hal is so fond of it. For his sake I wish that I excelled in many things—sometimes too I wish I were beautiful and yet I think he would not love me more if I were, and for myself I care not."

On the 6th "Isy is persuading me to get married—and Willie won't say one way or the other—and I—there are so many reasons for and against I know not what to say. I would so gladly have the happy knowledge that nothing could separate us—but I so fear it would not be right to burden him with myself under his present circumstances—God guide us."

On the 18th she makes the acquaintance of a lady who had recently married a widower: "She is very young, pretty and agreeable and looks I am sure as if she were full of fun. I should not like to be a second wife."

On the 22nd she has been ill: "I look very like an old German Frau, muffled up in shawls and handkerchiefs, and could dear Hal see me he would certainly be very sorry for the poor little white mouse, ten degrees whiter to-day than usual". ("The little white mouse" was clearly one of his pet names for her. See p. 248.)

On August 10th she had been much depressed by news of her father's financial troubles: "Returning home I wrote awhile to dear Hal, a sweet solace to my aching heart. How happy am I in having one who loves me so much and who in every sorrow will truly sympathize with me. Dear dear one, he has my whole affection and it seems to me as if none other could have drawn forth so much love. Our tastes and thoughts and feelings agree and in all things he answers the ideal my heart told me I could love—before I knew him. My love, based upon esteem and reverence, clings to the dear object with a happy consciousness of his worth. He is my life, my all—God ever bless him."

On August 20th she was at a ball: "From thinking of dearest Hal I made some very absurd mistakes in a Quadrille, setting to Alice my vis-a-vis when she came across, with the utmost gravity, to the great amusement of some friends who were seated near me". Next morning she takes a walk and describes the scene: "It was a lovely morning, the waves slightly ruffled by the breeze flashing with a thousand sun-sparkles—dashing against the rocks with lazy perseverence. Sydney Heads in the distance and dearest Hal close close beside me living in each thought. Had he been really by I had thought it tenfold more beautiful. How love changes one—once my enjoyment had been perfect in such a scene—now there was yet a want—the sympathy of him I so dearly love —and yet strange perversity I do think had he been there I should have been too absorbed in him to reflect much upon what surrounded me."

Her love and her anxiety over the dangers of his cruise, over her own ill-health and consequent unfitness to be his wife, over the dreary prospect of three years' separation, prompted her now and again to strange fantasies and gloomy forebodings.

"*May* 18*th*, 1849. This afternoon the bright sun suddenly departed and clouds and rain with a wild wind announced a storm which at length burst in full force—I was in my room at the time and as the lightning flashed in my face (I am never afraid of it) I spiritually went through a very sad scene. Methought the flash struck me blind and full of anguish I groped my way downstairs to Ory's room exclaiming 'I am blind, I shall never see again, I can never be his wife', and then we wept together. Then my utter helplessness and uselessness came before me as I thought of the many services I could never more render even to myself. I was a burden, a useless being in this world, and almost believing the picture I had sketched I cried bitterly."

"*June* 19*th*, 1894. I was so wretched all the evening fancying that Willie's parting words, 'You will never be married, Nettie', might come to pass that I sobbed as if my heart w^d break and in vain did the kind Will seek to comfort me. I thought of the perils from the sea—from illness—in the hot climate whither he was going and from the natives to which beside ordinary dangers he was exposed until my heart died within me and I pictured his death and my desolation. I know that it is wrong to anticipate evil but there are times when gloom hangs heavily over thought and will weigh it down with apprehension. Ah what a sunless sky would life present without him. Hope's evergreen consumed, Joy's laughter hushed in my heart's chamber. Memory gloomily brooding o'er the Past would weep in woe, each gem she lifted from the mine of Time contrasting with the present poverty. Heaven forgive me these repining thoughts. I tried and did at length in some degree conquer them—how I longed to pillow my head on his shoulder and tell him all I felt and hear sweet words of comfort that never yet failed to calm me when in sorrow."

On July 22nd, after being ill, she writes:

"Sometimes I have such bitter fancies—that he the dear one is no more—the ship returns and instead of his speedy coming a letter black-edged and sealed, harbinger of black grief, is brought to me—I know the ship is in—he has not come—I cannot open the letter, dreading to know what my heart forebodes—at length it is opened—with all the throbbing expectation of unbounded woe. As I surmised the writer is Dr Thompson and I skip the preamble which would prepare me for the truth and single out the confirmation of my fears— I do not appreciate the truth—believing still the words—not a tear escapes me but a faintness spreads over me—belief warring against expiring hope with painful throbbings stirs my heart. The gnawing of despair begins and yet I will not believe —Oh God, whatever I deserve, avert this evil from me. Spare me the bitterness of death in life—watch over my heart's treasure—spare and restore him—unite us and make us thine here and thine hereafter."

When we reflect how easily he might have met his death by going with Kennedy, we shall realize that her fears were not without cause.

Later, while he was in Sydney, she had a feverish cold: "I could not sleep, my head was burning, and horrid faces peeped at me thro' the curtains—and I almost fancied I saw you pale and dying and that you had come to take leave of me. The vision would not be shut out." But at the back of her mind was always the certitude of full mutual love.

The last section of her journal provides some charming pictures of the young couple together during the early months of 1850 (unfortunately his diary is blank for this period).

On March 7th they went together to a Ball at Government House:

"I felt very strange at entering with him and yet most happy. . . . Then came a Polka with the dear one—very nice, but not half so nice as a Schottische later in the evening. I half imagined we were fairies. I always loved dancing from a child —to dance at any time is delight to me, but with him it is bewitching—he holds me so that I scarcely touch the ground —I danced incessantly but never once felt tired."

Two days later she nearly fainted, but "then arrived darling Hal, which banished all illness—we descended to the little summer house on the rocks and talked even to my heart's content of our home and all that we would make it—until we were frightened away by seeing a boat put in to the little harbour and some person ascend the steps causing us to retreat."

On March 12th he was again at the house:

"We all had a round game of cards in which Hal most provokingly won all from me and asserted that his influence over me was so constant that it was exemplified even in the smallest things—then he impertinently whispered in my ear 'Give me a kiss'. How his eyes flash sometimes! I am half afraid to look at them—but it is not with anger—I have no fear of that, determined as I know him to be and hasty as he says he is. Dear Hal—he lingered behind the rest to give me a dear kiss until Mr Maclean too politely sent Nevil to intimate he was waiting for him. I never before thought Mr Maclean officious."

On the 16th, her half-sister Isy (Isabel) was married (a marriage of which Henrietta did not altogether approve, as the groom was but twenty while Isy was thirty-eight); and Huxley was "to act Papa" and give her away. On the day:

"Hal arrived and was for the first time introduced to my dear Mother whom he so 'snaked' that she was deep in her praises of him—does he not deserve them all and more—A short glimpse of her and perhaps the last he may ever have.

. . . At ten o'clock we drove to the church, on the way there
Hal suggesting all sorts of contretemps which did not happen.
The bridegroom and his brother with a Mr Allardice were in
waiting—but the clergyman not having arrived we seated ourselves in a pew, Hal still persisting (very contrary to his
capacity of Papa) to utter the greatest absurdities in the
gravest possible manner."

That evening she writes:

"Hal has coaxed his likeness from me—first made me
promise to give it and then when I refused gravely said if I
broke one promise I would all. 'Twas so mean of him—I gave
it directly and feel wretched—he promised he would restore it
and now says I shall never have it—that he is jealous of it—
oh it is too bad. Nearly three years have I had the miniature
and tho' it is not like him, time has endeared it to me and I
could cry that I shall not clasp it tonight as usual. Still he
wished it—I am not quite unhappy."

Two days later he again spent the afternoon with her:

"I asked him for the likeness—but he cruelly added another
burden to my load—I was not even to ask him for it—would
I do this to please him? I felt he was asking almost more than
I could perform—never more to ask for it—and he had moreover cut the miniature in halves—what I had so treasured he
had so used. Surely he had done it on purpose to vex me—
he was tyrannizing—he knew I could refuse him nothing and
he asked so much—slowly and with difficulty I quelled the
agony that filled my heart and promised not to ask again—
and then came a floating idea that he w^d give me back the face
—because he had once said it. It did not make me feel less at
giving it up and promising not to ask for it. For a moment
I felt he was unkind to try me—only for a moment—for I
remembered how few ways I had to shew my love for him.
I had yielded my will to his, even more a secondary affection;
and I was, if not happy, at peace, for he would see that I
would rather pluck the dearest object from my heart than
offend him."

And two days later on returning home she was told there was a parcel for her:

"A little box discovered itself and it flashed upon me that the lost likeness lay therein—and so it did, set in a pretty little locket which I could wear. I kissed it again and again, called dear Grandmamma to share my surprise (the pleasure was all my own) and then searched for a note which at first I had not seen—The dear note—I sobbed as I read it—he said he had repented of his trying me and w^d never more do it. It was such a dear affectionate note that if ever I doubted the depth of his love this had removed all doubt—I was so very very happy and yet I could not stop my tears—I answered it that evening—Mr Griffiths exclaiming 'What another note, 'tis as bad as the 16 you sent to Cape York—he will never read that', but I thought otherwise and went on."

Next day she "heard that Dr Thompson was taking a photographic likeness of Hal—how delightful to have a correct one". But it was not so "correct" after all, for a note has been added later: "very indistinct—with the sailor's cap".[1]
For a time Huxley was "laid up with a hurt in his foot". On seeing him again (he had come to dine) she writes "it was such a happiness to see and talk to him after so many days absence"—the many days, to be precise, numbering three.

"Hal 'snaked' Mrs Gilchrist, I think. Poor Dr Thompson was placed between the impenetrable proper Miss Thackers: he had my full share of pity. Dear Dr Thompson, I do so like him. How he must long to see again his wife and his child whom he has never seen. Much as I w^d wish to keep Hal here, I would not have the ship stay longer when I think of them— Hal and I are not the only beings in the world: 'tis a reflection I sh^d often make for I am too apt to be selfish."

On the 24th there was a cloud—but what a little one!

"The afternoon brought you, my own dear one—Alice and Mrs Griffiths were out. Mrs G. had taken the children to the

[1] This is presumably the photograph reproduced in Plate 1 (facing p. 2).

Point and we were all alone—but you were in such a strange
mood that I felt you did not make me glad. You were capri-
cious; if I talked you w^d have me silent and if I laughed it
grated on your ear and only at length, when I looked as sad
as I felt and suggested I w^d try crying, did you utter any kind
words or fold me lovingly to you—But I knew how often I
had felt so too and strove to be calm and then we talked long
and seriously of all you would do and then you gave me so
many dear kisses that I ceased to imagine you had been previously angry with me, which fear had well nigh crept into my
head. Before dinner time your fitfulness had returned and a
little nasty spirit possessed me to teaze you—till you warmly
told me I had better no. I then of course felt more wishful
than ever to do so and returned again and again to say a word
—half in sport and half in earnest—till I went up to dress for
dinner and told Alice part of my imaginary grievance. She
had guessed something from your altered manner when you
were walking on the green with us. At least she remarked you
were dull and not joyous as usual. I reasoned myself into no
very amiable mood much to Alice's amusement and so went
down to dinner with a white dress but a naughty dark heart,
punishing myself for your supposed harshness instead of you;
when you sought to catch my eye I would not give an answering
look—nor did I once address you—everything you said I mentally replied to and once (I must confess, that you may see all
the workings of my rebellious heart) when you were telling
Mrs Griffiths that you had brought much tortoise-shell from
the islands said to myself 'he could never give me any'—cross
as I was I could scarcely help laughing at myself for this absurd and unjust thought and when on the morrow afternoon
you brought me a comb made of it—I remembered my unkind
spiteful thought and inwardly blushed. But Alice to whom I
told all w^d not have me wretched all the evening and whispered you I was unhappy—and then dearest you talked and
kissed away all my evil fancies; indeed when you allowed that
you had felt ill before dinner I was very grieved that I had
not been more patient and good. How happily the rest of the
evening passed, peace stole into my heart and abode there and
when he had gone and I laid my head on my pillow I resolved

that I would never more torment myself and him again. Love will tarnish if 'tis always petted."

Next day, during a discussion about their future, he elicits more of her hidden fears, and she writes, "What right has Hal to read me my heart's book as he does?—I shall be frightened not only to think but to feel". "I accompanied him to the gate on leaving, a practice I shall certainly keep up—dear, dear Hal, if possible he is daily more loved by me. How shall I bear to part with him—for such a long long time as Fate has condemned me to."

On the morrow, being a Tuesday, she learns that "The Barneys had ensnared him into joining a Picnic. Perfectly monstrous—that he should enjoy himself away from me! Until Thursday then I lock up Hope and bring out Resignation—that day arrived I shall release the former and give it Impatience as a companion."

While he is away, she went down to the sea. "The Harbour looked so beautiful this morning as at an early hour I went down the rocks. The waters quivered under the rising sun. The land seemed thro' the soft haze to be emerging from them and the ships looked like beautiful huge birds with wings outstretched upon the sea. Mrs Griffiths is still as weak as ever—I must try and prevent her going about. Are you coming, Hal, or not?—It is an age since I saw you: you cannot know how I weary for your coming."

That afternoon he came. "I have just come up to bed half angry for Mr Griffiths thought I w^d get face-ache and prevented me going to the gate with Hal—and as I did not get a last kiss am very *böse* notwithstanding the many I received when Mr Griffiths went out to smoke his cigar. . . . We were quite undisturbed. One infliction was put on him, the carriage was ordered and we took a drive with the children by way of cover as Mrs Griffiths said but which Hal thought too patriarchal by far."

In the evening she pours out her heart on paper:

"Hal, dear Hal, how does my love for you increase, I feel so much more one with you than when last you were in. You draw out my thoughts and feelings—and appropriate them

most tyrannically—and yet 'tis perhaps one of the things that
has bound me with stronger love to you. You *are* a tyrant still
conquering by strength where influence fails, indeed you have
tonight acted very meanly about the 'shoulder dispute' and I
have half—only half a mind, remember—to give you up as
Will was constantly advising. Until we meet I will not decide,
—dearest, Good Night, I would not renounce my claim to
your love for all the world could offer—God bless you—I
have ordered Night Star to make us dream of each other."

The next day was March 29th, Good Friday. "Whilst reading aloud to Mrs Griffiths I suddenly thought of Hal's going
away and covering my face with my hands burst into tears.
Grandmamma comforted me so kindly and listened to all my
fears about my dear Father and Mother—I am sure there are
yet very bad days in store for us—I however recovered myself
and went on with my book."

In spite of griefs and fears, there was a radiance on her
spirit. "Mr C. went early to rest but I staid remembering Mr
Griffiths had a cigar to smoke in the verandah—I thought he
had forgotten it, but he went at last and then I was so happy
for dear Hal's arm was round me and as he drew me to him
and fondly kissed me I wished we might never part. Three
years—they seem immeasurable—how often will my heart
sicken and long to rejoin him and know it must wait and
weary. I am not murmuring, my own dear one, only regret-
ting. When I think how happy we shall be at the end, I am
more than content to wait and love and hope."

On April 1st, "How skilfully he thinks he has evaded the
first of April—but I have caught him—he will be very surprised to open his parcel to discover an old newspaper instead
of the music, and shᵈ he send it to Mrs Barney, quel horreur!"

He had gone off to Botany with some friends: the drive had
been dull and the children of the party had been naughty. "I
fancy this and the unprofitable drive had warmed the current
of his feelings against children—for he discoursed long upon
their proper management and the noise they were allowed to
make here—that it wᵈ drive him mad, etc. The more angered
he grew the more I laughed—it diverted me amazingly."

On April 9th, after he had left her, thinking how soon he

would be sailing "I cried passionately, and c^d with difficulty reason myself good again".

On the 11th he came to find them reading a new number of *David Copperfield*. "Hal had just been reading a letter from Mamma to me from some part of which he took it in his head that I was going to take part in all sorts of hardships—I told him not, but the conversation having so begun took a gloomy turn. He pictured his hopes frustrated thro' having over-rated his ability, even after years of well-directed energy, and asked me not if I w^d still love him—he knew that I still would —but if I could esteem him as before—for said he to be loved from compassion would be unbearable. The proud creature, that he should ever imagine my love could mix with such a feeling for him!—I told him that I reverenced as much as I loved him and believed that success or non-success was no criterion of merit, but he replied he would not give anything for the ability that could not compel fortune—Oh Hal, dear one, how wrong you are—many gifted ones who sh^d have succeeded have failed and if you should, after doing your best, is it right to repine? You are so young too—if you have health and long life what may not your determined will accomplish? Dearest of all was your assurance that could you only have me with you you would yet be fully happy."

On May 13th she caught a feverish chill and was in bed for some days, often in great pain and sleepless in spite of lauda-num. "Mrs Griffiths tried again and again to persuade me to see Hal but I would not"—apparently reluctant that he should see her suffering and ill. By the 17th she is up again, and he comes to dinner. "Mrs Griffiths amused them with views of Rome and the Continent while Hal, suffering angel, held a skein of rug wool which Mrs Griffiths wound—endeavouring, mean creature, to terrify me into owning his power by those strange piercing glances which, odious snake, he has never yet found to fail. My only chance is to avoid his eye and then I can be firm as himself."

On the 22nd, "At 10 o'clock Hal brought me a nice little horse to join him in a ride to New Town to Mamma Steele's where we were to accompany the Doctor and some others in a further ride. I was so happy all the way—it was the first time I had ever ridden out alone with him and I felt as if I belonged to the dear one more than ever. . . . We came home by a beautiful moonlight—Hal and I were leading the way by ourselves at a walk, Dr Steele not being disposed for fast riding. It was sadly pleasant for we could not help remembering what a long and weary while it would be ere we met after the parting so near at hand—but the dear one threatened to punish my tears with a kiss and being really alarmed he w^d do so—the three others being behind—I promised to be good."

On the 25th, "We went down the rocks to talk . . . and we were happy as even I, dissatisfied creature, c^d wish. The moon had risen ere we turned homeward and you dear Hal may perhaps recollect when you see this how you extracted my thoughts from me—refusing to come up the flight of steps till I had told you."

Next day he came to dine. "I had finished a very pretty purse I intended for Hal on his birthday. Unfortunately he was so charmed with it that he wanted to appropriate it directly but as that would have spoilt my plan I protested it was not for him and fearing its fate ran off and put it in a safe place. We had great fun all the evening about it—he vainly trying to coax me for it—until his old habit of trying the strength of his power over me came upon him and he asked only for one look at the purse—but I said no and persisted in it altho' he grew grave and said it was very little he asked—and I—I refused him such a trifle and w^d accordingly act likewise in greater matters. 'You will come tomorrow.' 'No— you will not do what I ask of you . . . I will not grant your wishes.' My heart ached—and often I was on the point of getting the purse but did not wish to give in—partly perhaps because Mrs G. knew of our contest. When they rose to go and Mr Hood had left the room, I could no longer keep in my tears and w^d not at first bid him goodnight believing he w^d not come on the morrow, when he was so kind and loving and good to me that I felt quite sorry for our little difference. I always punish myself most by any request I deny him."

On the 27th there was rumour of a change in Huxley's plans. "There was a dispute between the Captains of the

Meander and *Rattlesnake* as to which had the right of ordering her and it was very probable they might make another
cruise before going home." Later in the day there came a
message that the ship was to sail for home almost immediately.

The next day's entry is the last in the Diary. I will let it
speak for itself:

"Yesterday was a bitter day. I think I see the sailor now
bringing the news that you were to sail on Tuesday—see you
handing the note to Mr Griffiths and preventing me from
going to him for information, and then your leading me into
the drawing room and taking me and bidding me bear it
bravely—my own dear one! 'tis hard to bear anyway. I have
not cried today but the heaviness at my heart seems to weigh
me down—and I am so cold—you w^d never think your snow
house had any fire within—I am so grieved that we had that
silly difference yesterday and yet I do not think I was in any
way naughty—I wept bitterly when I came in about it and
prayed earnestly that I might be kind and conciliating if you
were ever ruffled when I became your wife—I shall so try
never to have a cross word between us my own dear one—one
might lead to so many and then I sh^d be most wretched. Do
you recollect our pleasant moonlight talk and walk last night,
my dearest—I have not forgotten one word you said and do
you remember and love me for my wish that I told you, as you
said, just to remember that lovely night by."

He came again that evening. "Night, $\frac{1}{2}$ past ten—You are
this instant gone, my own dear one. And I am still musing on
your dear words and dearer kisses. But one more day remains
to me my best beloved to spend with you and then the long
interval ere we meet. I could tell you much of the aching that
gnaws within my heart, of the painful struggles that I am
making to suppress my grief, but you know dearest by your
own heart all the agony I feel. Let us rather turn to the bright
future than dwell over the sad present. It may be far off but
'tis such a sunny spot that it is worth spending any time to gain
it. One thing can not cloud us in our journey towards it. We
have no doubt of the other's affection for I do believe our love

Plate 12

Thomas Henry Huxley and his wife, from a previously unpublished
photograph taken by Mrs. Bailey at Lynton in 1882.

will continue till death shall part us[1]—we have no regrets in the past history of our love and nothing but hopes for its future one. We have too had many pleasant meetings and happy hours together and have very much to be grateful for, for our inward course did certainly 'run smooth' whatever assailed us from without and these difficulties time faith and patience and Our Father's blessing shall overcome. We shall be so happy, my own dear one, for you will be my husband and I your wife—never never more to part. God Almighty bless and protect you my own darling Hal—you will never forget me—nor will you ever be forgotten by your loving-hearted Menen. Sunday 28th April 1850."

There is, however, one further citation to be made. Slipped into the pages of the Journal are a couple of sheets of notepaper with entries November 22nd, 1855, and January 12th, 1856—a few months after their marriage. It is clear they were deliberately put there.

"*Nov. 22nd* 1855. While sitting at tea this evening (my husband had gone to dine at the Philosophical Club) the girl brought in a letter. The address was so legibly written that I scarcely recognized the handwriting, yet my heart guessed rightly—It was from my darling husband, full of merry nothings yet meaning oh how much! written I know to cheer me because like a silly child just after he left me this morning he returned and found the tears in my eyes for the reason that he would not be at home in the evening. What a thoughtful loving soul he is. Let me never forget it.

"I have been reading Sydney Smith's *Memories*. Some parts touched me deeply—one I will if possible lay to heart, never to let a day pass without ministering in some way however briefly to the happiness of some fellow being. I have had several soul-absorbing wishes during my life-time—first, as a child, to be famous as a poetess—which as I came to measure justly my powers died away and was succeeded by what I fear was a meaner desire—to be universally loved. Since then I have become wise enough to know that it was an unhealthy appetite that excited the powers of pleasing for no positive

---

[1][In margin]: It did, it has to his last moments. Sep. 21st, 1895.

good—little more than vanity. The other desire now fills my soul—to *do* good, to *be* good—I cannot undo the finished past —wasted and abused—God help me to work in the future.

.   .   .   .   .

"What a pleasure is our little house to us—everything is so new and pretty I quite grieve to think there will ever come a time when the curtains and carpets shall look old and faded— but I think that like friends whom we have known in their youth they will still have charms for us. I cling very much to inanimate objects—even to old clothes from the numberless associations connected with them. An old white glove or piece of lace has often brought some long-gone-by party before me —a pen, some particular letter—it is a great effort to me to part with any object that has been long in my possession—only at length effected by shutting my ears to all fond whisperings of memory and opening them to the loud assertions of prac- tical utility. The indulgence of this taste is bad—it leads one to hoard up things which, of little use to the possessor, might be of great benefit to others. It is indulging sentiment at the cost of generosity—yet where such disposition is never or seldom evinced, I have not infrequently noticed a want of power to sympathize with one's fellow beings."

"*Jan.* 12th Sat. 1856. A few hurried lines from my darling husband have come saying he will be here 'to kiss the little white mouse by eleven'—I cried with joy—Oh how I love him. Better is he than father mother sister, or than child could be, for never had I such rich bestowal of love and sympathy. God keep him—us to each other. God make us to increase in good- ness—make the darkness light. Lieut. Sharpe called today and brought me a beautiful wreath of feather flowers. . . . How his coming recalled the old Sydney days when he was Mercury to me and Hal—fairy days tho' they were, still like all fairy times troubled by the presence of an evil fairy, but now—all is gone—all is bright and yet real—God be thanked for my dear husband—my kind dear friends, fair competency and pleasant home—How am I God's debtor! . . ."

With this we may leave Henrietta Heathorn and her husband. The official record of their story is in the *Life and Letters:* and the rest in the hundreds upon hundreds of letters, as yet unpublished, that they exchanged with each other whenever absent. All that need here be said is that their love and their happiness were destined to endure for forty-five years, through births and deaths, health and illness, struggle and success, until death took him and left her, with her memories of the past and her vivid interest in the present, to live out her benign old age to the full.

CHAPTER 11

The Diary: Homeward Bound
APRIL–OCT. 1850

—————————————

THIS final chapter is in the nature of a pendant. As Huxley himself says, the entries concerning the voyage home were made more to please Miss Heathorn than to keep a record for himself. In any case, the scientific purpose of the voyage was at an end, and the *Rattlesnake* was only concerned to reach England in the shortest possible time. Accordingly we find a rather different atmosphere in this section of the Diary. It is lighter, less of a Journal and more of a letter. It was indeed a long letter, daily added to for want of postal facilities in mid-ocean. And it well illustrates that wonderful epistolary gift which Huxley retained and constantly practised until the end of his life—a gift which served to illuminate and enliven his description of the simplest happenings.

· · · · ·

DID I not laughingly say something, dear Menen, about keeping a journal of the voyage home—that last evening that we were together? At any rate, I will do so, for it may amuse you hereafter.

I left Woloomooloo in a strange unnatural state of excitement on the night we parted. The effort I had made produced a sort of morbid disposition to merriment, painful merriment. I felt that each of us had been cheating the other, and that there was something horribly absurd in our doing so.

I feared to be late, too, and walked, or rather ran in at a

most tremendous pace—the exertion seemed cooling and calming to me and I was collected enough by the time I got on board.

All was in confusion—visitors, duns and dirt were everywhere. The survey of the *Bramble's* stores was not finished, and it was not certain when it would be. There was no chance of our sailing that night.

I went to bed, and continually woke up (rather than slept) till morning when to my delight, about half past seven, we began to get the anchor up.

It was a hazy, hot morning—the harbour like one of Martin's oil paintings—the sea glassy. A breath of wind came hot as from a kiln from the northwest, the sails were loosed and we were on *our way home*.

I went up on the poop and found several who like myself had come to take a last look of the spots dear to them. The Barneys were all assembled at the Scotts' and there was a waving of handkerchiefs going on.

But my eye was now and then turned, armed with the signalman's glass—quiet, quiet—to the other side of the harbour, and there I espied the dear one on the balcony—bare-headed too in that hot sun (for which I scolded her in my heart)— with glass directed towards the old ship. Did she see me? I know not. All I know is that the figure stayed there until we were far down the harbour—and then methought I could trace something like the waving of a handkerchief as it disappeared through the window of Griffith's dining-room. I watched and watched until we were between the heads, and then as the house, now a white speck, was shut in by the south head, I turned away and saw no more of Sydney. I said to myself that I had done with looking back—goodbye Sorrow, come Hope.

And therefore I went down with Simpson to have a glass of champagne—and, *silently,* drink to *our* success and happy reunion.

All our live stock came on board. M——y came on board in the middle of the night and was put under arrest—his wife and child came about 2 a.m.

The Crawford and Mrs Stanley were on the poop during our departure, but the former found it expedient to retire as soon as the swell became felt. Captain Stewart looked like a man who had been very drunk overnight and had just waked up to a sense of his situation in the watch house. Mrs Yule was I am sure mentally singing Jenny Lind's farewell.

We had a fine breeze as soon as we got outside, and we have been bowling along six or seven knots ever since.

I saw the last of the land of Australia last night—a dark grey line along the horizon backed by as splendid a sky as ever the setting sun lighted up. We part friends, O land of gum trees. I have much, much to thank you for.

A nice swell has got up to-day. All the women, save Mrs Stanley, below, and all the children sick—thank God. Mrs Cr. I believe was heard to inform her daughter to-day that she did not think they should be able to make any noise for a week, for which we have also great reason for thanksgiving.

At sunset, the lookout man was specially ordered to turn his regards astern—he could see no sail and I think that now Capt. Yule begins to think himself safe and breathes easily.

May 4th.

Such a vile night—half a gale of wind—the ship rolling heavily and no sleep to be had. Oh the vile odour, oh the noises! Göthe in his account of the siege of Mayence enumerates fifteen distinct sets of noises he heard going on one sleepless night. I heard:

1. Creaking of bulkheads.
2. Washing of sea against ship's side.
3. Whistling of wind.
4. One two three—haul! of sailors.
5. Sailors tumbling down on the deck.
6. Cat miauling.
7. Dog slipping down companion headlong.
8. Puppies yelping.
9. Fowls cackling.
10. Ducks quacking.
11. Goats bleating or rather moaning as Australian goats do.
12. Pigs grunting and squeaking.
13. Officer of watch shouting.
14. Boatswains' mate piping.

15. Miscellaneous people swearing.
16. Child crying.
17. Sentry striking the bell.
18. Cockatoo screeching.
19. Parrots twittering.
20. Water washing ankledeep to and fro in my cabin and the after gunroom.

And I think with ingenuity and a little trouble, I could find some more.

The ladies all thoroughly done up—or rather down and invisible. I beg pardon, the Misses Crawford and McGillivray were seen, but decidedly under a cloud.—No fear of any fantasia for some time.

This is my twenty-fifth birthday. I ought to be up and doing in the world if ever I mean to do anything. Twenty-five to thirty-five is the "mezzo cammin".

Sunday 8th.

Blowing fresh and the ship rolling heavily. I cannot reconcile myself to this life at all—it is more repellent the oftener I am subjected to it—but courage, every day is one day less now. Last Sunday evening, how different!

Monday.

Fine easy-going weather. The infant phenomenon walking about. I am very much afraid she is getting over her seasickness.

Tuesday.

My worst fears were realized this afternoon. We all suffered severely from an attack of Crawford this afternoon, the good lady, not content with yelling fearfully herself, must needs give the infant phenomenon a lesson, and they shrieked in chorus.

The very dogs were frightened as the lady brought forth her high notes, and barked vociferously, while the cockatoo and parrot outside the cabin screeched aloud, doubtless fancying some brother in captivity had hailed him. Something must

be done. The middies got a fiddle and fife under way immediately, and produced a temporary diversion—but the remedy
was as bad as the disease.

And the spinet—oh the spinet!—They tell me that the
spinet is only part of a compound machine consisting of piano,
chest of drawers, and portable mangle all in one! and all for
six pound ten.

There are rumours of our going to Concepcion in Chili—a
new leak has been discovered in the stern-post which though
not dangerous keeps the bread-room damp, several bags of
biscuits are already spoilt. I don't want to stop anywhere—
bother the bread!

9th.

This morning one of our captains of the forecastle died.
The poor man wounded himself some days ago with the bone
of a piece of beef which was being served out to the ship's
company. It was but a scratch, but diffuse inflammation succeeded, and he died in spite of all we could do. These deaths
whose cause, course and tendency we know and yet fail in
stopping disgust me with physic! I always think, might not
something more have been done? am I not more or less guilty
of this man's death from want of knowledge? The responsibility of a physician is something fearful. We shall have two
or three more deaths before reaching England. It is distressing
to pass men and know that their doom is already fixed, they,
poor fellows, unconscious as sheep before the shambles.[1]

Captain Yule gave his first official Entertainment to-day!!
a Red day.[2]

One of my messmates made a remark to me which amazingly tickled my fancy, though I did not laugh. I was reading
Macaulay's *Essays* and he asked me with great simplicity
"whether they were written in opposition to *Channings*"!

Mrs Crawford appears by the sound to be in great pain at
this moment—8 o'clock p.m.

[1][An interesting comment on medicine before the days of Pasteur and Lister.]

[2]Yule, who had previously commanded the *Bramble,* was appointed to the
command of the *Rattlesnake* on Stanley's death, but not without a dispute
(pp. 245–6); this may have led to Yule's fear of being intercepted (p. 255).

11*th.*

Blowing a gale of wind right in our teeth these two days.
Quel [*sic*] horreur! Quel supplice! The gunroom and my
cabin flooded, the preserved meats sending forth the most dire
odours—and no sleep to be had, for me at least. Till this
afternoon, I have not had an hour's sleep for 48 hours, so
violently have we been rolling. Now it is nearly calm again,
and our miseries are somewhat mitigated. All the reasonable
people want to go into New Zealand to have this vile leak in
the after gunroom stopped, but Yule is afraid of being intercepted, I believe, and won't take a hint.

We are so quiet to-night that it is quite delightful, and I
look forward to a night's rest with the greatest satisfaction.
The last two I have spent, partly in reading a book, and
partly in looking over your journal, dearest. It amuses me
beyond measure, it is so Franziska-ish, but I get quite angry
now and then to find whole pages gone and never replaced.
You would never have done this, dear Menen, had you known
the delight every word affords me, and the consolation that
the record of even the little vanities you are so scrupulous
about, gives me.

May 13*th.*

This morning, Inskip and I, in accordance with some hints
we had received that such an application would be successful,
made a formal complaint of the state of the gun-room to the
commanding officer—who forwarded the matter to Yule.
There was a cabinet council immediately, and the result is that
we are to put in to the Bay of Islands, and do what can be
done to stop the leaks. I am very glad, not only because I wish
to see New Zealand, but because I shall be able to send a letter
to dear Menen.

Will she not be surprised at receiving a letter from me in
ten days or thereabouts?

A chum of poor Taylor's who was in contant attendance
upon him has sickened with, I fear, the same disorder. I fear
he has somehow or other become inoculated. He is a very good
man, and I am anxious about him.

On Thursday the 16th, we entered the Bay of Islands and

anchored off Point Kororareka. This is a little village rather than a town, consisting of a few houses and stores scattered along the beach; a church and Roman Catholic chapel are conspicuous on the side of the hill. The site is pretty enough, the long fern giving a greenness to the aspect of the country which makes up in some measure for its want of trees. The military are stationed quite away from the town at Wahpu. I did not visit their settlement. At the time of our visit, they were 160 strong.

Meat, potatoes, and honey are to be had at reasonable prices at Kororareka, everything else dear and bad. The place I fancy had hardly recovered from its sack by Heki five years ago.

There was a report of some fine falls to be seen some eleven miles off up the Kidi Kidi river, and a party was made up to go thither in the cutter. Brady and I wished to see as much as we could of the country, and so determined to get leave till Monday, and walk on to Waimate and the chief Missionary station wh. lies about 10 or 12 miles from Kidi Kidi.

The Kidi Kidi river is a small stream with usually high and hilly banks. We ascended to within about a couple of miles of the falls and then a small rapid which becomes a fall at low water obliged us to land. At this point, there is a sort of branch station with a large store. The Missionary at the station is the Rev. Mr Kemp, and the store is kept by his sons. Commodities are here kept to exchange with the natives for produce. The Missionary was away, but his son treated us with great civility and almost obliged us to make use of one of the rooms of his home to dine in.[1] He gave us a guide to the falls in the shape of a little Maori boy who took us through about three-quarters of a mile of as nasty a swamp as I ever traversed. It was absurd to see us floundering through it in single file, with our light-heeled unencumbered guide dancing on before us.

The fall was very pretty; much the same style of place as the Chamarelle, only not so grand, being not more than sixty feet, but then in compensation, there was a much larger body

[1]See L. & L. i, 52, where he refers to a Mr and Mrs Burrows as among the missionaries, and is agreeably surprised at their attitude. "I had expected a good deal of *straight-hairedness* (if you understand the phrase) and methodistical puritanism, but I find it quite otherwise."

of water. Underneath, the unceasing action of the spray has hollowed a large cave, where tradition says a great number of Maori were once slain. The floor and walls of the cave are covered with verdure, ferns, Marsileae, and numerous other small cryptogamic plants forming a thick carpet. A coating of green slime too renders the passage into the cave on this side by no means easy.

Friday, May 24?

To-day at twelve o'clock, we were only four miles to the W. of the line of 100°. We have long passed it now, and consequently we shall have to make to-morrow Friday the 24th as well as to-day, in order to get rid of our gained day.

I wonder whether you will be at the ball to-night, my dearest. I hope so, for it will serve to divert your mind.

May 27, between 8 and 9 P.M.

The moon very brilliant, but light showers are falling all around us. There was the most beautiful lunar rainbow I ever saw, a perfect arch, bright coloured, and about 20° high—outside this at a considerable distance was a faint second arch of about the same intensity of colour as the ordinary lunar bows.

Last night, I had a long walk up and down the deck with the doctor, and a very interesting conversation at the same time. Something was said about our paying off and the dispersion that would then take place. I said with one or two exceptions, I greatly rejoiced at the prospect, but I could not help adding that I trusted that our friendship was not to come to so speedy an end. I told him how much I was indebted to him for the good understanding that has always existed between us, and how much I felt the uniform delicacy with which he had treated me. I was glad of the opportunity of saying this much—for Thomson is one of the few men for whose friendship I care and whom I thoroughly esteem. I felt that my hot temper had not always permitted me to act with perfect justice towards him, and though we never quarrelled, I felt as I told him that that was more owing to his even and amiable disposition than to my deserts. There are few people to whom my pride would have let me say this much, but I was not disappointed in him. He met me halfway, and more than halfway, and I feel sure that he has a real friendship for me. I am very glad that this kind of explanation has taken place between us —I did not feel sure before that he really esteemed me, and I liked him too much to be at all comfortable under that notion. I have always looked upon him as a better man in every sense than myself. Better tempered, with more self-control, and with a more solid and practical if not a sharper intellect. I could not but be amused at his want of self-knowledge when he said "That although placed by the service as my superior, he had never forgotten that I had far the advantage in intellect and knowledge". Much as this flattered me, I felt in sorrow how untrue it was—and could not rest until I had put in a vehement disclaimer.

Is it a poor vanity, or a just pride in his good opinion, even though wrong, that has made me write this down?

We talked a great deal of Alice Radford and McClatchie. He evidently likes Alice very much from what he has seen of her, and looks upon her as thrown away. Acknowledging all Archie's good qualities, he dwelt strongly on the defects in his temper and the influence they would be likely to have on Alice's happiness. I stuck up for Archie as I best might, but could not help feeling there was some truth in what he said. One thing I do *not* believe. He said he thought McClatchie would forget her and break off the connection. I said I did not think such a thing likely, and furthermore that I hoped most sincerely he would not, for I looked upon Alice as a sister—and I should call him to a heavy reckoning. And so I would, as if he were my own brother.

But it is utterly improbable—I have too much confidence in Archie with all his faults to entertain the idea for a moment.

I laughed and said, What did he think I would do? And what he said I shall not tell you, little Menen, so don't be curious.

And then he talked about his wife, and I about mine. He said he would never have married a woman whom he did not think would make a good mother to her children and I agreed with him—and told him that though unmarried I could form a perfect judgment of what sort of mother my wife would make.

I told him that I had had the opportunity of watching a most interesting series of experiments on that very point and that while I laughed at Nettie for her attachment to a child, I was in truth anxiously watching how she managed it, how she made it at once love and obey her, and how I *knew* from what I had seen, that all my requirements would be satisfied, and that I should love the mother of my children even better than my dear mistress. How I envied him in my heart that he could speak of his child. I felt more than ever the bitterness of our separation. I should like to see his wife. I think she must be a very nice creature. She is well loved at any rate.

May 31.

I have been thinking much of what my plans are to be when we arrive in England. I shall go first to Sir William Burnett. I shall tell him that it is my wish to remain in England and if possible in London for a twelvemonth, for the purpose of publishing my papers, but I shall tell him that I cannot afford to lose a year's time and a year's pay. Therefore can he or will he manage the matter so that I may be nominally attached to some naval hospital or wards for that time. I on my side only ask this on condition that I can obtain from Owen, Herschel, Forbes and others, favourable opinions as to the value of my papers.

If he will do this for me I shall work up my book, and at the same time prepare for my second examination at the University of London, so as to take my M.B. there.

Perhaps I may go in for honours, and then there is a chance of £50 a year for two years.

Perhaps living in London may be a *poser*—but I think at any rate I can continue to be attached to a hospital—Armstrong managed that. If my plan of living in London succeeds, I shall make use of my privilege as a member of the service to see the practice of the best hospitals. And I shall take three or four months' dissection. This will bring me to the end of 1857? And what is to be done then? that is not so clear, but I hope *s'eclaircira* as we go along. At any rate, my dearest, we are no further off than we always expected to be at the end of 1857 (supposing Capt. Stanley had lived). And my position will be infinitely improved to what it would have been had I only then just returned.[1]

June 15. 12 P.M.

After fair westerly breezes, we have now had a calm for three days. It is cool but beautiful weather. I have just watched the moon set in all her glory, and looked at those lesser moons, the beautiful Pyrosoma, shining like white-hot cylinders in the water. We have had numbers about us every night.

June 23rd. Lat. 50 S., long. 97 W., about.

The weather has become bitterly cold and we have had several showers of hail and snow to-day for the first time. The cold is nipping me up into a sort of animated mummy and besides that I feel regularly done, by the mental excitement which I have had for the last three days.

M. thought fit most inexplicably to re-open our old quarrel, by demanding the copy of a note of mine to him, written last February.[2]

This was on the night of the 20th. I never was so surprised by anything in my life and I never remember being in such a paroxysm of rage as I was for some hours afterwards. The unparalleled effrontery of the man in thus insulting me made me furious. I absolutely shook, so that I could hardly write or speak. I was absolutely surprised at the violence of my own anger and the complete possession the passion took of me.

Luckily for me, however, it did not weaken my understanding, and I therefore not only refrained from committing myself in any way, but at once seemed to see almost instinctively the course I ought to take. The next morning, I carried the whole matter to the quarter deck, and requested Simpson to report it officially to Capt. Yule. By his direction, I then made a written statement of the circumstances of the case. I had reason to believe that M. contemplated trying what he could

[1]The fact that the curtailment of the expedition was of benefit to Huxley's career seems not to have been appreciated by his biographers.

[2]See *L. & L.* i, 30. M. and Huxley had quarrelled, and the ship's clerk had spread rumours concerning Huxley's conduct as treasurer of his mess before joining the ship: there had been trouble with the accounts, M. hinted, and an impending scandal was just averted. It was these quite baseless insinuations which so infuriated Huxley. See also pp. 63–4 and p. 83, footnote.

do by civil law against me and I therefore applied to Yule to cause him to make such written admission as would be amply sufficient for my justification.

The next day, Yule sent for both of us and stated that he, Dayman and Simpson had formed a committee for the purpose of inquiring into the statements I had made, of hearing what proof I had to offer, and finally of suggesting the proper course to be taken.

A regular inquiry was to be held, notes being taken of all the evidence. Failure would have been most unpleasant to me, and my energies were therefore kept regularly on the stretch —to licit such evidence as I wanted from the various witnesses, and to show that I had made no unreasonable demands. The enemy employed all his cunning to defeat me, but it was no good. I soon felt that I was more than his match, and I turned his flank on every point. After two days' investigation, the three gave their decision to-day. I felt so confident that I had convinced them (besides having the step suggested to me as a stroke of policy) that I offered to abide by Yule's decision whatever it might be—if M. would do so. He, with ill-disguised reluctance acceded—knowing how ill it would look if he did not—and the consequence is that every one of my statements was declared proved and he was obliged to sign and place in the hands of the Commander a written confession approved by me, of the infamous assertions he made respecting me and of his admission that they were false and unfounded. I on my part, promised, in return, never to apply for this document, unless he attacked me.

I did not expect to gain so complete a victory. All that he has gained by his insolent attack has been that whereas before the fact of his being a scoundrel rested on my ex parte statement, it now rests on evidence proved before and admitted to be satisfactory by three neutral persons—Lieutenants in the Service. No man ever more completely "went out for wool and came back shorn".

Furthermore, by admitting the finality of Capt. Yule's decision, he has put it out of his power ever to annoy me again. And to say the truth, I don't think he will much care ever again to try that on.

But I may say with old Pyrrhus, another such victory would

be a defeat. I am too excitable for this kind of work and I feel regularly knocked up.

I did not sleep a wink all last night and instead amused myself by reading through *Emily Wyndham*, which is a right good story in some respects.

24th.

Bitterly cold. I wore your beautiful comforter and wrist-bands to-day, my dearest Nettie, for the first time—I wore the comforter round my chest under my waistcoat and it kept my physical heart as warm as your letters keep my moral heart.

July 4th.

If we have any luck at all and keep our present wind we shall double the dread cape in the next twelve hours. The altitude of the sun to-day was only 9° 54′ and the day not seven hours long. It's desperately cold, a sharp southerly wind blowing and the thermometer down to 22°. It has not risen to thirty for the last three days and we have had frequent snow showers. It suits me better than I expected—I wrap myself up in your comforter and my great-coat, dearest, and walk up and down the deck for two or three hours during the day. By the bye, what delightful things those wrist-affairs are, and the neatness of their appearance has excited much admiration. A brig, the *Adelaide,* has been in sight all yesterday and to-day—to-day within two or three miles. She signalled her name, but there was some blunder about her last signal, and we don't know where she comes from. Curious the interest one takes in a stupid little brig we should pass with contempt anywhere else.

Mrs Stanley has been confined to her cabin by the cold and I have just looked in to see how she was getting on yesterday and the day before. She must be amazingly lonely there.[1] She is remarkably well informed and has a good literary taste so that I really derived a good deal of pleasure from my little conversation with her. The other day, I got her the *New*

[1] In a letter of July 12th to his mother (*L. & L.* i, 54) he mentions that he has taken Mrs. Stanley's "Bougirigards" (budgerigars) under his care during the cold weather.

Times from Simpson. I wish I could do her any other good turn, for apart from a liking I have for her, she has afforded me many an hour's pleasure by lending me Macaulay's *History*, and Lamartine's *Histoire des Girondins*, to say nothing of *Mary Barton*. I have just finished the last—and a fine novel it is. I must send it out to you, Menen. I can testify to the general truth of its descriptions of the working classes in manufacturing towns—their dialect and ways—from what I have seen myself in Coventry. Mrs Stanley tells me it is by a Mrs Gaskill [*sic*], wife of a lawyer near Manchester.

If any subject ever strongly excited your sympathies, dear Menen, you would write very well. Your letters, although you write as I would have you, without calculation and carelessly, tumbling one thought above another, are always good—good simple saxon expressing clearly your thoughts and feelings— and you are a capital hand at little bits of mischievous description. And some of your letters, dearest, are beautiful—letters where your little heart speaks out—dear letters, that I would shew to no-one.

Arrived at Falkland Islands—*Monday, 8th; and 9th.*[1]

Left Berkeley Sound—*July 25th.*

And then, I was laid up for ten days in my cabin with the mumps, which was running through the ship.

Then Sloss [?] took it, and of course I made him have my cabin, so that I had no place to write in for some 6 or 7 days more.

Which fully accounts, my darling, for the [half page blank here].

Aug. 7th.

To-day at noon we were nearly in the same position as on the 9th February 1847—crossed our tracks, and completed our circumnavigation.

[1] For Huxley's impression of these, see *L. & L.* i, 53, in a letter to his mother. "I never felt anything so bitterly cold in my life. . . . The only thing to do is to eat, eat, eat, and the cold assists one wonderfully in that operation. . . . By four o'clock it is dark night, and as it is too cold to read, the only thing to be done is to vanish under blankets as soon as possible and take twelve or fourteen hours' sleep."

Aug. 8th.

Spoke the *Phoenician* bound for Sydney and 44 days from England. I and some others went on board and sent a hurried note to Nettie.

Aug. 18th.

For sixteen days now have we had a wind more or less foul, and consequently we are little more than inside the tropics. It is possible we may have to go to St Helena for water—but I do not think that we shall do so if it is to be helped.

I long to be home—this voyage uncheered by the hope of seeing you at the end, dearest, seems more insupportable to me than even our long cruises. And yet I am going to my friends and ought to rejoice.

25th.

We got the Trade at last yesterday in lat 13°—and are now bowling along at a fine pace. We shall in all probability have to put in to Terceira, one of the Western Islands, for water.

I am not sorry to have the chance of a last look at bananas and orange-trees,—so as to go home with the tropical vegetation fresh in one's memory.

Aug. 30th.

Crossed the line in almost exactly the same longitude as we crossed it 3 years and 8 months ago.

Sep. 2nd.

The wind has come to the W. of S. to-day and yesterday but up to this evening there has been a good breeze. To-night, however, the wind has fallen light, and it begins to rain. We are in lat 9° 5′ at noon and so well to the east that they think of going to the Cape de Verde islands instead of the Azores.

Old Stewart is decidedly cracked. We shortened sail last night, perhaps not quite necessarily, but the little man thought fit to give vent to the loudest reproaches about the management of the ship, swore that the Commander was keeping the vessel out purposely, and that he would represent it at the Admiralty. All this he roared out, stamping up and down the poop, to the great amusement of some of us who were lounging about.

If I had been old Yule, I would have taught him a lesson about it. In a civilian, such a gross violation of decency would have been bad enough, but in a man holding rank in the service and acquainted with its spirit, the thing is altogether atrocious.

I hear that Simpson talked to him about it to-day, but got no satisfaction.

Sunday, Oct. 6th, 1850.

Dearest Menen, I have not talked to you for a long time, but this has not been for want of many, many thoughts of you. Let me see, it's a whole month since I have written a word—and we have now just left the Azores. In consequence of our usual luck—fine calm weather with light variable winds —our passage from the Falklands became very much lengthened, and our supply of water fell seriously short. We had to go on an allowance of 3 pints per diem for all purposes, which is but just sufficient for all our animal wants, and sadly diminished our small stock of comforts.

So it was determined to call at the Azores. Our first intention was to go to Terceira but Fayal was nearest, and we were glad enough to put in there.

At dawn last Sunday, we knew that we ought to see the great peak of Pico, one of the islands, which rises a sharp cone for near 8000 feet. I went on deck before dawn (such an extraordinary exertion was no great merit, for I was called up to see a sick man) and there sure enough, right ahead of us was Pico, a sharp peak, rising straight out of the sea some thirty miles off. As the sun rose behind it, nothing could be more glorious than it appeared, dark and majestic, and crowned with a beautiful and richly coloured garland of clouds. I thought to myself what a grand thing it would be to be up on the top of that about sunrise and formed a resolution that if possible there I would be before we left the Azores.

I did nothing but talk about it all that day—and found

plenty of people who promised they would go too. However, many were called but few chosen, as you will see by and bye. Soon we had a clear view of Fayal, which is comparatively low, and the island of St George which lies further away from Fayal than Pico. Then the Magdalen rocks came in sight and finally we came to an anchor off the town of Horta (Fayal) about four in the afternoon.

I did not go ashore then, but looked after the commissariat. The people brought off lots of eggs at a very cheap rate, and vast quantities were immediately consumed on board.—There is something perfectly animal and filthy in one's ravenous appetite on first coming into harbour.

As for the town, it looked like all the Portuguese towns I have ever seen—very white and clean-*looking* with various churches and convents in a most hideous style of architecture.

The party returning from the shore reported that there was nothing to be seen—only the English consul was very polite and hospitable and had a very pretty unmarried daughter. Of course I thought it would be expedient to pay my respects at the earliest opportunity, especially as I was very desirous to ascertain the feasability [sic] of getting up the Pico. So I called the next morning and saw the consul Mr Minchin, a very kind and polite old military gentleman, and the daughter Miss Minchin—pretty enough but not much to my taste—and another daughter Mrs Creagh, not so pretty but much handsomer. I fell *in friendship* with her at first sight and she quite justified my instinct—turning out to be a most agreeable, kind, ladylike creature. Then there was her husband, a young major—unattached, and decidedly a fast man, but a gentleman withal, and whom I found a most essential adjunct to the Pico scheme.

The consul was a painter, and we talked about painting, and to my horror he asked me to bring my sketches ashore and come and dine with him. And I went and dined—and exhibited —and "snaked" myself into Mrs Creagh's good graces, while Simpson (tell it not in Gath) and Brady flirted with pretty Miss Nelly.

I have come to the conclusion, my dear Menen, that there must be something in my peculiarly ugly phiz which inspireth great confidence in woman-kind—a sort of old-man expression

—inasmuch as it has more than once happened to me, to be consulted by them within four and twenty hours after I had first had the honour of their acquaintance. So it was in the present case. Mrs Creagh had come out from England in a very debilitated state, and was not thoroughly recovered, and I had to put on additional gravity in order to listen to her complaints. I was very glad to have it in my power to do her some good, what between physic and lancet.

I have stated all this for your especial rumination, wicked one, inasmuch as you used, I remember, to treat my professional dignity with great slight. But that's just it, "a prophet hath no honour in his own country".

You will only be jealous if I tell you how one taught the sisters the Schottische—how one used to dine at the consul's every night and then practise it, and how much fun one had— so I won't say a word more about it. I will only tell you how I persuaded Nelly that your hair was "Australian Silk" and how, when Mrs Creagh gave me a very beautiful bouquet at parting, I told her it was lucky that the owner of the Australian silk did not see it.

Well they were most kind hospitable people, and I assure you I was quite sorry to leave our friends of six days' standing, when in spite of all Nelly's pretty persuasion, old Yule stolidly determined on sailing last Saturday.

While we were at Fayal, an Italian gentleman, Signor Augustin Robbio, a violinist, brought a letter of introduction to the consul—and one evening was kind enough to give us a specimen of his playing at the consul's home. I was very much pleased with his musical powers—as far as I can judge, they were of a high order. He visits England I believe in the Spring.

The American consul, Mr Datney, was very civil to us. His family was in some affliction as one of his sons had married the favourite daughter of that unhappy man Professor Webster [?] who was hanged the other day. I did not see her, but I am told that she is a clever person of great musical talent, but very apathetic. She seems to care nothing for the horrible catastrophe which has befallen her father. When her husband broke the news of the murder to her, she listened very quietly and when he had done only said "what an unfortunate occurrence". I think that is the sublime of bathos. I should have boxed her ears had I been her husband—I love a snow-house but not an iceberg.

But I have not yet told you about the ascent of the Pico— and that I shall leave for another time, as it is the middle of the night, blowing a gale of wind right in our teeth and the ship nearly pitching us under. Addio, little one. I shall read some of your journal. October 9th, 1850.

Oct. 13*th.*

The Party "what went up the Pico" consisted of Dunbar, Capt. Stewart, Tighe, Heath, Major Creagh, a half-Portuguese who spoke English very well, and myself. I had been ashore at Fayal all the morning of Thursday the day we started, and was half tempted not to go. The consul wanted me to dine with him, and I had once submitted to the lot in the shape of tossing, which decided against me. However, my invincible dislike to give up any project once formed was too much for me, and off I started for the ship at about two o'clock. Now two o'clock was fixed as the latest hour we were to start—but I got on board and dressed appropriately and still found plenty of time, greatly rejoiced after all at not giving up a resolution. Stewart was fretting and fussing away after the grub, Creagh talking to everybody all at once with incredible volubility, Dunbar ditto, Tighe snuffling, Heath quiet and resolute as usual and looking after proviant and requisites, very much in earnest—and it was nearly four before we left the ship for Pico, about five miles distant.

I began to laugh when we left the ship, and I don't think that I left off for about six hours. Such a queer trio as Dunbar, Creagh and Stewart I never had the luck to meet with before. After sundry ridiculous disputes as to navigation, we reached the town, dashing up through some heavy rollers which threatened to swamp us. Ourselves and our traps landed, any rational people would have commenced travelling, as we had some twelve miles to go to the proposed resting place, and the sun was near setting. But not we. First and foremost we went and took possession of an empty house the proprietor of which had kindly given us his key.

Then there was a great question about animals, Stewart and Dunbar protesting they would not and could not walk a mile. None were to be had, however, but there were hopes entertained that the priest who lived up at the other end of the long straggling town might be persuaded to lend a horse.

So, attended by all the population, who looked at us with faces not unlike those of an English mob round a Cherokee Indian, we trudged on. We had a tail of seven or eight Portuguese to carry our luggage and altogether formed quite a procession.

We had not gone very far before Creagh called a halt opposite one house and said we must go and see his friend one Signor Teira, a rich proprietor. So up we went and sitting on a sort of terrace devoured fruit while M. Teira was being found. While thus engaged a most ridiculous scene took place in the shape of a quarrel between Stewart and Dunbar, the former abusing the latter in the most unmeasured terms for certain improprieties. Poor Stewart, he lost his breath; he might as well have talked to a post. There was a rich, comic, stolid expression on his adversary's face all the while, beautiful to behold. It nearly killed me laughing, when at the end of Stewart's tirade, his reply consisted merely in mimicking the three last words thereof. The cream of the joke was that old Stewart was just as bad as the other himself.

Creagh is decidedly a "fast man", but this little scene rather palled on him and he asked me quietly if this style of conversation was common among naval officers. I rather enlightened him on that point, by assuring him that the two in this case quite understood one another. In fact they were excellent friends again in half an hour.

By and bye Signor Teira, a pleasing gentlemanly young man, made his appearance with a lot more Portuguese gentlemen. We must taste his wine, and very good it was, the second bottle especially was I think the most delicious Port I ever tasted. Imported direct from Lisbon and unadulterated it is quite a different thing from the fiery abomination you get in England.

The sun set apace, and at last we started again. A great deal of time was now lost in embassages to the Padre, who is a man not to be lightly treated in Portuguese places. Hopes were beginning to be entertained of bringing the matter to a successful issue, when Creagh swore a big swear that he wouldn't wait any longer and if anybody would come with him he would start sans guide sans provisions and sans everything. We who meant to go to the top, to wit, Heath, Tighe, and myself, immediately seconded the motion and off we went leaving the others to follow when they pleased. Creagh had a very indefinite idea of the road, which lies between high stone fences, built up of blocks of lava, but he knew there were two old ruined houses on the right hand side about seven miles off and insisted greatly on that point! Furthermore he was very particular in taking a compass bearing of the peak, the utility of which measure was not clear to any one but himself, inasmuch as we had to follow a road, not to go across country. Cross-country, indeed—it would puzzle all the steeple-chasers in or about Melton to manage that. The face of the country is cut up by high lava walls as I have told you with narrow lanes between them. These walls enclose fields or rather vineyards, but the vines are not grown on poles, but on stone fences of just the same character as the walls, running in parallel lines about four feet apart right across the field, so that the fields, as the vines did not cover the fences, had very much the look of immense currycombs.

However, no wise discouraged we started off at a sporting pace and walked (with a few stoppages for consultations as to the "diritta via" and a few doublings and returns not worth mentioning) some three or four miles. It was now dark. We neither heard nor saw anything of our friends, and beginning to entertain some not altogether unfounded doubts of the correctness of our course, we betook ourselves to the next cottage to inquire if our friends had not passed. The courteous old Portuguese peasant made us at home with much politeness, brought us fruit, and then his wife brought out a picturesque lamp dangling from a tripod and the little daughter made big eyes at us out of the dark shade within the house—we were a most picturesque party.

Well, we waited and waited, but no one came. We were too grand to go back, and having received some assurances (half understood, for not one of us could understand a dozen words of Portuguese) that we were in the right track we

started again. We trudged on, frequently looking back to catch a glimpse of the lights of our party (sometimes fancying we saw them) for about four miles—shin-breaking work it was too, and chill withal. At last we reached the Major's house, which however turned out most unaccountably to be on the left side of the road, and here were determined to wait, especially as it was beginning to rain smartly and we had no covering and no water. The house was miserable and half unroofed. Some of the thatch made us a fire, and at the imminent risk of our heads, no plaster or mortar being employed in Pico architecture, we dislodged a rude rafter for firewood. Then we set fire to the bush outside and, not knowing what mischief we might be doing, took infinite pains to put it out again.

Finally, when the rain pattered through the thatch and a couple of hours had elapsed, we began to abuse our companions for leaving us in the lurch. Firewood began to run short, and we had debates worthy of an American Congress as to the propriety of "annexing" the door of the hut, but considerations of justice I am happy to say prevailed. Then we held a council of war, and as we all agreed that nothing could be done without the commissariat, we determined on marching down hill again. A bitter resolution this was, and many were the anathemas on our friends below. We had not gone very far, however, before we saw a light below us and rejoicing in the arrival of our party we all rushed back to the hut, determined not to let them know our misgivings. We waited patiently some time, and at last appeared a single Portuguese with a lantern. All he had to say was "You come back—signors not come". Fancy how cantankerous we got, how *mürrend* we descended, and how John Portugal got small thanks. But again we had not proceeded half a mile before we saw more lights and had in answer to our cooee a loud hail; this time it was our veritable tail, commissariat and all. Such a rich procession, first various flambeau bearers; then Dunbar *à pied*, trudging laboriously up the hill; then Stewart *à cheval*, on a little beast of a pony and looking for all the world like Silenus; then a whole troop of blackguards carrying tent and tentpoles, baskets of fruit, water, etc. etc.

The delay had been all about the Padre's horse, but we soon forgot all about that, in the imbibition of certain liquids round our fire. But we were not allowed to rest here, our guide telling us that we must go further on, so we formed again and marched two or three miles further—up hill continually—till we reached some empty cottages, after the same style as that we had left. It was now nine or ten o'clock and as we who meant to go up (Stewart and Dunbar had long before declared their intention of waiting for us at the first resting place) determined to see the sun rise from the peak, we had not more than an hour to spare.

Stewart was constituted cook and immediately set to work upon a stew, which being concocted was put on a fire outside, one of us mounting guard to see that our Portuguese friends did not make free with its savoury contents.

Heath brewed a pot of tea, inside. Dunbar lay on his back and did nothing but make us laugh, and Creagh was afflicted with a continual succession of small angular lumps of lava wh. *would* run into his back. The "Portugals" carried it clearly written on their faces that they thought us a party of mad Englishmen. And I don't wonder at it.

Having greatly comforted and refreshed our inward man, the five of us—to wit, Creagh, Heath, Tighe, Lane and myself, with our guide and three or four Portuguese bearers—proceeded on our journey. The road now became nothing but the bed of a dry torrent, and even with our torches required much circumspection. Still we walked continually between the high lava walls. On, on—I never had such a queer walk. Then we marched through a queer long cleft in the rock some thirty feet deep, and not more than two wide, with perpendicular sides all overhanging with fern. Up, up continually. At last we came to a clear space, without fences, where "the difficult air of the mountain top" blew freely on our faces. Here we walked over a springy turf, saturated with moisture. The Peak looked quite close, black and frowning. And as for us we seemed mere pigmies in the wide spaces. Odd basin-shaped cavities of old craters were lit up fantastically as we crossed, our shadows thrown long and weird on the smooth turf. At one place was a pool of water, the last we should meet with we were told, and we took the opportunity to refresh. Still we ascended until we came to a low wall with a wicket gate, and here we were told it was no use going any further as we should probably break our necks if we went on without the moon's light. Creagh's energy on this and like occasions was something delightful. He gesticulated and sputtered in Portuguese English and gave them to understand that we were a kind of people who rather took a pleasure in breaking our necks, if it so pleased us, that we were very different from them—d——d Portuguese as they were—and that go on we would. Eventually the dispute was compromised into an hour's rest. So we gathered heather for our beds and each wrapping himself up in his plaid or coat, went peacefully to sleep. In about an hour I woke and I was just looking at the Great Bear and wondering if I had really slept an hour, when Creagh who was close to me sang out, "I say, Doctor, time to start; haven't you been snoring!", immediately jumping up and beginning to bully the Portuguese, which seemed to be a great relief to his excitable feelings. It was now about two o'clock. All our worst climbing was before us, but we were in capital order, and worked on in capital style.

The rarefaction of the air began to give one a little uneasiness about the throat, but that was merged in the satisfaction of being so high up, and after one or two rebellions on the part of the guides, which were greeted by Creagh's eloquent appeals to their fears, cupidity, or jealousy as the case might be, the first grey of dawn found us not above a mile from the base of the crater. But here we left Lane, the half-Portuguese; he said he had a pain in his legs and gave up without a struggle. We left him to make his way back, the Major taking occasion to draw a great moral on the comparative endurance of English and Portuguese.

We reached the base of the crater and it was still dawn. We were all in high spirits and I had just remarked that I felt as little tired as when I started, when I found myself seized with a sudden attack of my old enemy, palpitation of the heart, so bad that I was obliged to lie down. Stand I could not in spite of all my efforts, so I told them to go on, that I should be well presently and would join them, as I believed I should. However, there I stuck for about a couple of hours, unable to make any exertion, and cursing my stars at being thus balked.

We had ascended on the west side of the Peak too, so that there was no chance of my absolutely seeing the sun rise, and

I began to be rather disgusted. But I was amply repaid for all my trouble as the sun rose. Where I was, was more than 7000 feet above the sea, within 6 or 700 feet of the top of the Peak, so that had I reached the top my view would not have been perceptibly more extensive. How can I describe to you the glory of the scene. Far—thousands of feet—below me lay a huge mass of fleecy white clouds, gorgeously tinged here and there as they caught the rays of the sun. In the midst of them was an opening, and there lay framed the island of Fayal. From the great distance of the horizon, sea and sky were melted into one grey mass, and Fayal looked like an exquisite little painting on a rich grey ground. And then as the light increased you might spy the ship, a mere speck in the bay of Orta, and in the channel between the islands a white spot here and there, which you knew and yet could hardly believe was a boat's sail. I never shall forget it as long as I live. I had my sketch book in my haversack but it would have been presumption in Titian and Claude and Turner if they could have been rolled into one to attempt to depict such a sight. Furthermore my condition was not exactly favourable to artistic pursuits.

My reverie over the sunrise had been somewhat interrupted by the importunity of two Portuguese boys who had been left behind with me, and who not understanding the good cause I had to be quiet, were continually shouting to me to "cōme on, you". I felt a morbid desire to break both their heads. As I would not ascend, they began to descend while shouting to me to "cōme on, you", but as descending was as difficult to me as ascending I remained where I was, until I became sufficiently recovered as to crawl along a little way towards my tormentors. As I did this I suspect in rather a lame, tumbledown sort of manner, it seemed at length to enter their stupid heads that there might be something wrong and one came back to me. By way of explaining, I took his hand and put it upon my heart which was going pit-a-pat at a great rate. He felt it with a great air of commiseration and then gradually sliding his hand over the other side, to my astonishment I found his finger sliding into my waistcoat pocket, where my spare cash lay. I gave my friend to understand that this was not quite correct, and then made him help me down to his companion who was some distance below us with a keg of wine, just the thing I wanted.

When I reached this worthy, I demanded wine at once, but deuce a bit could I get until I handed over a six-pence a drink. I was angry at the impertinence of the blackguard but as I was not exactly in a position to quarrel with him I acceded to his demand. The keg was pulled away each time and not given back till the demand "You give shilling" was complied with. The best of the joke was we had bought the wine so that it was absolutely mine.

I got much better with the wine and wrapping myself up had a doze until the three who went to the top, Heath, Creagh and Tighe, returned. They had had a hard climb, and had not seen very much more than I, though that did not much alleviate my disgust at my shortcoming.

We began to descend, and on our way I told Creagh as rather a good joke what had befallen me with my friends the boys. He was mightily wroth and threatened great things. (He had had occasion to knock down one gentleman after we parted.) I begged of him to take no notice of the affair and I thought it was all over, but it was not, as you will hear in the end.

When we reached the hut where we left Stewart and Dunbar on the previous night, the former had according to his agreement prepared us a grand breakfast of eggs and milk and Irish stew. I sat and drank and then being regularly knocked up went fast asleep inside the hut.

In the meanwhile Creagh had informed Stewart of the conduct of the boys, and he most outrageously proceeded at once to administer naval justice upon the unfortunate principal delinquent.

Being rather too fat and short-winded to perform such a feat himself, he bribed a Portuguese who was standing by and who was a sort of constable in the village, with a couple of shillings, to catch the culprit. Then he had him "seized up" nautical fashion and with a cob made up by himself for the occasion he administered personally a preliminary dozen lashes, with a will I have no doubt, then getting tired he handed over the cob to the constable and by the aid of the universal persuader, a shilling, got *him* to give the remaining three dozen, contenting himself with merely superintending. It was a tolerable cool proceeding in a foreign country and I wonder they did not give him a touch of the knife, but I suppose they looked upon us as "those mad Englishmen who always have pistols about them".

I should have put a stop to the whole affair had I been conscious of it, but I was unfortunately in a dead sleep the whole time.

We got on board again without further adventures, by about four o'clock, so that our whole expedition had not taken us more than 24 hours. I dressed, went ashore, dined at the consul's and afterwards danced schottisches and polkas with his daughters, not getting on board again till about 1 o'clock in the morning.

I did not feel at all tired until a day or two afterwards, and then not much.

On Saturday they had got up a very pleasant excursion for us into the country, but old Yule, bother him, would not stop and we sailed about two o'clock on that day. I really felt quite sorry to part with our friends, particularly Mrs Creagh (don't be jealous!)—there was so much genuine kindness, apart from mere civility, about them. But such is our life in the Service.

We had a splendid westerly gale for two days, and fully expected to have been in England last Sunday (the 18th) but (our luck!) it suddenly dropped and most unaccountably a strong E. gale sprang up in our teeth. This lasted, abating in violence, until yesterday, when a light westerly wind again sprang up, and now bids fair to carry us home. I do not now wish that word—home—from my heart, dearest. I did four years ago. But now I feel most truly, that where you are there is my true home. There is where all my loves and all my anxieties are centered. Those whose care and affection reared me into manhood seem but as aliens, compared with you. The scenes of my childhood and youthhood seem but as strange compared with dear old Holmwood, and the bush paths where we twain have walked hand in hand. Why is this? Your heart will tell you.

.   .   .   .   .

Here ends Huxley's Diary. However, I append two items. The first is trivial enough—the tailor's bill for Huxley's naval get-up, which was found among some miscellaneous papers— but it helps to round out the picture of the young Assistant Surgeon as he set out on his voyage. Here it is:

T. H. Huxley Esqre, Asst. Surgeon R.N.
London, *April 7th,* 1846
DR to G. & W. H. GILLOTT,
Tailors and Habit Makers
No. 36, Strand.

1846		£	s.	d.
Mar. 16th.	A Superfine Blue Full Dress Coat	6	10	–
	A do. Undress do.	4	10	–
	A do. do. Jacket	2	4	–
	2 fine White Cashmere Waistcoats	2	–	–
	A fine Blue Cashmere Waistcoat		18	–
	2 prs Blue Trousers	3	8	–
	A Cocked Hat with bullion loop Tassels	4	10	–
	A Japanned Case for do.		10	6
	An Uniform Cap 1 in. band	1	2	–
	A rich gilt town-made Sword	4	–	–
	A rich gold Sword Knot		15	6
	A rich Embroidered Full Dress Belt	1	18	–
	A Patent leather Undress do.	1	–	–
	An Airtight Japanned Suit Case with lock and key and brass name plate engraved	1	–	–
	An Oiled Silk Cover for Cap		5	–
	12 Huckabac Towels		15	–
	3 Black Silk Cravats		18	–
	A Stout deal Chest with Padlock, etc.	3	18	–
	Pewter fittings and Water Can		17	6
	12 Boxes of Blacking		6	–
	3 Shoe Brushes		4	6
	6 lbs Soap		3	6
	Marking Towels		1	–
24th.	A rich Bullion Epaulette	2	10	–
	A do. Strap	1	8	–
	A Japanned Case		4	–
	An Embroidered Crown for Cap		6	–
		£46	2	6

$7\frac{1}{2}$ p. cent for cash.

The second, here reproduced in facsimile, is the quotation inscribed by Huxley on the inside back cover of the notebook containing the Diary. It is so intensely characteristic of his attitude of mind throughout his active life that I can think of no fitter end to this volume.

"Thätige Skepsis"

"An active Scepticism is that which unceasingly strives to overcome itself and by well directed Research to attain to a kind of Conditional Certainty."

Appendix

ATFER this volume had been set up in page proof, I received a letter from Mr. J. Richardson, of Edinburgh, saying that he possessed several unpublished letters written, shortly after the return of the *Rattlesnake* to England, by my grandfather to Dr. Thomson, the ship's doctor, of whom he speaks so admiringly in several places in the Diary, and a number written by Dr. Thomson to his wife during the voyage itself. By his courtesy and that of Mrs. Richardson, of North Berwick, daughter of Dr. Thomson, and of the Executors of the late Professor J. Arthur Thomson, I am able here to reproduce the most interesting passages in their correspondence.

I will begin with those from Huxley's pen. They cast an interesting light on the difficulties he experienced in getting his scientific papers published by the Admiralty (p. 3; and *L. & L.* i, 55–60, 71–75), his unsuccessful application for a Professorship at Toronto (p. 3; *L. & L.* i, 77ff.), and his early election to the Royal Society. They also show that Huxley's friendly relations with MacGillivray had come to an end; his attitude now was one of dislike and all but contempt. They further illustrate Huxley's keen interest in any and every scientific point arising from the voyage, as evinced by his letter of December 10th, 1851, concerning the mysterious epidemic experienced on the homeward voyage; and finally contain some good examples of his epistolary style.

41 North Bank
Regent's Park
Dec. 4th, 1850

My dear Doctor,

You will be glad to hear that yesterday I took up my appointment to the *Fisguard* with six months' leave, renewable at the end of that period.[1]

---

[1] The *Fisguard* was at Woolwich, and the duties of the appointment were nominal: *L. & L.* i, 56.

I got it chiefly I think in consequence of a letter which Owen was kind enough to volunteer to write to the First Lord on my behalf. As to publication, I am pretty certain of a portion of the Royal Society's money—and besides I have the Royal, Linnean and Zoological Society's *Transactions* open to me, the "Men in Authority" professing their willingness to insert anything of mine.

One of the papers I sent home has been very well published in the *Phil. Trans.* for 1849. I wd. send you a copy if I knew how, without its costing you in carriage a great deal more than it is worth.

If people would only let me alone, and not invite me out to dinners and parties, I should be getting on very well—but I find the world altogether "too . . . hotitiful".

I see a great deal of Fanning's people. They are a most agreeable set, particularly as they have fairly inducted me one of the family.

I have hardly expected to hear from you yet (notwithstanding your promise) and I would not even now disturb your quiet home happiness were it not that I ought to send in my certificates from you, and that any further delay will look like neglect. Can you spare an hour to write them for me?

I would give something to see you with the infant Hercules, if you get into a green field together. I hope he has learnt by this time to have a due reverence and affection for his stranger papa.

I almost feel as if I had a right to send my kind regards to Mrs Thomson, but I leave that to your discretion,

And remain,

Yours ever,

T. H. HUXLEY

My brother and sister desire their very kind remembrances.

41 NORTH BANK
REGENT'S PARK
Jany. 27th, 1851

MY DEAR DOCTOR,

Old Yule has written to me (as he does not know your address) to forward the enclosed. He has asked me to read it and give my opinion. My answer is "Scott is not going to Hospital—acted entirely upon his own discretion and is responsible for his own acts.

"The probabilities were, when we were paid off, that he would be well in a few days and Dr. Thomson, of course, advised him in accordance with the probabilities.

"He took the doctor's advice, but had he persisted in going to Hospital, of course he could have done so."

The old man is in a funk for fear he should be called upon to give some explanation—though what he has to do with it I don't very clearly see.

I can't forbear sending a sketch of the old gentleman as he will probably appear when called upon for an explanation.

Suckling dined with us yesterday. He is in fine feather and looks as if he meant to live to ninety.

Dayman is going out to the Cape of Good Hope—there to take charge of certain surveying operations. I suppose they will give him his step when he has been out some time.

I dined with Brady and his lady-love the other day—she seems a nice quiet person.

Did you ever hear anything so ridiculous as the attempts what have been made to make him out a Don Juan? I hear you bore testimony to his having never left the moral pedestal. . . .

. . . Simpson I hear nothing of. McGillivray is in town working at his book. I see him occasionally—*on business* only.

Yours faithfully,

T. H. HUXLEY

41 NORTH BANK
Feby. 5th, [1851]

MY DEAR DOCTOR,

. . . I sent your note on to old Yule; whether he has received it or not I cannot say, as he has not had the good manners to acknowledge it.

The old gentleman is Lt. Yule still—promotion cometh not from the East nor from the West for him, but I believe he is to have the next ship that is given.

You should have seen him the other night at the Geographical Society —pointing out the charts with a long stick. They were all being exhibited apropos of a letter of Capt. Stanley's to the Secretary sent from Cape York, and containing the abstract of results which you remember he made McGillivray give him.

Yule and Dayman were there per order of Adml. Beaufort to exhibit. McGillivray read his paper, and I looked on, and laughed.

I get asked all sorts of questions about the latter by people, and have to keep my tongue within my teeth as much as possible. He is not the man whose praises one can dilate upon.

I saw Mrs Chas. Stanley a few days ago; she is I think getting better. She is always the same, and is I believe really glad to see me. But the old lady seems to me to be inclined to be patronising, and as I don't put up with that from anybody, I have uniformly declined the invitations I have received—foolish pride, you will say—but I am too poor to afford to be meek.

You do not tell me if there is anything I can do for you up in this great Babylon,—if there is you know how happy I shall be to be your commissioner; but perhaps you had better give that message to Mrs Thomson, I am sure my sister would be delighted to be of any service. Deuce knows how—that is a mystery above me—only I know that ladies in the country are frequently glad to have a London Commissioner.

I have had no news from Australia for an age.

Ever yours,

T. H. HUXLEY

Dr. Thomson.

41 NORTH BANK
April 27th, 1851

MY DEAR DOCTOR,

. . . Do you not mean to come up and bring Mrs Thomson to see the Great Exhibition? I should like very well to see the opening of it but I positively can't afford three pounds for a season ticket when I should most probably only go once or twice.

25,000 season tickets have been already issued so they won't miss me. Why don't you exhibit some of your Calotypes?[1] It might do you good when you take to the peripatetic cart we used to talk about.

As to my own affairs—they are progressing very favourably—not much in the direction of pudding possibly, but well enough in the way of praise.

I don't think I told you that I was a candidate for the F.R.S. this year. About 2 or 3 years ago they made some new regulations by which admission was rendered far more difficult than it used to be and I should not have dreamt of putting my name up if I had not understood that the having a paper printed in their *Transactions* was one of the best claims. When I found this was the case I got my very kind friend Forbes to get up my certificate. There were 38 candidates, out of whom the council, by the new rules, had to select 15—and somewhat to my surprise though I must confess greatly to my gratification I hear that I am one of the "segregated."[2]

The election of these happy few takes place as a matter of course in June.

The only drawback is that it will cost me fourteen pounds. I hope however to make it worth the money.

I find my brother's house is not a house of work but quite the reverse —so I am going to migrate to a den of my own—

No 1 Hanover Place,
Clarence Gate,
Regent's Park.[3] . . .

41 NORTH BANK
June 8th, 1851

MY DEAR DOCTOR,

You will I know be glad to learn that I have just been elected an F.R.S. and can now sport a tail to my name. Isn't that a privilege? However, it goes down with the world and I hope some day to turn it to advantage.

The *Voyage of H.M.S.* has not yet appeared. I have been so bothered about the book with inquiries about its coming out, that I took the trouble the other day to make inquiries of the fountainhead—the primary mud-volcano himself—about it. He tells me that it is to appear in the middle of July.

[1]An early photographic process: sometimes called "Talbotypes" after the inventor.

[2]For further details see *L. & L.* i, 67.

[3]"Which sounds grand, but means nothing more than a sitting-room and bedroom in a small house" (*L. & L.* i, 65).

He has been getting into all sorts of messes, quarrelling with his publisher, dawdling over his work, until he has got into difficulties.

I am told that old Suckling beat up his quarters lately and was so struck with the condition of distress in which he found him as to leave £5 for him. Is it not like the old man?

The Royal Society has refused to give me any portion of the Grant—entirely as a matter of principle. They say it is too bad for the Government to try to put the publication of the work of their own offices on to the Royal Society's shoulders, and that if this is what they mean by their grant of £1000, agree they may just take it back again.

I believe it will turn out all the better for me—as some of the principal men offered to back any application of mine to the Treasury with their personal influence.

My first six months of leave is up (who could believe it?) and I have applied to have it renewed indefinitely on condition of my reporting progress every six months.

Sir William[1] was civility itself the last time I saw him.

Don't you mean to come up to town and see the great Exhibition of Exhibitions? You will repent it all your life if you do not. It is a sight which it has not yet entered into the imagination of man to conceive. . . .

No. 1 Edward St.
St. John's Wood Terrace
July 27th, [1851]

My dear Doctor,

Since I wrote you last I have been down at Ipswich attending a meeting of the British Association—as I daresay you will have seen if you have looked over the reports of the proceedings in the *Literary Gazette* or *Athenaeum.*[2] For my own part, I went down not by any means to advance science, but to be "advanced" myself—by getting the Association as a body to recommend Govt. to publish my work. This they have agreed to do, and so I shall be backed by all the scientific influence that is to be obtained, viz., by the Royal Society and British Association conjointly.

It is curious that the only two recommendations of grants from Govt. to individuals, made by the British Association, should have been to Asst. Surgeons in the Navy. The other was to Hooker, who is just married.

[1]Sir William Burnett, Director-General of the Navy Medical Service: see *L. & L.* i, 23.

[2]See *L. & L.* i, 72. Huxley also enjoyed himself there, at the celebrated Red Lion Club (*L. & L.* i, 91).

I have no doubt now about obtaining what I want—from the Treasury. The Admiralty have nothing to do with it, thank Heaven.

I have great thoughts of applying for a Professorship of Natural History vacant at Toronto. It is worth at least £300 a year and that is nearly as good as £500 over here. Unless they use private interest against me I am pretty sure of getting it—as I have all the bigwigs here with me. It would be a great deal better than the service.

Do you know anything about Toronto? I know you have been in those parts.

I am busy over the illustrations of my book at present. If they publish it as I wish there will be about 20 plates, the size of the *Philosophical Transactions*.

I don't propose to be under anybody's patronage unless the Government choose to consider their grant as such—and I mean to write a concise preface, setting forth without malice or extenuation, in the quietest but most forcible way in the world, the mode in which the Admiralty act up to their professions as set forth in the preface to their *Manual*. I will try if I cannot make the way clearer for those who may follow after me.

MacGillivray has deceived every one, as might have been expected— Boone complains bitterly to me about him—and with great justice. Boone has advanced him £50 on the book, and can neither get that repaid nor can get the conclusion of the book out of him. I have done all I can, but McGillivray has lied to me so thoroughly, that I am altogether disgusted.

At the same time, the whole matter is so completely one of private contract between Boone and McGillivray that I do not see how any one can interfere, more efficiently.

I have not now the slightest faith that the book will come out at all— and if it does the name of that disreputable scamp will be enough to damn it. . . .

                                        I am,
                                      Ever yours,
                                        T. H. HUXLEY

                                        4 UPPER YORK PLACE
                                          ST. JOHN'S WOOD
                                          Dec. 10th, [1851]

MY DEAR DOCTOR,
    "Expectans expectavi"—I waited for the calotypes and they didn't come—so my project of killing two birds with one stone, *i.e.* thanking you for them and answering your letter, is defeated. Do you ever intend to publish or make any use yourself of the notes of our marvellous

"Dopo" epidemic? I mean that which began with the death of poor Taylor.[1] I have mentioned the circumstances of that disease to several people of eminence (Carpenter and others) and they all strongly advise the publication of its details. Now, as I tell them, any account of it must come from you and not from me as a matter of etiquette, to say nothing of my having no notes.

Now are you disposed to take the trouble of drawing up a paper on the subject, for the Epidemiological Society, or one of the Journals? I almost fancy I hear a very decided negative—and if so, have you any objection to let me have your notes and draw up a history of the disease in your name? I will then see that it is properly published. It seems to me much more proper that anything of the kind should be in your name rather than mine, but if you have any scruples on that point it can be in both.

Of course if you will do it yourself so much the better.

You ask me about the emoluments of Toronto. The paid salary is £350 a year Toronto currency, wh. I believe is about £300 Sterling, besides fees. This is better than anything I am likely to get in the service for the next ten years, to say nothing of the balance of comfort and satisfaction. The out-of-the-way-ness of it is the great drawback—but with the rapidly improving facilities for communication, that is perhaps not so great a bugbear as it looks.

I hope you have seen McGillivray's book. It is very creditable I think. Tell me what you think of the illustrations—they have murdered mine in the engraving. . . .[2]

Believe me,
Ever yours faithfully,
T. H. HUXLEY

41 NORTH BANK
Dec. 19th, [1851]

MY DEAR DOCTOR,

Many thanks for the Calotypes—they are certainly as fine as any I have ever seen. Your own is especially sharp and life-like, and wonderfully like. As for your son's, of course I can't judge of the likeness but I can quite believe it—as he has all that peculiarly sturdy, *planted,* look—a sort of jolly defiance to the world in general—which I have heard of as his characteristic. A most indubitable chip!—it makes me laugh whenever I look at him.

[1]This refers to the deaths recorded on pp. 254–255.

[2]MacGillivray's book is dated 1852, on the title page; presumably Huxley had seen an advance copy. Boone (p. 285) was the publisher. I can find no references elsewhere to the difficulties mentioned in earlier letters (pp. 284, 285).

I know Brith[?] and shall talk to him about the "Dopo". Doubtless there are many parallel cases to be found, but the disease is certainly not known as it ought to be—I mentioned it to Carpenter the other day and I have spoken of it to other eminent men and all seem to think is very desirable it should be made known.

I can hear nothing of my success or failure at Toronto until the middle of January. The election is made in this manner—out of the candidates proposing themselves three are selected by the Senate of the University—of these one is appointed by the Governor-General, Lord Elgin. It is therefore necessary to make interest in both quarters. With such strong testimonials as I possess, and those magical three letters F.R.S., which go for as much as Lord Burleigh's nod in the colonies—I cannot doubt of being one of the "selected" of the Senate. To become the "elect" of Lord Elgin is another business. If any of the varied forms of suctorial proceeding—toadying or intriguing—have weight with his Lordship then I am done, because I would not condescend to them at any price. But what I have done—and thought I had a right to do it—was to secure his attention to my testimonials by sending out a copy of them *direct*—accompanied by a strong letter recommendatory from Lord Stanley of Alderley and enclosed in, I trust, a sufficiently manly and independent one from myself.

The Stanleys *volunteered* their assistance when they heard of my being a candidate. You may be pretty sure I did not ask it.

I hear further that Gray, the head of the British Museum, has written out to Lord Elgin on my behalf.

I believe too that some friends of mine have moved the Speaker of the House of Commons (there) and the Chancellor to do their "demdest" in my favour, so that you see while putting our "trust in the Lord" we have not forgotten that other maxim of "keeping the powder dry". I won't intrigue myself, but I won't be done by intriguer if I can help it.

As for competition I hear of nobody I care about—there is a Dr Ayres in the field and one or two others—but the honest truth is—and you will not suspect me of conceit in a statement meant for your private eye alone—that there is no man in England young enough to be a candidate—who could get together the weight of influence that I have done. No one has been more surprised than myself at the hearty way in which the bigwigs have put their shoulders to the wheel to help me—I can't at all account for it.[1]

---

[1]The vacancy was advertised in the summer of 1851. The decision was repeatedly postponed, and eventually, over two years later, the relative of an influential Canadian politician was appointed. Tyndall was also rejected for another chair at Toronto at about the same time. See *L. & L.* i, 77–79.

The following extracts from Dr. Thomson's letters to his wife are of interest as amplifying or illuminating Huxley's account of the voyage. We first have a vivid picture of the discomfort aboard the *Rattlesnake* in a storm, and the unseaworthiness of the ship (see p. 10, note, p. 55, and p. 56, note).

H.M.S. "RATTLESNAKE"
FUNCHAL ROADS, MADEIRA
20th December, [1846]

. . . the wind that was blowing a fresh breeze, ripened into a gale and the full powers of the ship were put to the test. Gradually one by one all those that were unseasoned retired, finding themselves deadly seasick, and the ship began to take in water in regular seas along the main deck. All the cabins were flooded, the water in mine was about six inches deep, and the old tub from the violent straining began to leak in great quantity abaft, injuring all and sundry provisions and stores. The scene amongst the midshipmen was one which I shall never forget. Nearly one and all of them were sick and so far gone as totally to disregard the destruction which was going on amongst their property from the leak abaft. Their mess-place was flooded and at some times to the depth of nearly 18 inches and this great flood of water rushing violently from side to side during the rolling of the ship carried along with it everything that was movable, desks and gun-cases and books, many of the desks were completely resolved into their elements. Amidst all this turmoil and confusion I was tolerably comfortable, the only damage which I sustained was having the whole stock of my linen soaked through with the filthy water; but our sea stock of living animals suffered most, the unfortunate ducks were picked up dead in bucketfuls. This state of things continued for about four days.

The next extract shows that Huxley's comments on the "Neptunizing" when crossing the Line (p. 17) were far from ill-founded. In fact Huxley only mentions the increase of the sick list, not the death recorded by Thomson.

H.M.S. "RATTLESNAKE"
RIO DE JANEIRO
24th Jany., [1847]

. . . We had to undergo the usual ceremony of shaving when we crossed the line and your humble servant was first on the list as candidate. I am sorry to say that although attended with a great deal of amusement and fun it is not altogether devoid of dangerous and even fatal consequences. One of our own men fell a sacrifice, dying in three days after of violent inflammation and congestion, and another who for two or three days was vibrating between life and death will be an invalid to witness the untoward results of that day's sport.

The following two letters refer to the Third Cruise. That dated 24th May 1848 shows that Thomson as well as MacGillivray found plenty to interest them in the way of natural history (see Chapter 5), while the second gives ample confirmation of the monotony of the cruise and the effect that it had upon the minds and tempers of the officers condemned to it.

> H.M.S. "RATTLESNAKE"
> OFF DUNK ISLAND
> Lat. 17′58 S., long. 146′9 E.
> 24th May 1848

The time passes on very comfortably, for the country affords ample opportunity to the botanist and to the natural historian of making researches into their different departments from the abundance of the natural products. Whenever the weather permits I am on shore with my gun and haversack and keep toiling through scrub and over hill in quest of whatever appears rare. With a perpendicular sun the perspiration pours down off me and my clothes are as wet as if I had walked through a pond, and roasting with thirst how delightful to come across any little water. At other times I am for half a day up to the neck in water looking after shells, with many of which I have already replenished my cabinet.

> H.M.S. "RATTLESNAKE", at SYDNEY
> 30th January 1849

. . . but when I last left Sydney I never dreamt of such perfect isolation as we experienced during our cruise and vainly thought, perhaps because I fervently wished, that some stray chances might occur of keeping up communications and transmitting money by way of India. Being disappointed in that I have done my best in what I could do. Since our leaving Cape York the cruise has been as monotonous and tiresome as I can well imagine any voyage to be. We called at Port Essington and remained there for five days only to give our ship's company a little more sickness and if possible to make what was sufficiently unpleasant already still more so. To speak of this place as a settlement is a mere abuse of words—the country in the neighbourhood is the most wretched, the climate the most unhealthy, the human beings the most uncomfortable, and the houses in a condition the most decayed and rotten. I have no doubt of its being shortly abandoned by the Government. We sailed from Port Essington 16 Nov. and made a long passage of ten weeks to Sydney. I had some faint hope that we might have visited Swan River and this would have made a pleasant break but no such luck was destined for us. We had to run over the course without a rest or without a breath and listlessly and lazily the old ship did her work. During the whole of this time and for near two months before leaving Cape York we had been almost completely reduced to salt provisions, indeed almost absolutely to ship's allowance, and as you will remember the old proverb a hungry man is an angry man, each one on board exhibited himself quite in a new light, showing ebullitions of temper and disposition for which he previously had not received credit. I can remember even now with what satisfaction I could, when a fitting occasion happened, vomit forth a whole bellyful of bile against some unfortunate messmate, and what a pleasing relief followed upon this medical treatment; and how often did I contrast my then wretched state with the simple comforts of home. . . .

Finally, the last three entirely confirm the light thrown upon Captain Stanley's conduct and character by Huxley. The first shows that a change of disposition manifested itself in Stanley during the Third Cruise. The second is strong supporting testimony for Huxley's ironic comments and bitter outbursts on the conduct of the Fourth Cruise (pp. 154, 163, 165, 181, 202). And the last is interesting for the light it sheds on the progress of Stanley's irritability, and on the consuming fire of his ambition to rank among the great names of English discovery.

H.M.S. "RATTLESNAKE"
5th March 1849

. . . I am very glad that the gaieties which were so frequent on board when we were last at Sydney are a good deal thrown aside. I suppose that it arises from the cordiality of feeling between the Captain and officers not being so great as formerly. The Captain instead of pursuing the system which I have generally seen adopted by captains, of entertaining at his own table, found it more economical to join with the officers and give parties more seldom but more gay, but now I sincerely hope that that arrangement has been knocked on the head, for while it was in operation I never hesitated to express my aversion to what forced me to pay for what I cared nothing. A very great difference of feeling now exists in the ship from what did this time last year. The Captain has treated some on board very badly, constantly snarling at them from an ungovernable temper which he has and scarcely treating them with ordinary civility, and this has tended to rouse up their animosity to him. Very curiously your humble servant has never experienced such treatment but on the contrary has been rather encouraged to a friendship which he has as invariably declined.

H.M.S. "Rattlesnake", at Cape York
9th October 1849

. . . In two days after leaving Moreton Bay we encountered a very fierce gale of wind that lasted for five days, in which the *Bramble* parted company from us. We met again off the coast of the Louisiade . . . And now we had arrived on the field of our surveying operations, but how to tell in what manner these operations were conducted, I feel myself hardly able and finally as adopting a proper and precautionary step I would suggest to you (and my own dearest Mary, I have good confidence that a secret may be entrusted to you) that what I say in the sequel on this subject may be kept to your own *dear bosom* or at least divulged only to those from whom there is no fear of its going farther. . . .

. . . The Louisiade is a large chain of islands stretching in an easterly direction from the south point of New Guinea. Each island is encircled by a reef which frequently also stretches from one island to another, thus enclosing small seas in which there are very good anchorages where there are breaks in the reefs to form an entrance. In the coral seas you must be aware that there exists this peculiarity with the reefs of that formation that outside of them to seaward no soundings can be procured at many hundred fathoms depth, so that a ship cannot anchor unless she can get to landward side of the reef into these small seas which I have mentioned. To find out therefore one of these anchorages was our first object. And in this we succeeded, solely through the instrumentality of the *Bramble,* after a search of five days. At this time I never saw greater fear exhibited than was done by Captain Stanley, although I must confess that after consulting my own judgment I could not discover the smallest cause for such. Indeed I began to augur that all my anticipations of interest and pleasure that I formed had been false and that the realization would be more tedious, monotonous and irksome than what were experienced during our last cruise.

This part of the world has doubtless been visited by many navigators, although history records only the names of two Frenchmen—Bougainville and D'Urville, who have explored these shores and by both of them in a very hurried manner, for I think that D'Urville charted all the work on which we have been employed, in the short space of three days, and so accurately too that after our prolonged survey of four months we have not been able to find fault with it. But at the commencement of our operations it was currently reported that this chart of the Frenchman would not be of the slightest assistance to us, nor could it be relied upon as being at all accurate, and these surmises were thrown out that those on board might be blinded to imagine that our voyage was really one of discovery and would be attended with unheard-of dangers.

Truly our voyage might have been one of discovery, but not in the sense above implied, but in a very different sense. For the Frenchmen, although they cruised along these shores and surveyed them for the purposes of navigation, never landed and were therefore wholly ignorant of their productions, etc. In this department might we with proper claim have been considered discoverers; but this was denied us. The prudence —did it not absolutely amount to fear and cowardice?—of the Captain would not allow us to enjoy the advantages that were held out to us. And now we have left this great *terra incognita* after a four months' cruise along its shores without knowing anything more or being able to communicate to the world anything more than was known of it before our visit. But now it almost makes me sick to think of the opportunities for seeing a country which was unknown as to its nature, its productions, etc., that have been thrown away. When we first procured anchorage the new broom was at work and continued in operation for a short period. The survey was begun with an attention to minuteness and accuracy that was scarcely expended on our former survey where it was so much demanded, and in this way without making much progress a great proportion of the season was spent, when it was found that there was not time to conduct the remaining portions of the survey in the same manner; and as misfortunes never come singly the weather became hazy, unsettled and rainy and very badly suited for our purposes. We had therefore to shuffle through the work as we best could. . . .

. . . I cannot now conceal my chagrin and disappointment at the course which was adopted of restraining us from going on shore among the natives for I thought that so much that would interest might be observed, but be that as it may it cannot now be remedied and what are byegones let rest as such. . . .

H.M.S. "RATTLESNAKE", at SYDNEY
February 1850

. . . All this we did but we spent a shorter time about it than I had anticipated, partly I imagine from the fact that the Captain's health began to break down, said to be from the great responsibility of his duties. From whatever cause his illness arose, whether from his peculiar habits or from extreme anxiety, it was of a formidable character and gave me great alarm. There was a complete prostration of strength and of his nervous constitution and his mind wandered for a few days during his convalescence which even at present is not very far advanced. His temper which is always very waspish became unbearable and of the most iritable character; he treated every one except your humble servant with a petulance and discourtesy that obliged me to remonstrate with him about the childishness of his conduct and forced from me the necessity of dissuading him from the performance of his duties, for that unless he relieved himself from the anxiety of office I could not feel myself responsible for his life. How it has been that I have acquired an ascendancy over him I cannot tell but the fact is no less true and is the observation of every one on board. Towards him I have acted on the principal that it was better that he should seek my society than that I should show any great predilection for his and on all occasions where I have imagined that he was inclined to tread too closely on my toes I have resisted quietly and without any bluster and he like a snail has drawn in his horns quickly enough. But now that we have arrived at Sydney I sincerely feel for his bereavements—his father and brother are both dead and his brother's wife has been left in Van Diemen's Land in great distress. Apparently therefore he has had a great deal to distress him and for a day or two after our arrival here I was fearful that such disastrous tidings would have produced a strong and injurious revulsion on his very weak constitution—but he never showed the slightest outward demonstration of any such. He seemed to have received from Admiral Beaufort's flattering letter regarding the work he has done something which acted more strongly in an exciting direction than the former news did in a depressing one. His mind indeed has one fixed idea which rules all his actions—the wish to rank amongst the scientific and *savans* [sic] of England fills his mind by day and is the subject of his dreams by night and in this he may succeed but it can be only for a short time for he is but a superficialist in all his knowledge and the realization of his vision of ambition must be a short one.

INDEX

Index

Plate 13

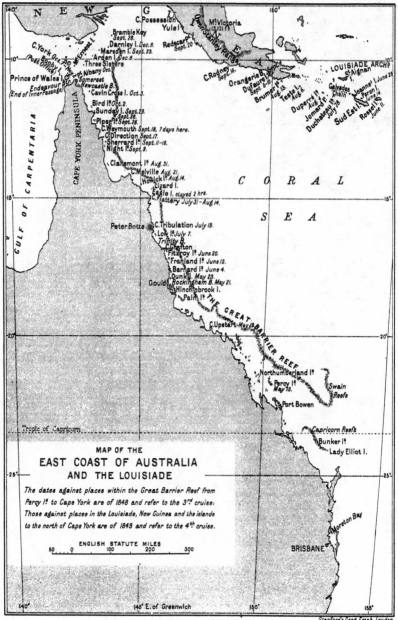

MAP OF THE

EAST COAST OF AUSTRALIA
AND THE LOUISIADE

*The dates against places within the Great Barrier Reef from
Percy I. to Cape York are of 1848 and refer to the 3rd cruise;
Those against places in the Louisiade, New Guinea and the islands
to the north of Cape York are of 1849 and refer to the 4th cruise.*

ENGLISH STATUTE MILES

50   0   100   200   300